Simplified Independence Proofs

BOOLEAN VALUED MODELS OF SET THEORY

This is Volume 31 in
PURE AND APPLIED MATHEMATICS
A series of monographs and textbooks
Edited by PAUL A. SMITH and SAMUEL EILENBERG
Columbia University, New York

A complete list of the books in this series appears at the end of this volume.

Simplified Independence Proofs

BOOLEAN VALUED MODELS OF SET THEORY

J. Barkley Rosser

Mathematics Research Center
United States Army
University of Wisconsin
Madison, Wisconsin

1969

ACADEMIC PRESS New York and London

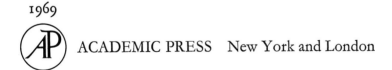

ACADEMIC PRESS, INC.
111 Fifth Avenue, New York, New York 10003

United Kingdom Edition published by
ACADEMIC PRESS, INC. (LONDON) LTD.
Berkeley Square House, London W.1

LIBRARY OF CONGRESS CATALOG CARD NUMBER: 69-13479
AMS 1968 SUBJECT CLASSIFICATION 0265,0242

PRINTED IN THE UNITED STATES OF AMERICA

Preface

In this text we show how to construct models for set theory in which the truth values of statements are elements of a Boolean algebra. By proper choices of the Boolean algebra one can then derive such conclusions as the following, all of which are predicated on the assumption that the axioms of set theory are consistent.

1. Even if one adjoins the axiom of choice to the axioms of set theory, one still cannot write down an explicit formula by means of which the real numbers can be well-ordered; consequently the axiom of constructibility is independent of the axioms of set theory even after adjoining the axiom of choice.
2. From the axioms of set theory alone it is not possible to prove that the real numbers can be well-ordered; consequently the axiom of choice is independent of the axioms of set theory.
3. The continuum hypothesis cannot be derived from the axioms of set theory even after adjoining the axiom of choice.

Generalizations of the third conclusion are also derived.

The notion of using Boolean valued models for independence proofs was put forward in the fall of 1965 by Robert Solovay. During the subsequent two years, it was extensively developed by Solovay and Dana Scott and their students and associates. At about the same time a somewhat similar development was being carried on quite independently in Czechoslovakia by Vopěnka and his associates. A published work of Vopěnka [11] is the first of a succession of publications in which one can follow the steps of this development. Vopěnka [12] gives a self-contained presentation of the ultimate theory that emerged from the development, with citations of the earlier partial results.

The developments of Scott and Solovay have appeared so far only in limited editions of notes which were reproduced by such means as Ditto (often from handwritten originals) and privately distributed. A definitive treatment (see Scott and Solovay [8]) is in preparation by Scott and Solovay to appear in the *Proceedings of the American Mathematical Society Summer Institute on Axiomatic Set Theory, 1967*, which was held at the University of California at Los Angeles, July 10 to August 5.

The exposition by Scott and Solovay is addressed to expert specialists. Also, most attention is given to studying the novelties of the model, and the proofs of independence appear rather incidentally. Somewhat the same is true of the Vopěnka exposition. Since there is extensive interest in the independence results among nonspecialists, the present text was prepared to make the independence results accessible to a wide audience.

Cohen's [2, 3] original proofs of independence by forcing arguments were of such depth and conceptual novelty as to dishearten all but the most motivated professional logicians. By contrast, the proofs by Boolean valued models are fairly simple and involve familiar concepts. They can be followed by an interested mathematician who has a modest familiarity with axiomatic set theory. For the benefit of such readers, the basic construction is presented in full detail with ample explanations (in Chapter 3). Although the model depends on Boolean algebra, only a small amount of knowledge in this area is needed. All information about Boolean algebra that is needed is presented with ample explanations (in Chapter 2), so that a nonmathematical reader with no previous knowledge of Boolean algebra can follow the proofs fully.

In addition to the items listed in the bibliography, there were a number of sets of notes that were used by the author. Scott provided several of these, as well as a preliminary draft of reference [8], and also discussed a number of points in the notes. The model given in Chapter 3 is close to one that was given in some notes by Kenneth Kunen dated February 1966. Also, Chapter 9 benefits from a letter dated November 3, 1967 from Kunen, and from a subsequent discussion with Kunen. Much help in the preparation of Chapters 5 and 8 came from discussions with C. C. Chang.

Most of the preparation of this text was carried out while the author was on leave from the University of Wisconsin, 1966–1967. During this time, he received half his support from the Wisconsin Alumni Research Foundation and the other half from the National Science Foundation under Grant GP5913. During the fall and winter of 1966 the facilities of the Aiken Computation Laboratory of Harvard University were made available to him. During the spring and summer of 1967 the facilities of the Oxford University Computing Laboratory were made available to him. In the academic year of 1967–1968, he had much technical help, including the typing of the manuscript, from the Mathematics Research Center of the United States Army, under Contract DA-31-124-ARO-D-462.

The author wishes to express his gratitude for the assistance he has received from various individuals and institutions, as acknowledged above.

J. BARKLEY ROSSER

Madison, Wisconsin
January 1969

Contents

PREFACE v

GLOSSARY OF SYMBOLS xii

LOCATION OF THEOREMS xiii

LOCATION OF DEFINITIONS xv

Chapter 1. **General Remarks**

A. Background Materials 1
B. Assumptions 2
C. Summary of Results 2
D. A Paradigm for the Proofs 3
E. A Guide for the Casual Reader 7

Chapter 2. **Boolean Algebra**

A. Topological Spaces 12
B. Properties of Boolean Algebras 20
C. Automorphisms 27
D. The Countable Chain Condition 31

Chapter 3. **The Basic Model**

A. Axioms of the Restricted Predicate Calculus 34
B. Axioms of Equality and Extensionality 41
C. Methods for Defining Members of V 51
D. The Basic Set Theory Axioms 65
E. Ordinals and Cardinals in the Model 75
F. The Axiom of Choice 81

Chapter 4. **The Independence of $V = L$**

A. Preliminaries 89
B. Proof of GCH 90
C. Subsets of $\check{\omega}$ 92

Chapter 5. **Analogies with Forcing**

A. Comparison of Specific Proofs 99
B. Replacing Boolean Algebra by Forcing in Proofs? 102

Chapter 6. **The Independence of AxC**

A. The Key Idea of the Proof 105
B. The Choice of Γ 106
C. Subsets of $\check{\omega}$ 107
D. The Real Numbers Are Not Well-Ordered 113

Chapter 7. **The Independence of the Continuum Hypothesis**

A. The Key Result 116
B. Additional Cardinality Results 119

Chapter 8. **The Generalized GCH—the Bounded Case**

A. Statement of Easton's Theorem 127
B. Specification of the Boolean Algebra 131
C. Substitutes for the Cohen Combinatorial Lemma 132
D. Cardinality Relations 140
E. Proof of Easton's Theorem 145
F. A Note on the Proof 155

Chapter 9. **The Generalized GCH—the Unbounded Case**

A. Preliminary Considerations 156
B. Specification of the Boolean Algebra 158
C. Definition of the Universe 165
D. Definition of the Boolean Value of a Statement 169
E. Proof of the Axioms of Set Theory, Except the Power Set Axiom 174
F. Cardinality Relations 182
G. The Axiom of the Power Set 182
H. Proof of Easton's Theorem 201

Chapter 10. **Resolution of Conceptual Difficulties**

A. What Is Truth? 202
B. Appeal to Strong Axioms 208

Bibliography 214

SUBJECT INDEX 215

Glossary of Symbols

We list here only symbols special to this book. The number opposite each symbol is the page on which it is defined or explained. Many symbols common in logical writings are used. Their meanings can be found by appealing to the Glossary of Special Logical Symbols given by Rosser [7, p. xii]. Standard mathematical terms are not listed in either glossary.

AxC	2	$\prod_{i \in I} P_i$	24	SC	74
GCH	2	$\mathcal{G}$	31	$\aleph(a)$	78
X	12	Γ	31	CCC	78
B	12	$\Vert \cdots \Vert$	34–36,	$\aleph_{\check{\alpha}}$	80
Λ	13		42–46	Ord	81
Cl(P)	13	$\models$	36	Hyp(Γ)	82
Co(P)	14	$\Vert a \in b \Vert$	42–46	Mord	83
Cc(P)	15	$\Vert a = b \Vert$	42–46	q	93
Cc^2(P)	15	V	43–47	B_P	100
Cc^3(P)	15	V_α	43–47	$\mathbf{B}^n_{i,J}$	106
Cc^4(P)	15	Od	43	$\mathcal{G}_J$	107
A	17	D	44	S_a	108
0	17	$\mathcal{G}_a$	47	s_a	108
1	17	Φ	54	q_μ	109
$\wedge$	17	$a^{(S)}$	59	s_N	121
$\vee$	17	SD	59	$\sum$	123,148
$'$	17	Img	62	E	129
$\{0, 1\}^I$	20	$\check{s}$	62	Cf	129
B_i^n	20	$\{b, c\}$	66	θ	131
$\Rightarrow$	22	$\bigcup b$	68	$s(P)$	132
$\Leftrightarrow$	22	$\{a\}$	68	P^L	133
$\leq$	22	$\langle a, b \rangle$	68	P^U	133
$\sum_{i \in I} P_i$	23	$a \cup b$	68	M	211

Location of Theorems

The number opposite each theorem, corollary, or lemma is the page on which its enunciation commences.

Theorem 2.1	13	Theorem 2.28	27	Theorem 3.18	62
Theorem 2.2	13	Theorem 2.29	28	Theorem 3.19	63
Theorem 2.3	13	Theorem 2.30	29	Theorem 3.20	63
Theorem 2.4	13	Theorem 2.31	29	Theorem 3.21	63
Theorem 2.5	13	Theorem 2.32	32	Theorem 3.22	63
Theorem 2.6	13	Lemma	32	Theorem 3.23	64
Theorem 2.7	14	Theorem 3.1	36	Corollary	64
Theorem 2.8	14	Theorem 3.2	38	Theorem 3.24	64
Theorem 2.9	14	Lemma	39	Theorem 3.25	65
Theorem 2.10	14	Theorem 3.3	40	Theorem 3.26	66
Theorem 2.11	15	Lemma A	47	Theorem 3.27	66
Theorem 2.12	15	Lemma B	47	Theorem 3.28	67
Theorem 2.13	15	Theorem 3.4	49	Theorem 3.29	68
Theorem 2.14	16	Corollary	50	Theorem 3.30	69
Theorem 2.15	16	Theorem 3.5	50	Theorem 3.31	70
Theorem 2.16	16	Theorem 3.6	51	Corollary	72
Theorem 2.17	16	Theorem 3.7	53	Theorem 3.32	72
Lemma	16	Theorem 3.8	54	Theorem 3.33	72
Theorem 2.18	17	Theorem 3.9	54	Theorem 3.34	74
Theorem 2.19	22	Theorem 3.10	54	Theorem 3.35	76
Theorem 2.20	22	Theorem 3.11	56	Theorem 3.36	76
Theorem 2.21	23	Theorem 3.12	57	Corollary	76
Theorem 2.22	24	Theorem 3.13	59	Theorem 3.37	77
Theorem 2.23	25	Theorem 3.14	60	Theorem 3.38	77
Theorem 2.24	25	Theorem 3.15	60	Theorem 3.39	77
Theorem 2.25	25	Corollary	61	Theorem 3.40	78
Theorem 2.26	25	Theorem 3.16	61	Theorem 3.41	78
Theorem 2.27	26	Theorem 3.17	62	Theorem 3.42	78

Theorem 3.43	78
Theorem 3.44	79
Theorem 3.45	80
Theorem 3.46	80
Theorem 3.47	80
Theorem 3.48	81
Theorem 3.49	82
Theorem 3.50	82
Theorem 3.51	82
Theorem 3.52	83
Theorem 3.53	83
Lemma	86
Theorem 3.54	87
Theorem 3.55	87
Theorem 3.56	87
Theorem 4.1	90
Theorem 4.2	92
Theorem 4.3	93
Theorem 4.4	94
Theorem 4.5	95
Theorem 4.6	97
Theorem 6.1	108
Theorem 6.2	108
Theorem 6.3	109
Theorem 6.4	110
Theorem 6.5	110
Theorem 6.6	113
Theorem 6.7	115
Theorem 7.1	118
Theorem 7.2	120
Theorem 7.3	121
Theorem 7.4	122
Theorem 7.5	123
Theorem 7.6	124
Theorem 7.7	124
Theorem 7.8	125
Theorem 7.9	126
Easton's Theorem	130
Theorem 8.1	131
Theorem 8.2	133
Theorem 8.3	133
Theorem 8.4	137
Theorem 8.5	137
Theorem 8.6	138
Theorem 8.7	139
Theorem 8.8	140
Lemma 1	141
Lemma 2	142
Theorem 8.9	144
Corollary	144
Theorem 8.10	144
Theorem 8.11	144
Theorem 8.12	145
Lemma 1	146
Lemma 2	146
Lemma 3	147
Lemma 4	147
Theorem 8.13	148
Lemma	148
Corollary	149
Theorem 8.14	150
Lemma 1	150
Lemma 2	150
Lemma 3	151
Lemma 4	152
Lemma 5	154
Theorem 9.1	161
Corollary	161
Theorem 9.2	162
Corollary	164
Theorem 9.3	165
Theorem 9.4	166
Theorem 9.5	166
Theorem 9.6	169
Lemma	170
Theorem 9.7	172
Theorem 9.8	173
Theorem 9.9	182
Theorem 9.10	185
Theorem 9.11	186
Lemma	186
Theorem 9.12	187
Lemma 1	187
Lemma 2	187
Lemma 3	188
Lemma 4	190
Lemma 5	190
Lemma 6	190
Lemma 7	191
Theorem 9.13	191
Theorem 9.14	193
Theorem 9.15	194
Lemma 1	195
Lemma 2	195
Lemma 3	197
Lemma 4	198
Lemma 5	198
Lemma 6	199
Lemma 7	200
Lemma 8	200

Location of Definitions

The number opposite each definition is the page on which its enunciation commences.

Definition 2.1	12	Definition 2.15	28	Definition 8.1	129
Definition 2.2	13	Definition 2.16	31	Definition 8.2	130
Definition 2.3	13	Definition 3.1	54	Definition 8.3	131
Definition 2.4	14	Definition 3.2	59	Definition 8.4	132
Definition 2.5	14	Definition 3.3	62	Definition 8.5	133
Definition 2.6	15	Definition 3.4	81	Definition 8.6	133
Definition 2.7	15	Definition 3.5	82	Definition 8.7	148
Definition 2.8	17	Definition 3.6	83	Definition 8.8	149
Definition 2.9	17	Definition 4.1	93	Definition 8.9	149
Definition 2.10	22	Definition 6.1	108	Definition 9.1	160
Definition 2.11	23	Definition 6.2	108	Definition 9.2	162
Definition 2.12	23	Definition 6.3	109	Definition 9.3	164
Definition 2.13	24	Definition 7.1	123		
Definition 2.14	27	Definition 7.2	123		

CHAPTER ONE

General Remarks

A. Background Materials

Of the various materials appearing in texts listed in the bibliography, it will be necessary for the reader to be fairly familiar with the restricted predicate calculus. We shall assume the treatment given in the first six chapters of Rosser [7]. We shall also use the notation of Rosser [7], especially the use of dots [7, pp. 96 and 19–23]. The notation does not really affect the operations of the restricted predicate calculus, and the reader will find it satisfactory to use whatever treatment he is familiar with.

To read Chapters 7–9, the reader should be quite familiar with the theory of ordinals and cardinals in set theory. He may follow either the treatment of Gödel [5] or Bernays and Fraenkel [1]; we shall rely on the latter. Further acquaintance with set theory itself is not needed at most points, but would be quite helpful at all points. Only a modest acquaintance with the theory of ordinals or cardinals is needed to read the first six chapters.

The reader need have no acquaintance at all with the idea of forcing, or with proofs of independence based on it. Chapter 5 discusses the relationship of the present proofs to those using forcing, but this material is not used in any of the developments given here, and the chapter can be omitted if desired.

B. Assumptions

The arguments of the next eight chapters are considered to be carried out within set theory, under the assumption of AxC (the axiom of choice) and GCH (the generalized continuum hypothesis). This involves certain conceptual difficulties; an outline of how to resolve these is given in Chapter 10. That we can get a proof of the independence of AxC (while assuming it) is made plausible by the following argument. Suppose the axioms of set theory are free from contradiction. Then no contradication will result if we adjoin AxC and GCH, as is shown by Gödel [5]. With the help of AxC and GCH we construct within set theory a model for which the axioms of set theory hold but AxC fails. (By taking the truth values of statements to be elements of a Boolean algebra, we are led to unorthodox definitions for "$\in$" and "$=$," and hence to unorthodox definitions for the derivative notions. This accounts for the altered behavior in the model.) But if AxC were indeed provable from the axioms of set theory, then AxC must hold in the model since the axioms of set theory hold in the model. So two contradictory statements would hold in the model. However, each statement of the model is a statement of set theory (though with an unorthodox interpretation). So two contradictory statements would hold in set theory, which cannot be the case if it is consistent.

C. Summary of Results

Assuming AxC does not necessarily ensure that one can write a formula which will well-order a given set. The statement that there is a well ordering relation and the presentation of a prescription for such a well-ordering relation are quite different affairs. In Chapter 4 it is shown that even if one adds AxC and GCH to the axioms of set theory one does not possess the machinery to write down an explicit formula by means of which the real numbers can be well-ordered. If the axiom of constructibility $V = L$ (see Gödel [5]) where provable, one would be able to write down such a formula, and not only for the set of real numbers. Therefore

$V = L$ is independent of the axioms of set theory plus AxC and GCH.

Even if AxC is not derivable from the axioms of set theory, one might be able to prove that certain special sets can be well-ordered. In Chapter 6, it is shown that one cannot prove that the real numbers can be well-ordered. Not only can one not write down an explicit formula which well-orders the real numbers, but one cannot even prove theoretically the existence of an unspecified well-ordering using only the axioms of set theory. Naturally, one cannot prove the stronger statement AxC.

In Chapter 7 it is shown that one cannot derive the simple continuum hypothesis from the axioms of set theory plus AxC. Naturally, one cannot derive the stronger GCH.

The question of what alternatives to GCH are consistent with the axioms of set theory plus AxC was answered in almost complete generality by Easton [4], by means of a forcing argument. Easton's result is derived in Chapters 8 and 9 by means of Boolean valued models. The precise statement is fairly complicated, and the reader should refer to the opening paragraphs of Chapter 8 for this statement and the necessary explanations.

D. A Paradigm for the Proofs

The proofs of independence which we shall present all have a striking similarity to a famous classical proof of independence, namely one of the proofs of the independence of Euclid's parallel postulate. A survey of the high points of this classical proof will provide a useful guide for our subsequent developments. We summarize key points from the discussion of Young [13, pp. 91–147].

We say that two lines AB and DE in the same plane are parallel if they never meet, however far extended. Suppose we have a line AB, and a point P not on AB (see Fig. 1.1). The parallel postulate says that through P there is a line DE parallel to AB, and only one such parallel line. In his treatise on geometry, Euclid enunciated a number of postulates embodying "self-evident" properties of

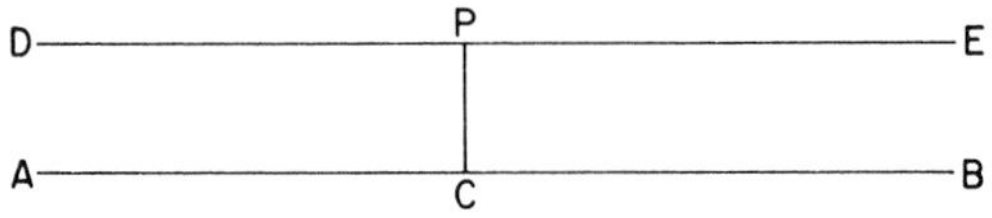

FIG. 1.1. Parallel lines.

points, lines, distances, etc., and then undertook to deduce from them all other known properties. Things went well through Proposition 28 of the first book. This proved that through *P* there is a line *DE* parallel to *AB*; essentially the proof is got by dropping *PC* perpendicular to *AB*, and then erecting *DE* perpendicular to *PC*. However, to prove that there is only one parallel to *AB* through *P*, Euclid invoked a special Postulate 5. (See Young [13, p. 99] for fuller details.) The tradition is that Euclid felt that Postulate 5 lacked the attribute of being "self-evident," and that he had expected to be able to prove it from the other postulates. At any rate, for over 2000 years, mathematicians felt challenged to try to prove Postulate 5 from the other postulates; none succeeded.

Saccheri (1667–1733) had attempted a proof by *reductio ad absurdum* by denying Postulate 5 and seeking a contradiction. Finally, in the early nineteenth century. Lobachevsky, Bolyai, and Gauss came up with the breathtaking suggestion that perhaps there is not a contradiction to be derived from a denial of Postulate 5. They were so bold as to suggest that denying Postulate 5 merely gave an interesting "non-Euclidean" geometry, and they made extensive developments of it. It is hard now to appreciate what an audacious performance this was. Philosophers of the highest authority then said that the physical universe must of necessity be Euclidean. Equally, a "non-Euclidean" geometry must be inconsistent. Once the inconsistency were revealed, then indeed one would have a proof of Postulate 5 by *reductio ad absurdum* as Saccheri had attempted. It has now been established by experimental evidence that the physical universe is in fact not Euclidean. However, 150 years ago, such a suggeston smacked of heresy.

For a good part of the nineteenth century, many people persisted in the belief that "non-Euclidean" geometry must certainly be inconsistent, and that eventually a clever mathematician would discover the inconsistency. Finally it was proved conclusively that "non-Euclidean" geometry is consistent. That is, there genuinely is no proof of Postulate 5 from the other postulates; it is not merely the case that no one has been penetrating enough yet to discover the proof.

How could one prove such a thing? Eventually, many proofs were found. One which is particularly illuminating for our own development is given by Young [13]. Many people associate the name of Klein with it, but Young [13, p. 141] states that Cayley gave the key idea first. In summary, it proceeds as follows. We start with the Euclidean plane. This disarms all who wish to deny the existence of "non-Euclidean" geometry. The postulates attribute certain properties to points, lines, distances, etc. We now define some things which are not exactly points, lines, distances, etc., but which are enough like them to have all the properties stated in the postulates, except the parallel postulate. Specifically, we shall take as "points" only the points interior to the unit circle (see Fig. 1.2), and shall take as "lines" those line segments lying inside the unit circle. Many postulates hold immediately, for instance, that through two distinct "points" there passes

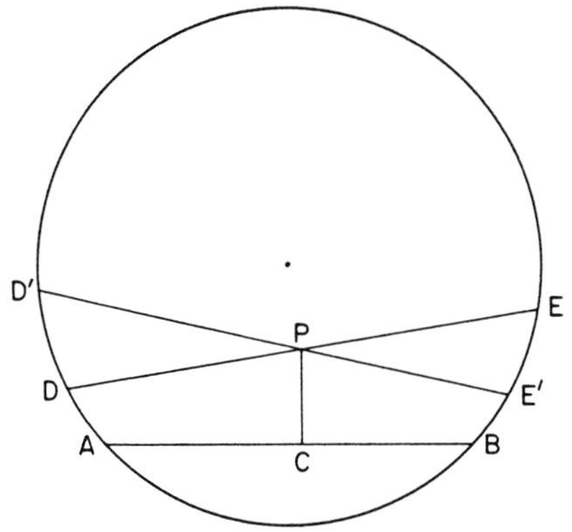

FIG. 1.2. Non-Euclidean geometry.

one and only one "line." However, the parallel postulate clearly fails. This is evident in Fig. 1.2. DE is parallel to AB because each has been extended as far as possible, but they do not meet. Similarly $D'E'$ is parallel to AB. In order to validate some of the other postulates, one must make quite marked changes in the definition of distance. The details are given by Young [13, pp. 133–140], but basically the "distance" between two "points" is a multiple of the true distance; this multiple is taken ever greater as the points are taken farther from the center of the unit circle. Indeed, the "distance" from the center of the circle to its circumference is infinite, so that the illusion of an unbounded plane is created. By judicious adjustment of the multiplying factor between the distance and the "distance" it is possible to satisfy all of Euclid's postulates except Postulate 5. The latter is incontestably false.

This makes it conclusive that Postulate 5 cannot be derived from the other postulates.

Note that to show the independence of Postulate 5, Cayley assumed a Euclidean plane to start with. That is, he began by assuming the truth of Postulate 5. As we mentioned in Section B, we begin similarly by assuming AxC and GCH, preparatory to proving their independence. This is not self-defeating, because we then modify somewhat the notions of "set," "well-ordering," "cardinal number," etc., just as Cayley introduced modified "points," "lines," "distances," etc. Indeed, we need the presence of powerful principles such as AxC and GCH to be able to prove that our unorthodox "sets," etc. have the desired properties, just as Cayley needed Postulate 5 to prove the properties of his "points," "lines," "distances," etc.

Note further that Cayley did not modify his "points," "lines," etc. very much. After all, he wished to invalidate only Postulate 5. All other postulates were to remain valid. Thus his "points" were actual points; he just didn't use all possible points.

Similarly we shall wish to keep valid all of our axioms except AxC or GCH. So we shall wish to make only fairly minor modifications. Our "sets" will be sets; we just will not use all possible sets. Other concepts will be kept as similar as possible to the classical form.

E. A Guide for the Casual Reader

As noted previously the independence proofs to be presented do not make any use of the conceptually difficult notion of forcing, which was invented by Cohen as an instrument for independence proofs. For most specialists in logic, this is not a particular consideration as they will already have mastered the notion of forcing. However, there will be many readers with main interests elsewhere who feel a curiosity about the independence of AxC and the continuum hypothesis. These were considered central unsolved problems for more than half a century, and many persons would like to gain some comprehension of how such proofs of independence can be carried out, provided they can do so without an extended excursion into unfamiliar matters.

The present treatment has the advantage of requiring fewer novel concepts, as compared with a treatment using forcing. However, there is still a mass of detail (whether forcing is used or not). Thus, to show independence of an axiom, we must show that the Boolean valued model which we introduce satisfies all the other axioms, namely, six for the restricted predicate calculus, two for equality, and eight or more specific set theory axioms. Thus at least sixteen separate validations are required to establish the result. However, one need not check all these to understand the basic ideas of the proof. Similar ideas are used for many of the validations. If suitable validations are checked, the principles involved become clear, and a casual reader may then be satisfied to trust that the proofs supplied for the rest are sound. We here offer a guide to the reader who wishes to gain a fundamental comprehension with a minimum of reading.

It will suffice to go through a single proof of independence. The independence proofs for the axiom of constructibility (Chapter 4), the axiom of choice (Chapter 6), and the continuum hypothesis (Chapter 7) are not interdependent, and one may choose any one of them. However, the proof of the independence of the axiom of choice is appreciably more complex; it is recommended that before attempting it one should first look at the proof of independence for the axiom of constructibility, which uses considerations which are similar and so will illumine the proof for AxC.

For the reader who is familiar with the theory of transfinite cardinals, the proof of independence for the continuum hypothesis will be the simplest, since it avoids any need to consider automorphisms of Boolean algebras. On the other hand, the proof of independence for the axiom of constructibility can be carried out without reference to cardinal numbers, and so may be more appealing to some readers. However, certain common preliminaries will be needed by all readers.

The reader who wishes to look at only one (or two) of the proofs cited above should eschew the rather general approach used in Chapter 2. This general approach is useful in Chapters 8 and 9, but will only be a distraction for a casual reader. In Definition 2.1, specialize X to be as in (2.24); for the various independence proofs, we take $I = \omega$ for the axiom of constructibility, $I = \omega \times \omega$ for AxC, or $I = \omega \times \omega_2$ for the continuum hypothesis. Then the basis sets of Definition 2.1 are given by (2.26) if $I = \omega$ or by (6.2) in the other cases. Axioms 2.1 and 2.2 are then readily verified.

The reader who is well acquainted with topological spaces can skip directly to Definitions 2.8 and 2.9. The reader without such acquaintance should read all intervening definitions and theorems, and perhaps check the proofs of about every third theorem. Theorem 2.18 is crucial, but its proof may be skipped by those familiar with both topological spaces and Boolean algebra. Otherwise, one checks as much of the proof as seems necessary to get a feel for such manipulations. Certainly one must be able to follow the proof given after (2.33) that each basis set is a regular open set (and hence an element of the Boolean algebra). To the extent that Theorems 2.19 and 2.20 seem to involve anything unfamiliar, some attention should be paid to their proofs.

The next few pages (through Theorem 2.26) concern supremums and infimums. These are basic for the treatment of quantification, and should be understood. However, Theorem 2.27 will not be used in any of the independence proofs cited.

To follow the independence proofs for the axiom of constructibility or AxC, the material on automorphisms in Section C of Chapter 2 must be understood. However, it can be skipped completely for the proof of independence of the continuum hypothesis. For Chapter 2, Section D, which deals with the countable chain condition, the situation is completely reversed. It is used for the independence proof for the continuum hypothesis, but not for the axiom of constructibility or AxC.

Only for the proof of independence of AxC do we need to maintain the full degree of generality specified in the second paragraph of Chapter 3. For the proof of independence of the axiom of constructibility, we take Γ to consist of all subgroups of $\mathscr{G}$; all matters involving Γ will then reduce to trivialities. For the proof of independence of the continuum hypothesis, we simply expunge all material which involves $\mathscr{G}$ or Γ. Thus (3.20)–(3.24) are deleted, as are (3.30), (3.34), (3.36), and Theorem 3.7. One further proceeds as though Γ were the set of all subgroups of $\mathscr{G}$. Thus in Theorem 3.9, (3.45) holds and $a \in V_{\alpha+1}$ holds without exception, Theorem 3.12 holds for all extensional Φ, and so on. One proceeds as though Hyp(Γ) is always satisfied (see Definition 3.5).

The rest of Section A of Chapter 3 is basic, and should be read carefully. Section B of this chapter is also basic. However, the rather tedious proof (done by examining a number of cases) that (3.15)–(3.19) hold (beginning with Lemma A and running up to Theorem 3.4) is not very illuminating, and could be taken on faith with no loss of understanding.

The introductory paragraphs of Section C (up to Theorem 3.7) contain a summary of much of the material of the section. After reading this, one might elect merely to read the theorems of this section, and to trust that the proofs suffice. Theorems 3.14–3.21 are of particular use later, and it is perhaps advisable to check the proofs of Theorems 3.15 and 3.19 to verify that one comprehends precisely what is involved. Theorem 3.7 is crucial for the independence proofs of the axiom of constructibility and AxC (but is not used at all for the continuum hypothesis).

In Section D, the proof of Theorem 3.33 is quite illustrative. If one understands this proof, one could well believe that the proofs of the other difficult theorems of the section proceed by variations of the same idea.

Section E is not used at all in the proofs of independence of the axiom of constructibility and AxC, but is basic for the continuum hypothesis (it is quite essential to understand the proof of Theorem 3.44, but one could well accept the other theorems without checking their proofs).

Section F is devoted to showing that if Γ is the set of all subgroups of $\mathscr{G}$, then the axiom of choice holds in the model. Unless one has a morbid curiosity about the exact workings of the model, one should omit any further details. Indeed, when we come to prove the independence of AxC, we shall be very careful to choose Γ in another fashion, so that AxC will fail to hold in the model.

At the end of Chapter 3, it has been verified that all the axioms of set theory (except AxC in special cases) hold in a model based on a fairly general Boolean algebra. In Section A of Chapter 4, a particular Boolean algebra is chosen, and in Section C of the same chapter it is shown that the axiom of constructibility fails in the corresponding model. Thus the axiom of constructibility is independent of the other axioms of set theory. To comprehend the proof, the reader will have to go through Sections A and C of Chapter 4 in fair detail. Section B provides an extra dividend, in that it shows that GCH also holds in the model. Thus one cannot derive the axiom of constructibility even if one adjoins GCH to the other axioms of set theory. How carefully one reads Section B depends upon how suspicious one feels about the independence of the axiom of constructibility after adjoining GCH. It should be pointed out that if one undertakes to check the proofs in Section B of Chapter 4, one will find that they depend on the material of Section E of Chapter 3 which one could otherwise omit.

To comprehend the proof of the independence of the axiom of choice, one must read Chapter 6 in reasonably full detail. By a suitable choice of Γ, we obtain a model in which AxC fails although the other axioms hold. As we mentioned earlier, it will help the understanding if one first reads Sections A and C of Chapter 4 (but one should definitely omit Section B of Chapter 4).

Section A of Chapter 7 establishes the independence of the continuum hypothesis. It can be read quite independently of the other independence proofs (references to Theorems 6.3 and 6.4 of Chapter 6 cause no difficulty, since these theorems are independent of the rest of Chapter 6). If one is sufficiently familiar with Section E of Chapter 3, one can read Section A of Chapter 7 very easily. Then the proof of independence is complete. Section B is adjoined to answer some additional questions which are suggested by the independence of the continuum hypothesis. These questions, with their answers, are stated in the opening lines of Section B. The proofs which follow become quite involved, concluding with a special case of the very complicated results of Chapters 8 and 9. The reader's interest will dictate how much he will choose to read. It should be noted that one does not need to introduce the notion of automorphisms of Boolean algebra, so that lack of reference to $\mathscr{G}$ and Γ persists. However, extensive familiarity with the theory of transfinite ordinals and cardinals is assumed.

CHAPTER TWO

Boolean Algebra

A. Topological Spaces

The Boolean algebras which will be particularly useful to us are based on topological spaces. We shall need the notion of regular open set, which receives relatively little attention in texts on topological spaces. However, the total information we need about topological spaces is very little indeed. Furthermore, it will be more useful to us if this information is derived from an old-fashioned approach that is not now commonly used. For this reason, and to make the present treatment self-contained, we shall derive herein all the material we need. We lay down the following definition.

Definition 2.1. Let X be a nonempty set of (abstract) points; we use x and y to denote points of X. Let there be certain distinguished nonempty subsets of X, called basis sets; we use B to denote a basis set. Let the basis sets satisfy the following axioms:

Axiom 2.1. For each point $x \in X$ there is a basis set B such that $x \in B$.

Axiom 2.2. If $x \in X$ is in each of two basis sets B_1 and B_2, then there is a basis set B_3 such that $x \in B_3$ and $B_3 \subseteq B_1 \cap B_2$.

***Definition* 2.2.** We say that P is an open set iff it is a sum of a set of basis sets.

With this definition, our X is a topological space in the usual sense. However, we shall use very few of the consequences of this fact.

***Theorem* 2.1.** The sum of any set of open sets is an open set.

PROOF. This is obvious.

***Theorem* 2.2.** Each basis set is an open set.

PROOF. This is obvious.

***Theorem* 2.3.** X is an open set.

PROOF. Use Axiom 2.1. to conclude that X is the sum of all the basis sets.

***Theorem* 2.4.** Λ is an open set.

PROOF. Λ is the sum of an empty set of basis sets.

As we are using the notations of Rosser [7], we conform with his use of Λ to denote the null set.

***Definition* 2.3.** We write $\mathrm{Cl}(P)$ for the set of all points x such that each basis set which contains x must contain also a point of P.

We refer to $\mathrm{Cl}(P)$ as the closure of P.

***Theorem* 2.5.** If $P \subseteq X$, then $P \subseteq \mathrm{Cl}(P)$.

PROOF. This is obvious.

***Theorem* 2.6.** If $P \subseteq Q$, then $\mathrm{Cl}(P) \subseteq \mathrm{Cl}(Q)$.

PROOF. Assume $P \subseteq Q$ and $x \in \mathrm{Cl}(P)$. Let B be a basis set which contains x. Then it must contain a point of P. But $P \subseteq Q$. So B contains a point of Q.

Theorem 2.7. $\mathrm{Cl}(P \cup Q) = \mathrm{Cl}(P) \cup \mathrm{Cl}(Q)$.

PROOF. As $P \subseteq P \cup Q$ and $Q \subseteq P \cup Q$, we have by Theorem 2.6 that $\mathrm{Cl}(P) \subseteq \mathrm{Cl}(P \cup Q)$ and $\mathrm{Cl}(Q) \subseteq \mathrm{Cl}(P \cup Q)$. So

$$\mathrm{Cl}(P) \cup \mathrm{Cl}(Q) \subseteq \mathrm{Cl}(P \cup Q).$$

To show inclusion in the reverse direction, let $x \in \mathrm{Cl}(P \cup Q)$ and $\sim x \in \mathrm{Cl}(P)$. So there is a basis set B_1 which contains x but contains no point of P. Let B_2 be a basis set which contains x. By Axiom 2.2, there is a basis set B_3 which contains x such that $B_3 \subseteq B_1 \cap B_2$. As $x \in \mathrm{Cl}(P \cup Q)$, B_3 must contain a point y of $P \cup Q$. But $B_3 \subseteq B_1$, so that $y \in B_1$, so that y is not in P. Hence $y \in Q$. But $B_3 \subseteq B_2$, so that B_2 contains a point of Q. As this is true for each B_2 which contains x, we conclude $x \in \mathrm{Cl}(Q)$.

Theorem 2.8. If P is an open set, then $P \cap \mathrm{Cl}(Q) \subseteq \mathrm{Cl}(P \cap Q)$.

PROOF. Let $x \in P \cap \mathrm{Cl}(Q)$ and let B_1 be a basis set which contains x. As $x \in P$ and P is an open set, there is a B_2 which contains x and is included in P. By Axiom 2.2, there is a B_3 which contains x such that $B_3 \subseteq B_1 \cap B_2$. But $B_2 \subseteq P$, so that $B_3 \subseteq P$. As $x \in \mathrm{Cl}(Q)$, B_3 must contain a point of Q. As $B_3 \subseteq P$, this point must be in P also, and hence in $P \cap Q$. But $B_3 \subseteq B_1$, so that B_1 contains a point of $P \cap Q$.

Definition 2.4. We write $\mathrm{Co}(P)$ for $X - P$.
We refer to $\mathrm{Co}(P)$ as the complement of P.

Definition 2.5. We say that P is a closed set iff there is an open set Q such that $P = \mathrm{Co}(Q)$.

Theorem 2.9. P is an open set iff there is a closed set Q such that $P = \mathrm{Co}(Q)$.

PROOF. This is obvious.

Theorem 2.10. If P is a closed set, then $P = \mathrm{Cl}(P)$.

PROOF. By Theorem 2.5, $P \subseteq \mathrm{Cl}(P)$. To prove inclusion in the other direction we prove $\mathrm{Co}(P) \subseteq \mathrm{Co}(\mathrm{Cl}(P))$. So let $x \in \mathrm{Co}(P)$. By Theorem 2.9, $\mathrm{Co}(P)$ is an open set. So there is a basis set B which contains x and is included in $\mathrm{Co}(P)$. So B does not include a point of P. Hence x is not in $\mathrm{Cl}(P)$. Thus x is in $\mathrm{Co}(\mathrm{Cl}(P))$.

Theorem 2.11. $\mathrm{Cl}(P)$ is a closed set.

PROOF. Write Q for $\mathrm{Co}(\mathrm{Cl}(P))$. By theorem 2.9, it suffices to show that Q is open. For each $x \in Q$, let B_x be the set of basis sets which contain x and are included in Q. Clearly

$$\sum_{x \in Q} B_x \subseteq Q.$$

To show inclusion in the reverse direction, let $x \in Q$. That is, x is a point not in $\mathrm{Cl}(P)$. So there must be a basis set B which contains x but contains no point of P. Then B contains no point of $\mathrm{Cl}(P)$, since by Definition 2.3 this would require that B contain a point of P. So $B \subseteq \mathrm{Co}(\mathrm{Cl}(P))$. That is, $B \in B_x$. So

$$x \in \sum_{x \in Q} B_x.$$

Definition 2.6. We write $\mathrm{Cc}(P)$ for $\mathrm{Co}(\mathrm{Cl}(P))$.

Definition 2.7. We write $\mathrm{Cc}^2(P)$ for $\mathrm{Cc}(\mathrm{Cc}(P))$, $\mathrm{Cc}^3(P)$ for $\mathrm{Cc}(\mathrm{Cc}(\mathrm{Cc}(P)))$, etc.

Theorem 2.12. If $P \subseteq Q$, then $\mathrm{Cc}(Q) \subseteq \mathrm{Cc}(P)$.

PROOF. If $P \subseteq Q$, then $\mathrm{Cl}(P) \subseteq \mathrm{Cl}(Q)$ by Theorem 2.6. Complementation of both sides gives our theorem, since this reverses the order.

Theorem 2.13. If P is an open set, then $P \subseteq \mathrm{Cc}^2(P)$.

PROOF. By Theorem 2.5, $P \subseteq \mathrm{Cl}(P)$. Complementation of both sides gives $\mathrm{Cc}(P) \subseteq \mathrm{Co}(P)$. Then by Theorem 2.6, $\mathrm{Cl}(\mathrm{Cc}(P)) \subseteq \mathrm{Cl}(\mathrm{Co}(P))$. As P is open, $\mathrm{Co}(P)$ is closed, by Definition 2.5, so that $\mathrm{Cl}(\mathrm{Co}(P)) = \mathrm{Co}(P)$ by Theorem 2.10. So $\mathrm{Cl}(\mathrm{Cc}(P)) \subseteq \mathrm{Co}(P)$. Complementation of both sides gives our theorem.

Theorem 2.14. Cc(P) is an open set.

PROOF. By Theorem 2.11, Cl(P) is a closed set, so that Cc(P) is an open set by Theorem 2.9.

Theorem 2.15. If P is an open set, then $\mathrm{Cc}(P) = \mathrm{Cc}^3(P)$.

PROOF. Applying Theorem 2.12 to the conclusion of Theorem 2.13 gives $\mathrm{Cc}^3(P) \subseteq \mathrm{Cc}(P)$. However, taking P to be Cc(P) in Theorem 2.13 (which we are entitled to do by Theorem 2.14) gives $\mathrm{Cc}(P) \subseteq \mathrm{Cc}^3(P)$.

Theorem 2.16. $\mathrm{Cc}^2(P) = \mathrm{Cc}^4(P)$.

PROOF. Take P to be Cc(P) in Theorem 2.15, which we are entitled to do by Theorem 2.14.

Theorem 2.17. If P is an open set, then

$$\mathrm{Cc}^2(P \cap Q) = \mathrm{Cc}^2(P) \cap \mathrm{Cc}^2(Q).$$

PROOF. We first prove a lemma.

Lemma. If P is an open set, then $P \cap \mathrm{Cc}^2(Q) \subseteq \mathrm{Cc}^2(P \cap Q)$.

PROOF. By complementation of both sides of the conclusion of Theorem 2.8, we get

$$\mathrm{Cc}(P \cap Q) \subseteq \mathrm{Co}(P) \cup \mathrm{Cc}(Q).$$

Then by Theorem 2.6 and Theorem 2.7,

$$\mathrm{Cl}(\mathrm{Cc}(P \cap Q)) \subseteq \mathrm{Cl}(\mathrm{Co}(P)) \cup \mathrm{Cl}(\mathrm{Cc}(Q)). \tag{2.1}$$

However, by the same argument as in the proof of Theorem 2.13, $\mathrm{Cl}(\mathrm{Co}(P)) = \mathrm{Co}(P)$. So complementation of both sides of (2.1) gives our lemma.

Using Theorem 2.12 twice with the lemma gives

$$\mathrm{Cc}^2(P \cap \mathrm{Cc}^2(Q)) \subseteq \mathrm{Cc}^4(P \cap Q).$$

Then by Theorem 2.16

$$\mathrm{Cc}^2(P \cap \mathrm{Cc}^2(Q)) \subseteq \mathrm{Cc}^2(P \cap Q). \tag{2.2}$$

By Theorem 2.14 we can in the lemma simultaneously replace P and Q by $\mathrm{Cc}^2(Q)$ and P, giving

$$\mathrm{Cc}^2(P) \cap \mathrm{Cc}^2(Q) \subseteq \mathrm{Cc}^2(P \cap \mathrm{Cc}^2(Q)).$$

Combining this with (2.2) gives

$$\mathrm{Cc}^2(P) \cap \mathrm{Cc}^2(Q) \subseteq \mathrm{Cc}^2(P \cap Q). \tag{2.3}$$

As $P \cap Q \subseteq P$ and $P \cap Q \subseteq Q$, we can apply Theorem 2.12 two times to each of these to get $\mathrm{Cc}^2(P \cap Q) \subseteq \mathrm{Cc}^2(P)$ and $\mathrm{Cc}^2(P \cap Q) \subseteq \mathrm{Cc}^2(Q)$. So

$$\mathrm{Cc}^2(P \cap Q) \subseteq \mathrm{Cc}^2(P) \cap \mathrm{Cc}^2(Q).$$

Combining this with (2.3) gives our theorem.

Definition 2.8. We say that P is regular iff $P = \mathrm{Cc}^2(P)$.

If P is regular, then by Theorem 2.14 P is an open set. So it is customary to speak of the regular open sets as those sets P such that $P = \mathrm{Cc}^2(P)$.

Definition 2.9. We take A to be the set of regular open sets of X, and define

$$0 = \Lambda \tag{2.4}$$

$$1 = X \tag{2.5}$$

$$P \wedge Q = P \cap Q \tag{2.6}$$

$$P \vee Q = \mathrm{Cc}^2(P \cup Q) \tag{2.7}$$

$$P' = \mathrm{Cc}(P). \tag{2.8}$$

Theorem 2.18. If A, 0, 1, $\wedge$, $\vee$, and $'$ are as in Definition 2.9, then

$$0 \in A \qquad 1 \in A \tag{2.9}$$

$$0 \neq 1 \tag{2.10}$$

$$0' = 1 \qquad 1' = 0. \tag{2.11}$$

Also, if P, Q, and R are members of A, then

$$P' \in A \tag{2.12}$$

$$P \wedge Q \in A \qquad P \vee Q \in A \tag{2.13}$$

$$P \wedge 0 = 0 \qquad P \vee 1 = 1 \tag{2.14}$$

$$P \wedge 1 = P \qquad P \vee 0 = P \tag{2.15}$$

$$P \wedge P' = 0 \qquad P \vee P' = 1 \tag{2.16}$$

$$P'' = P \tag{2.17}$$

$$P \wedge P = P \qquad P \vee P = P \tag{2.18}$$

$$(P \wedge Q)' = P' \vee Q' \qquad (P \vee Q)' = P' \wedge Q' \tag{2.19}$$

$$P \wedge Q = Q \wedge P \qquad P \vee Q = Q \vee P \tag{2.20}$$

$$\begin{aligned} P \wedge (Q \wedge R) &= (P \wedge Q) \wedge R \\ P \vee (Q \vee R) &= (P \vee Q) \vee R \end{aligned} \tag{2.21}$$

$$\begin{aligned} P \wedge (Q \vee R) &= (P \wedge Q) \vee (P \wedge R) \\ P \vee (Q \wedge R) &= (P \vee Q) \wedge (P \vee R). \end{aligned} \tag{2.22}$$

PROOF. Clearly $\mathrm{Cl}(0) = 0$, so that by (2.8) $0' = \mathrm{Co}(0) = 1$. But clearly $\mathrm{Cl}(1) = 1$, so that by (2.8) $1' = \mathrm{Co}(1) = 0$. This verifies (2.11), and incidentally establishes $0'' = 0$ and $1'' = 1$. By (2.8) and Definition 2.8, this says that 0 and 1 are regular open sets, which verifies (2.9). As X is nonempty, (2.10) follows from (2.4) and (2.5).

Incidentally, by (2.8) and Definition 2.8, the relation (2.17) merely says that P is a regular open set; thus (2.17) holds because A is the set of regular open sets. If $P \in A$, then P is an open set, and so by Theorem 2.15, $\mathrm{Cc}(P) = \mathrm{Cc}^3(P)$. By (2.8), this says $P' = \mathrm{Cc}^2(P')$. So P' is a regular open set, verifying (2.12). By Theorem 2.16 and (2.7), $P \vee Q = \mathrm{Cc}^2(P \vee Q)$, so that the right side of (2.13) holds.

We next verify the right side of (2.19). By (2.7) and (2.8), $(P \vee Q)' = \mathrm{Cc}^3(P \cup Q)$. As P and Q are open sets (being in A), we conclude that $P \cup Q$ is an open set by Theorem 2.1. So by Theorem 2.15, $(P \vee Q)' = \mathrm{Cc}(P \cup Q)$. Then by Theorem 2.7, $(P \vee Q)' = \mathrm{Co}(\mathrm{Cl}(P) \cup \mathrm{Cl}(P)) = \mathrm{Co}(\mathrm{Cl}(P)) \cap \mathrm{Co}(\mathrm{Cl}(P))$. By (2.6) and (2.8), we have finally $(P \vee Q)' = P' \wedge Q'$.

This with (2.17) gives us effectively de Morgan's laws. Using these, we can verify either side of one of the clauses of Theorem 2.18 if the other side has been verified. We illustrate by verifying the left side of (2.13). If P and Q are in A, then P' and Q' are in A by (2.12), and so $P' \vee Q'$ is in A by the right side of (2.13), and finally $(P' \vee Q')'$ is in A by (2.12). But by the right side of (2.19), we have $(P' \vee Q')' = P'' \wedge Q''$, and so by (2.17) we get

$$(P' \vee Q')' = P \wedge Q. \tag{2.23}$$

So the left side of (2.13) holds. If we prime both sides of (2.23), we get $(P \wedge Q)' = (P' \vee Q')''$, and then the left side of (2.19) follows by (2.17).

As yet another illustration of using (2.19) and (2.17) to derive one side of a clause from the other, we note that the left side of (2.14) holds by (2.4) and (2.6). Putting P' for P gives $P' \wedge 0 = 0$. Priming both sides, and using (2.19) gives $P'' \vee 0' = 0'$. Then the right side of (2.14) follows by (2.17) and (2.11).

In view of this, we shall verify only one side of the remaining clauses. By (2.5) and (2.6), we verify the left sides of (2.15), (2.18), (2.20), and (2.21). By Theorem 2.5, if $P \in A$, then $P \subseteq \mathrm{Cl}(P)$. Hence $P \cap \mathrm{Co}(\mathrm{Cl}(P)) = \Lambda$. By (2.4) (2.6), and (2.8), this gives the left side of (2.16).

We conclude by verifying the right side of (2.22). By (2.6) and (2.7),

$$(P \vee Q) \wedge (P \vee R) = \mathrm{Cc}^2(P \cup Q) \cap \mathrm{Cc}^2(P \cup R).$$

By Theorem 2.1 and Theorem 2.17

$$\begin{aligned}(P \vee Q) \wedge (P \vee R) &= \mathrm{Cc}^2((P \cup Q) \cap (P \cup R)) \\ &= \mathrm{Cc}^2(P \cup (Q \cap R)).\end{aligned}$$

By (2.6) and (2.7), this gives the right side of (2.22).

B. Properties of Boolean Algebras

It is customary to say that a Boolean algebra is a set A with members 0 and 1 and functions $\wedge$, $\vee$, and $'$ which satisfy (2.9)–(2.22). This is the description given by Halmos [6, p. 5]. Incidentally, we are using the notation given by Halmos [6] for Boolean algebras.

Note that we have specified that A should be a set. This greatly simplifies many developments. In Chapter 9, we shall allow A to be a class. (See Cohen [3, p. 74] or Gödel [5, p. 3].) In so doing, we lose many properties of a Boolean algebra, and subsequently find the developments much more difficult.

The simplest Boolean algebra is that in which $A = \{0, 1\}$, and $\wedge$, $\vee$, and $'$ are defined by (2.11), (2.14), (2.15), and (2.20). The other relationships are easily verified. This Boolean algebra will be of little interest for us, since its use would only reproduce the familiar two-valued logic, and so would produce no novelties.

For our purpose, we need a more sophisticated A. Typical of the kind we will use is the following. Choose a nonempty index set I, and take

$$X = \{0, 1\}^I. \tag{2.24}$$

That is, the points of X are functions x defined over I with values in $\{0, 1\}$. That is, for each $i \in I$ we take $x(i)$ to be 0 or 1.

For each $i \in I$ and each $n = 0$ or 1, we define the subbasis set B_i^n to be the set of all points x for which $x(i) = n$. That is,

$$B_i^n = \{x \mid x(i) = n\}. \tag{2.25}$$

Then we take the basis sets to be the nonempty intersections of finitely many subbasis sets. (We discard empty intersections, such as $B_i^0 \wedge B_i^1$.) That is, if N is a nonnegative integer, $f(j) \in I$ for $1 \leq j \leq N$ and $g(j) = 0$ or 1 for $1 \leq j \leq N$, then B is a basis set if $B \neq \Lambda$ and

$$B = \bigcap \{B_{f(j)}^{g(j)} \mid 1 \leq j \leq N\}. \tag{2.26}$$

Moreover, B is a basis set only if it can be expressed in the form (2.26). Taking N to be 0 gives X as a basis set.

The notation in (2.26) is that of Rosser [7, p. 238]. Other common notations for this are

$$B = \bigcap_{1 \leq j \leq N} B_{f(j)}^{g(j)}$$

and

$$B = \prod_{1 \leq j \leq N} B_{f(j)}^{g(j)} .$$

We readily verify Axioms 2.1 and 2.2. Furthermore, for each i,

$$B_i^0 = \mathrm{Co}(B_i^1). \tag{2.27}$$

As B_i^0 and B_i^1 are both open sets by Theorem 2.2, we see that B_i^0 and B_i^1 are both closed sets by Definition 2.5 and Theorem 2.9. So by Theorem 2.10

$$\mathrm{Cl}(B_i^0) = B_i^0 \tag{2.28}$$

$$\mathrm{Cl}(B_i^1) = B_i^1. \tag{2.29}$$

Then by (2.8) and (2.27)

$$(B_i^0)' = B_i^1 \tag{2.30}$$

$$(B_i^1)' = B_i^0. \tag{2.31}$$

Hence

$$(B_i^0)'' = B_i^0 \tag{2.32}$$

$$(B_i^1)'' = B_i^1. \tag{2.33}$$

So each B_i^0 and B_i^1 is a regular open set. Then by (2.26) and (2.13), each basis set B is a regular open set. Thus, by Theorem 2.18, we get a Boolean algebra in which there is a plentiful supply of elements, especially if I is taken to be a large set. Boolean algebras generated in this particular manner have other useful properties, to which we will call attention at the proper point.

We need certain additional properties of Boolean algebras. Until otherwise stated, these will be derived solely on the assumption that A, 0, 1, $\wedge$, $\vee$, and $'$ satisfy the various clauses of Theorem 2.18.

Theorem 2.19. In a Boolean algebra we have

$$P \vee (P \wedge Q) = P \qquad P \wedge (P \vee Q) = P \tag{2.34}$$

$$(P \wedge Q') \vee Q = P \vee Q \qquad (P \vee Q') \wedge Q = P \wedge Q \tag{2.35}$$

$$P \wedge Q = P \quad \text{iff} \quad P \vee Q = Q. \tag{2.36}$$

PROOF. We have
$P \vee (P \wedge Q) = (P \wedge 1) \vee (P \wedge Q) = P \wedge (1 \vee Q) = P \wedge 1 = P.$
This gives the left side of (2.34), and the right side follows by (2.17) and (2.19). We have $(P \vee Q') \wedge Q = (P \wedge Q) \vee (Q' \wedge Q) = (P \wedge Q) \vee 0 = P \wedge Q$. Then the left side of (2.35) follows by (2.17) and (2.19). If $P \wedge Q = P$, then $P \vee Q = (P \wedge Q) \vee Q$ so that $P \vee Q = Q$ follows by the left side of (2.34). Conversely, if $P \vee Q = Q$, then $P \wedge Q = P \wedge (P \vee Q) = P$.

Definition 2.10. We define

$$P \Rightarrow Q \quad \text{for} \quad P' \vee Q \tag{2.37}$$

$$P \Leftrightarrow Q \quad \text{for} \quad (P \Rightarrow Q) \wedge (Q \Rightarrow P) \tag{2.38}$$

$$P \leq Q \quad \text{iff} \quad P \wedge Q = P. \tag{2.39}$$

Theorem 2.20. In a Boolean algebra we have

$$P \leq P \tag{2.40}$$

$$\text{if} \quad P \leq Q \quad \text{and} \quad Q \leq P, \quad \text{then} \quad P = Q \tag{2.41}$$

$$\text{if} \quad P \leq Q \quad \text{and} \quad Q \leq R, \quad \text{then} \quad P \leq R \tag{2.42}$$

$$0 \leq P \quad \text{and} \quad P \leq 1 \tag{2.43}$$

$$\text{if} \quad P \leq Q, \quad \text{then} \quad P \wedge R \leq Q \wedge R \tag{2.44}$$

$$\text{if} \quad P \leq Q, \quad \text{then} \quad P \vee R \leq Q \vee R \tag{2.45}$$

$$P \wedge Q \leq P \quad \text{and} \quad P \leq P \vee Q \tag{2.46}$$

$$P \leq Q \quad \text{iff} \quad Q' \leq P' \tag{2.47}$$

$$P \leq Q \quad \text{iff} \quad P \Rightarrow Q = 1 \tag{2.48}$$

$$P = Q \quad \text{iff} \quad P \Leftrightarrow Q = 1. \tag{2.49}$$

PROOF. We obtain (2.40) by (2.18), (2.41) by (2.20), and (2.42) by (2.21). To show (2.45), suppose $P \leq Q$. Then $P \wedge Q = P$ by (2.39), so that $P \vee Q = Q$ by (2.36). So $(P \vee R) \vee (Q \vee R) = (P \vee Q) \vee (R \vee R) = Q \vee R$. So $(P \vee R) \wedge (Q \vee R) = P \vee R$ by (2.36), which is $P \vee R \leq Q \vee R$. The reader should have no trouble proving the remaining clauses of the theorem.

We say that R is an upper bound of a set of elements iff $P \leq R$ for each P in the set. By (2.46), $P \leq P \vee Q$ and $Q \leq P \vee Q$. So $P \vee Q$ is an upper bound of the set $\{P, Q\}$. We say that S is the supremum of a set of elements iff it is an upper bound of the set and is $\leq$ each upper bound of the set. Suppose R is an upper bound of the set $\{P, Q\}$. That is, $P \leq R$ and $Q \leq R$. Then by (2.45), $P \vee Q \leq R \vee Q$ and $R \vee Q \leq R \vee R = R$, so that $P \vee Q \leq R$. Thus $P \vee Q$ is the supremum of the set $\{P, Q\}$. This motivates the following definition.

Definition 2.11. If the set of elements P_i for $i \in I$ has a supremum S, we call this the sum of the P_i, and write

$$\sum_{i \in I} P_i = S. \tag{2.50}$$

Clearly, if I is the null set, then the supremum is 0. That is

$$\sum_{i \in \Lambda} P_i = 0. \tag{2.51}$$

Definition 2.12. If the supremum exists for each set, we say that the Boolean algebra is complete.

We readily verify the generalizations of the right sides of (2.18) and (2.20). The generalization of (2.21) takes the following form.

Theorem 2.21. If for each j

$$\sum_{i} P_{ij} = S_j \tag{2.52}$$

and

$$\sum_{j} S_j = S, \tag{2.53}$$

then

$$\sum_{i,j} P_{ij} = S. \tag{2.54}$$

The reader should have no trouble devising a proof. If needed, reference could be made to Lemma 3 on p. 27 of Halmos [6].

A generalization (which we shall need) of the left side of (2.22) is the following.

Theorem 2.22. We have

$$Q \wedge \sum_{i \in I} P_i = \sum_{i \in I} (Q \wedge P_i) \tag{2.55}$$

in the sense that, if $\sum P_i$ exists, then so does the right side of (2.55) and (2.55) holds.

PROOF. As $P_i \leq \sum P_i$, we have $Q \wedge P_i \leq Q \wedge \sum P_i$, so that $Q \wedge \sum P_i$ is an upper bound of the $Q \wedge P_i$. To show that it is a supremum, let $Q \wedge P_i \leq R$ for each i. Then (using (2.35))

$$P_i \leq Q' \vee P_i = Q' \vee (Q \wedge P_i) \leq Q' \vee R.$$

So $\sum P_i \leq Q' \vee R$. Then (using (2.35) again)

$$Q \wedge \sum P_i \leq Q \wedge (Q' \vee R) = Q \wedge R \leq R.$$

Given a set of elements P_i for $i \in I$, we define a lower bound and an infimum analogously to the upper bound and supremum. It is easy to see that $(\sum P_i')'$ is an infimum if $\sum P_i'$ exists (if $R \leq P_i$, then $P_i' \leq R'$ so that $\sum P_i' \leq R'$). This motivates the following definition.

Definition 2.13. If $\sum P_i'$ exists, we make the definition

$$\prod_{i \in I} P_i = \Big(\sum_{i \in I} P_i'\Big)'. \tag{2.56}$$

This provides the generalization of (2.19).

Clearly the Boolean algebra is complete if and only if each set has an infimum. Analogous to (2.51), we have

$$\prod_{i \in \Lambda} P_i = 1. \tag{2.57}$$

Also we have analogs of previous theorems.

Theorem 2.23. If for each j

$$\prod_i P_{ij} = S_j \tag{2.58}$$

and

$$\prod_j S_j = S, \tag{2.59}$$

then

$$\prod_{i,\,j} P_{ij} = S. \tag{2.60}$$

Theorem 2.24. If

$$\prod_{i \in I} P_i = P \tag{2.61}$$

then

$$\prod_{i \in I} (Q \vee P_i) = Q \vee P. \tag{2.62}$$

We shall have frequent use for the following obvious results.

Theorem 2.25. We have

$$\sum_{i \in I} P_i = 0 \tag{2.63}$$

if and only if

$$P_i = 0, \qquad i \in I, \tag{2.64}$$

and we have

$$\prod_{i \in I} P_i = 1 \tag{2.65}$$

if and only if

$$P_i = 1, \qquad i \in I. \tag{2.66}$$

The following result is of the greatest importance.

Theorem 2.26. If A is the set of regular open sets of X and the Boolean algebra is determined by Definition 2.9, then the Boolean algebra is complete.

PROOF. By (2.6) and (2.39) we have $P \leq Q$ if and only if $P \subseteq Q$. Let

$$S = \mathrm{Cc}^2(\bigcup \{P_i \mid i \in I\}). \tag{2.67}$$

Since each P_i is open, we have $\bigcup \{P_i \mid i \in I\}$ is open, by Theorem 2.1. So by Theorem 2.13, $\bigcup \{P_i \mid i \in I\} \subseteq S$, Hence $P_i \subseteq S$ for each $i \in I$ by Theorem IX.5.5, Part II, on p. 241 of Rosser [7]. Also, $S \in A$ by Theorem 2.16. So $P_i \leq S$, and S is an upper bound. To prove it is the supremum, suppose $Q \in A$ and $P_i \leq Q$ for each $i \in I$. Then $P_i \subseteq Q$, so that $\bigcup \{P_i \mid i \in I\} \subseteq Q$ by Theorem IX.5.8, Part II, on p. 242 of Rosser [7]. Then two uses of Theorem 2.12 give $S \subseteq \mathrm{Cc}^2(Q)$. But, as $Q \in A$, we have $\mathrm{Cc}^2(Q) = Q$ by Definition 2.8.

For our applications, it is vital that the Boolean algebra be complete. However, as the Boolean algebras which we shall use will consist mostly of the regular open sets of a topological space, Theorem 2.26 assures us of the needed completeness.

Henceforth we shall assume that the Boolean algebra is complete.

Theorem 2.27. Let A be defined as in Definition 2.9. Let $P \in A$ and $Q_i \in A$ for $i \in I$. Suppose

$$P \wedge \sum_{i \in I} Q_i \neq 0. \tag{2.68}$$

Then there is a basis set B and an index i such that

$$B \subseteq P \wedge Q_i. \tag{2.69}$$

PROOF. Let x be a point in $P \wedge \sum Q$. By Definition 2.2, there is a basis set B_1 with $x \in B_1$ and $B_1 \subseteq P$. Then

$$B_1 \wedge \sum Q_i \neq 0 \tag{2.70}$$

since it contains x. We cannot have

$$B_1 \wedge Q_i = 0 \tag{2.71}$$

for each i, since this would give

$$B_1 \wedge \sum Q_i = 0 \tag{2.72}$$

by Theorems 2.22 and 2.25. So there is an $i \in I$ such that

$$B_1 \wedge Q_i \neq 0. \tag{2.73}$$

Therefore by (2.6) there is a y with $y \in B_1$ and $y \in Q_i$. By Definition 2.2, there is a basis set B_2 with $y \in B_2$ and $B_2 \subseteq Q_i$. By Axiom 2.2, there is a basis set B with $y \in B$ and $B \subseteq B_1 \cap B_2$. This B satisfies (2.69).

C. Automorphisms

In some cases, automorphisms of the Boolean algebra play an important role.

Definition 2.14. A mapping G is an automorphism of the Boolean algebra A iff it is one-to-one, its range and domain are both A, and for P, $Q \in A$ we have

$$G(P \wedge Q) = G(P) \wedge G(Q) \tag{2.74}$$

$$G(P \vee Q) = G(P) \vee G(Q) \tag{2.75}$$

$$G(P') = (G(P))'. \tag{2.76}$$

Theorem 2.28. If G is an automorphism of the Boolean algebra, then

$$G(0) = 0 \tag{2.77}$$

$$G(1) = 1. \tag{2.78}$$

Also, if P, $Q \in A$, then

$$G(P \Rightarrow Q) = G(P) \Rightarrow G(Q) \tag{2.79}$$

$$G(P \Leftrightarrow Q) = G(P) \Leftrightarrow G(Q) \tag{2.80}$$

$$P \leq Q \quad \text{iff} \quad G(P) \leq G(Q). \tag{2.81}$$

Finally, if $P_i \in A$, then

$$G\Big(\sum_{i \in I} P_i\Big) = \sum_{i \in I} G(P_i) \tag{2.82}$$

$$G\Big(\prod_{i \in I} P_i\Big) = \prod_{i \in I} G(P_i). \tag{2.83}$$

PROOF. Take a $P \in A$. Then $G(0) = G(P \wedge P') = G(P) \wedge G(P') = G(P) \wedge (G(P))' = 0$. The proof of (2.78) is similar. No difficulty arises in proving (2.79)–(2.81). By means of (2.81), we can conclude that the property of being a supremum or infimum is preserved under G, so that (2.82) and (2.83) follow.

A typical automorphism for our purposes will be constructed as follows. Having defined X by (2.24), we can transform X into itself by interchanging B_i^n with B_j^n $(n = 0, 1)$ at all places where either occurs. This is a one-to-one transformation which is its own inverse. It carries basis sets into basis sets, and hence open sets into open sets, and thus regular open sets into regular open sets. It induces a transformation G on the Boolean algebra A which is readily seen to be an automorphism. One can also transform X into itself by interchanging B_i^0 with B_i^1; this also induces an automorphism on A.

Theorem 2.29. The only elements of A which are invariant under all automorphisms induced by interchanging B_i^0 with B_i^1 are 0 and 1.

PROOF. Let $P \in A$ be invariant. If $P \neq 0$, then there must be a basis set of the form (2.26) included in P, since P is an open set. Now interchange $B_{f(N)}^0$ with $B_{f(N)}^1$. Since P is invariant

$$\left(\bigcap \{B_{f(j)}^{g(j)} \mid 1 \leq j \leq N-1\}\right) \cap B_{f(N)}^{1-g(N)}$$

is also included in P. Hence the sum of this and the basis set (2.26) in included in P. That is

$$\bigcap \{B_{f(j)}^{g(j)} \mid 1 \leq j \leq N-1\} \subseteq P.$$

Proceeding in this manner, we conclude that $X \subseteq P$, and so $P = 1$.

Definition 2.15. We shall speak of

$$\{f(j) \mid j \in J\}$$

as the support of the set of points

$$\bigcap \{B_{f(j)}^{g(j)} \mid j \in J\}.$$

In terms of this, one may characterize the basis sets (2.26) as those nonempty products of subbasis sets which have a finite support.

Theorem 2.30. If J is an infinite subset of the I of (2.24), then

$$\prod_{j \in J} B_j^{g(j)} = 0$$

$$\sum_{j \in J} B_j^{g(j)} = 1.$$

PROOF. Suppose

$$\prod_{j \in J} B_j^{g(j)} \neq 0.$$

Then it must include some basis set

$$\bigcap \{B_{f(j)}^{h(j)} \mid 1 \leq j \leq N\}$$

since it is a regular open set. Let $j^* \in J$ but j^* not in the support of the basis set. Then some point x with $x(j^*) = 1 - g(j^*)$ will lie in the basis set. But no such point can lie in

$$\prod_{j \in J} B_j^{g(j)}.$$

Hence this latter must be 0. Now by (2.30) and (2.31)

$$\Big(\sum_{j \in J} B_j^{g(j)}\Big)' = \prod_{j \in J} B_j^{1-g(j)} = 0.$$

Theorem 2.31. Suppose J is a subset of the I of (2.24) such that $I - J$ is infinite. Suppose P is an element of the Boolean algebra such that, for each i and j in $I - J$, P is invariant under the automorphism induced by interchanging B_i'' with B_j''. Then P is the supremum of a set of basis sets whose supports are subsets of J.

PROOF. Suppose $P = 0$. Then it is the supremum of an empty set of basic sets. So let $P \neq 0$. Then by Definition 2.2. it is a nonempty sum of basis sets. As in the proof of Theorem 2.26 we conclude that P is indeed the supremum of this set of basis sets. Let B be one of these basis sets. Suppose the support of B is not a subset of J. Then we can write

$$B = Q \cap B_i^n$$

where $i \in I - J$ and

$$Q = \bigcap \{B_{f(j)}^{g(j)} \mid 1 \leq j \leq N \;\&\; f(j) \neq i\}.$$

Now interchange B_i^n with B_j^n, where j is not in the support of Q. Since P is invariant, we conclude

$$Q \cap B_j^n \subseteq P.$$

Therefore

$$Q \wedge (B_i^n \vee B_j^n) \subset P.$$

Doing this for each $j \in (I - J) - S$ where S is the support of Q, we conclude

$$Q \wedge \sum_{j \in (I-J)-S} B_j^n \subseteq P.$$

As $(I - J) - S$ is an infinite set, we conclude by Theorem 2.30 that

$$Q \subseteq P.$$

If the support of Q is not a subset of J, we may repeat the process. As B has a finite support, we will come in a finite number of steps to a basis set R such that

$$B \subseteq R \subseteq P$$

and the support of R is a subset of J. Doing this for each basis set which is included in P, we conclude our theorem.

It is clear that the inverse of an automorphism is again an automorphism. For instance, by (2.74),

$$G(G^{-1}(P) \wedge G^{-1}(Q)) = G(G^{-1}(P)) \wedge G(G^{-1}(Q)) = P \wedge Q.$$

Therefore

$$G^{-1}(P) \wedge G^{-1}(Q) = G^{-1}(P \wedge Q).$$

If G and H are automorphisms, we define the product GH by

$$(GH)(P) = G(H(P)). \tag{2.84}$$

It is verified trivially that GH is again an automorphism. Thus it is natural to speak of a group $\mathscr{G}$ of automorphisms.

In some cases we shall wish to speak of a filter Γ of subgroups of $\mathscr{G}$. By this we require that every member of Γ be a subgroup of $\mathscr{G}$. Also

$$\mathscr{G} \in \Gamma \tag{2.85}$$

$$\text{if} \quad \mathscr{H}, \mathscr{K} \in \Gamma, \qquad \text{then} \quad \mathscr{H} \wedge \mathscr{K} \in \Gamma \tag{2.86}$$

$$\text{if} \quad \mathscr{H} \in \Gamma \quad \text{and} \quad \mathscr{H} \subseteq \mathscr{K}, \qquad \text{then} \quad \mathscr{K} \in \Gamma \tag{2.87}$$

should hold for all subgroups $\mathscr{H}$, $\mathscr{K}$ of $\mathscr{G}$. We shall require that the filter be strongly normal, which means that we ask that:

$$\text{if } G \in \mathscr{G} \text{ and } \mathscr{H} \subseteq \mathscr{G}, \quad \text{then } \mathscr{H} \in \Gamma \text{ iff } G\mathscr{H}G^{-1} \in \Gamma. \tag{2.88}$$

The simplest filter is the one consisting of all subgroups of $\mathscr{G}$. Clearly it is strongly normal. We shall use this filter in most cases, but shall occasionally need to use something more complex.

D. The Countable Chain Condition

Not every Boolean algebra is complete. However, for our purposes use can be made only of those which are, so that we shall need to require this in all developments henceforth. There is another property, not possessed by all Boolean algebras, which we shall wish to use in many of our developments.

Definition 2.16. A Boolean algebra A is said to satisfy the countable chain condition if every disjoint set of nonzero elements of A is countable. (Two elements P and Q of a Boolean algebra are disjoint iff $P \wedge Q = 0$; a set E is disjoint iff every two distinct elements of E are disjoint.)

This definition is given by Halmos [6, p. 61].

It will commonly be desirable that the Boolean algebras we expect to use satisfy the countable chain condition. Not all do, but many do, as witness the next theorem.

Theorem 2.32. Suppose X is defined by (2.24) with basis sets defined by (2.26). Then the Boolean algebra defined by Definition 2.9 satisfies the countable chain condition.

PROOF. Indeed, we shall prove the slightly stronger result that every disjoint set of nonzero open sets of X is countable. Therefore, take a disjoint set of nonzero open sets. Each nonzero open set must contain a basis set, by Definition 2.2. Basis sets contained in disjoint open sets must clearly be disjoint. So for each nonzero open set we choose a basis set included in it, and have a disjoint set of basis sets.

Each basis set has the form (2.26), where we may as well insist that if $i \neq j$, then $f(i) \neq f(j)$; otherwise we could make do with a smaller value of N or else $B = 0$.

Lemma. If each member of a disjoint set of basis sets has exactly N distinct factors, as in (2.26), then there are at most $(N+1)!$ members of the set.

PROOF BY INDUCTION ON N. First take $N = 1$. If $j \neq k$, then $B_j^n \cap B_k^m \neq 0$. So there must be a single j such that each basis set has the form B_j^n. But there are at most two such, namely B_j^0 and B_j^1. So the lemma holds when $N = 1$. Now assume the lemma for N, and let E be a disjoint set of basis sets determined by (2.26) with $N + 1$. If E is empty, we have finished. So let $B \in E$. For $1 \leq j \leq N + 1$, consider the factor $B_{f(j)}^{g(j)}$. of B. Write $\theta(j)$ for the class of all members of E which contain $B_{f(j)}^{1-g(j)}$ as a factor. Each element of E except B must be in at least one of the $\theta(j)$, else it would not be disjoint with B. Since each element of $\theta(j)$ contains $B_{f(j)}^{1-g(j)}$ as a factor, and the pairs of elements from $\theta(j)$ are disjoint, the pairs would still be disjoint if we simply removed the factor $B_{f(j)}^{1-g(j)}$ from each element. But then each element has N factors. So the hypothesis of the induction says that each $\theta(j)$ contains at most $(N+1)!$ members. There are $(N+1)$ of the $\theta(j)$, so that altogether they contain at most $(N+1)((N+1)!)$ elements. We must add one more to take account of B. So E has at most $(N+1)((N+1)!) + 1$ elements, which is in fact less than $(N+2)!$. Thus our lemma is verified.

The theorem follows trivially from the lemma.

In Chapters 8 and 9 we introduce basis sets defined more generally than by (2.26). Thereupon, we lose the countable chain condition. This entails considerable complications to find a useable substitute.

CHAPTER THREE

The Basic Model

A. Axioms of the Restricted Predicate Calculus

In later chapters, we shall use special Boolean algebras. However, for the present chapter except where explicitly stated otherwise we assume only that we have a complete Boolean algebra. That is, the clauses of Theorem 2.18 all hold, and every set of elements has a supremum and infimum. We shall not need until the later chapters to specify that the Boolean algebra consists of the regular open sets of a topological space, as in Definition 2.9.

We shall assume that we have specified a certain group $\mathscr{G}$ of automorphisms of the Boolean algebra, and a certain filter Γ of the group $\mathscr{G}$. For the present chapter, we need only assume that Γ is strongly normal. This we do assume. Special choices of $\mathscr{G}$ and Γ will be made later.

We shall proceed shortly to a definition of a universe V of objects. Simultaneously with the definition of V will be given a definition of the predicates $\in$ and $=$. That is, when our definition is complete, we shall have specified for each pair of objects a and b of V two elements P and Q of the Boolean algebra, which elements are to be associated with the statements $a \in b$ and $a = b$, respectively. These shall be called the "Boolean values" of $a \in b$ and $a = b$, respectively. We shall use $\|a \in b\|$ and $\|a = b\|$ to denote these Boolean values of $a \in b$ and $a = b$, respectively.

More complex statements are to be built up from these, following the definition on p. 208 of Rosser [7]. Namely:

(a) Each variable or member of V is a term.
(b) If p and q are terms, then $(p \in q)$ and $(p = q)$ are statements.
(c) If x is a variable and X is a statement, then $(x)X$ is a statement.
(d) If X and Y are statements, then $\sim X$ and $(X \,\&\, Y)$ are statements.

Free and bound occurrences of variables are defined in the usual manner (see Rosser [7, pp. 208]). It is considered that members of V are constants. Specifically, they are not variables, either free or bound.

Assuming that the Boolean values $\|a \in b\|$ and $\|a = b\|$ have been specified for each a and b in V, we specify inductively the Boolean values for other statements without free variables as follows:

$$\|\sim X\| = \|X\|' \tag{3.1}$$

$$\|X \,\&\, Y\| = \|X\| \wedge \|Y\|. \tag{3.2}$$

If $F(x)$ is a statement containing no free occurrences of any variable except x, then

$$\|(x)F(x)\| = \prod_{a \in V} \|F(a)\|. \tag{3.3}$$

We might remark that V is a class and not a set. Thus, at first sight it would appear that the right side of (3.3) does not constitute a proper definition. However, the class of values taken by $F(a)$ is a subclass of the set of all members of the Boolean algebra, and hence is a set. Thus, on the right of (3.3.) we are asking for the infimum of a set of elements (rather than a class of elements). As we are assuming that the Boolean algebra is complete, the desired infimum exists.

From the definitions of $X \vee Y$, $X \supset Y$, $X \equiv Y$, and $(Ex)F(x)$ given by Rosser [7, pp. 14, 15, and 90], we conclude

$$\|X \vee Y\| = \|X\| \vee \|Y\| \tag{3.4}$$

$$\|X \supset Y\| = \|X\| \Rightarrow \|Y\| \tag{3.5}$$

$$\|X \equiv Y\| = \|X\| \Leftrightarrow \|Y\| \tag{3.6}$$

$$\|(Ex)F(x)\| = \sum_{a \in V} F(a). \tag{3.7}$$

The reader should note most carefully that we are using the word "statement" exclusively as defined by means of (a), (b), (c), and (d) on p. 35. Hence, by means of (3.1), (3.2), and (3.3) we can, for each statement X with no free variables, determine a unique Boolean value $\|X\|$ by starting from the Boolean values for the ultimate constituents of X and building up. Suppose that X contains free variables, but that no matter how these are replaced by members of V the resulting statement without free variables has the Boolean value 1. Then we set $\|X\| = 1$.

We shall write $\vDash X$ to denote that X has the Boolean value 1. That is

$$\vDash X \quad \text{iff} \quad \|X\| = 1. \tag{3.8}$$

Our procedure to prove that some specific statement X_0 is not derivable in set theory is to establish two results:

(1) Every statement derivable in set theory has the Boolean value 1.

(2) The statement X_0 does not have the Boolean value 1.

In the present chapter we establish the result (1). It can be rephrased as entailing that if $\vdash X$ then $\vDash X$. It is established by showing that if X is an axiom of set theory, then $\vDash X$, and that if Z can be derived from X and Y by the rules of set theory and $\vDash X$ and $\vDash Y$, then $\vDash Z$.

We will follow the formulation of Rosser [7], in which the sole rule is *modus ponens*. So the application of the rules of set theory is taken care of by the following theorem.

Theorem 3.1. If $\vDash X$ and $\vDash X \supset Y$, then $\vDash Y$.

PROOF. Assume $\|X\| = 1$ and $\|X \supset Y\| = 1$. Then by (3.5) and (2.37), $\|X\|' \vee \|Y\| = 1$. But $\|X\|' = 0$, so that $\|Y\| = 1$. Suppose that X and Y contain free variables. Then $\vDash X$ and $\vDash X \supset Y$ require that $\models X_V$ and $\models X_V \supset Y_V$, where X_V and Y_V are obtained by replacing the free variables of X and Y by members of V. Then, by the analysis just given, $\models Y_V$. However, this holds for each replacement. So $\models Y$.

Thus it will suffice to show that for each axiom X of set theory we have $\models X$. We do this forthwith for the axioms of the restricted predicate calculus. We use the axioms given by Rosser [7, p. 101].

We first interpolate a few remarks about the role of the Boolean algebra in verifying the axioms of the restricted predicate calculus. Boolean algebra was invented by George Boole in an attempt to find a more satisfactory treatment of probability. The problem was to reconcile the concept that there is a fifty percent chance of getting heads when a coin is flipped with the classical doctrine that a statement must be true or false. Consider the statement, "When I next flip this coin, it will land heads up," If one is going to insist that the statement must be either true or false, then either the coin will certainly land heads up, or it will certainly land tails up. Then what meaning is to be attached to the statement that I have a fifty percent chance of getting heads, and the same for tails?

Boole's proposal was to invent additional truth values. Instead of insisting that the statement, "When I flip this coin, it will land heads up," must take either the value truth or the value falsehood, he would allow other possible truth values. Thus, if the coin is symmetric, and is as likely to land heads up as tails up, he would assign a truth value B_1 to the statement. If the coin is loaded so that it is twice as likely to land heads up as tails up, he would assign the value B_2 to the statment. If the coin has a head on both sides, then indeed the statement is true, and he would assign it the value 1. If the coin has tails on both sides, then the statement is false, and he would assign it the value 0.

Boole worked out a set of rules for the manipulation of these values. A set of such values and Boole's rules for their manipulation constitute a Boolean algebra.

Since we are assigning Boolean values to statements, we could be considered to be assigning probabilities to statements. Thus classically, if one has sets a and b then either a is a member of b or else it is not. That is "$a \in b$" must take either the value 1 or 0.

If we are willing to admit that there is a fifty percent likelihood that a is a member of b, then we could set

$$\|a \in b\| = B_1,$$

where B_1 is the Boolean value assigned to the statement that a symmetric coin will land heads up.

If Boole's assignments of values to statements were to be satisfactory for the treatment of probability, then they would have to obey the rules of logic. Thus one may assign values other than 0 or 1 to each of "It will rain" and "The streets will be wet," but one must assign the value 1 to "If it rains the streets will be wet." That is, Boole's rules for manipulating his truth values must be so chosen that logically true statements always have the value 1 assigned. Indeed, they are so chosen, and this is why we will succeed in proving that the axioms of the statement calculus (see Rosser [7, Chapters II and IV]), take the value 1.

Boole did not try to deal with statements $F(x)$ involving a variable x. To do this, one has to introduce quantifiers. These are related to infimums and supremums by (3.3) and (3.7). We still wish logically true statements to take the value 1. To ensure this when infimums and supremums are involved, we must extend Boole's original stipulations by requiring that the Boolean algebra be complete. We have imposed this requirement. It suffices to assure that all axioms of the restricted predicate calculus take the value 1, as we now proceed to show.

Theorem 3.2. If X is an axiom of the restricted predicate calculus, then $\models X$.

PROOF. The methods of proof for each of the first three axioms

$$X \supset XX$$

$$(X \;\&\; Y) \supset X$$

$$X \supset Y \,.\supset .\, \sim(Y \;\&\; Z) \supset \sim(Z \;\&\; X)$$

are similar, and we shall illustrate by giving the proof for the third, which is the least trivial. By (3.1), (3.2), (3.5), and (2.48), it suffices to prove

$$P \Rightarrow Q \leq (Q \wedge R)' \Rightarrow (R \wedge P)'.$$

By de Morgan's laws and (2.37), this is the same as

$$P' \vee Q \leq (Q \wedge R) \vee R' \vee P'.$$

By (2.35), this is the same as

$$P' \vee Q \leq (Q \vee R') \vee P'.$$

As $Q \leq Q \vee R'$, this follows by (2.45).

If X, Y, and Z contain free variables, the above analysis applies to each instance obtained by replacing these free variables by members of V. Hence we conclude that such replacements give the Boolean value 1 for the axiom. Hence the axiom is valid even when free variables are present. The same argument also verifies that

$$\vDash (x_1)(x_2)\cdots(x_n)(X \supset Y . \supset . \sim(Y \,\&\, Z) \supset \sim(Z \,\&\, X)).$$

Lemma. $\vDash X \supset . Y \supset Z$ if and only if $\|X\| \wedge \|Y\| \leq \|Z\|$.

PROOF. By (3.5), (3.8), and (2.37),

$$\vDash X \supset . Y \supset Z \qquad \text{iff} \qquad \|X\|' \vee (\|Y\|' \vee \|Z\|) = 1.$$

By de Morgan's laws and (2.37)

$$\|X\|' \vee (\|Y\|' \vee \|Z\|) = (\|X\| \wedge \|Y\|) \Rightarrow \|Z\|.$$

So our lemma follows by (2.48).

We now consider the axiom

$$(x) . F(x) \supset G(x) : \supset : (x)F(x) \supset (x)G(x).$$

By (3.3) and our lemma, it suffices to prove

$$\Big(\prod_{a \in V} \|F(a) \supset G(a)\|\Big) \wedge \prod_{a \in V} \|F(a)\| \leq \prod_{a \in V} \|G(a)\|. \tag{3.9}$$

However as $\prod$ is the infimum, we have

$$\prod_{a \in V} \|F(a) \supset G(a)\| \leq \|F(b) \supset G(b)\| \tag{3.10}$$

and

$$\prod_{a \in V} \|F(a)\| \leq \|F(b)\|. \tag{3.11}$$

By (3.5), (2.37), and (2.35)

$$\|F(b) \supset G(b)\| \wedge \|F(b)\| = \|F(b)\| \wedge \|G(b)\| \leq \|G(b)\|. \quad (3.12)$$

By two uses of (2.44), we can conclude from (3.10) and (3.11) that

$$\left(\prod_{a \in V} \|F(a) \supset G(a)\|\right) \wedge \prod_{a \in V} \|F(a)\| \leq \|F(b) \supset G(b)\| \wedge \|F(b)\|.$$

So by (3.12)

$$\left(\prod_{a \in V} \|F(a) \supset G(a)\|\right) \wedge \prod_{a \in V} \|F(a)\| \leq \|G(b)\|.$$

Multiplying on the right for all $b \in V$ gives (3.9).

The generalization to the case where $F(x)$ and $G(x)$ may contain other free variables besides x is easily handled, as is the case where one prefixes universal quantifiers to the axiom.

The axiom

$$X \supset (x)X$$

where there are no free occurrences of x in X presents no difficulties.

Finally, the axiom

$$(x)F(x, y) \supset F(y, y)$$

contains free occurrences of y, and perhaps other variables. Replace y by $b \in V$. So we need to show

$$\models (x)F(x, b) \supset F(b, b).$$

That is, we must show

$$\prod_{a \in V} \|F(a, b)\| \leq \|F(b, b)\|.$$

Since $\prod$ is an infimum and $b \in V$, this is immediate.

Incidentally, this final argument establishes the next theorem, which gives a useful extension of the restricted predicate calculus to the present situation, where statements may contain constants as well as variables.

Theorem 3.3. If $b \in V$, then

$$\models (x_1)(x_2) \cdots (x_n)((x)F(x, b) \supset F(b, b)).$$

From Theorems 3.1 and 3.2, we can say that if $\vdash X$ is a theorem in the first six chapters of Rosser [7], then $\vDash X$. More than that, the analysis of Rosser [7, pp. 123–133] establishes that we are entitled to use Rules G and C in demonstrating for a statement X that $\vDash X$.

B. Axioms of Equality and Extensionality

Let us recall Cayley's proof of the independence of the parallel postulate. To invalidate the parallel postulate, he had to introduce "points," "lines," etc. which differed slightly from classical points, lines, etc. However, as he wished the other postulates to remain valid, he made as few changes as practicable. We are at a similar point. To invalidate AxC, we must introduce "sets," "class membership," "equality," etc. which differ from classical sets, class membership, equality, etc. However, as we wish the other axioms to remain valid, we will make as few changes as practicable.

Let us look closely at the concept of class membership. If a is a member of b, we say that $a \in b$ is valid. A way to associate this with truth values is to identify 1 with truth and 0 with falsehood. Then we can say that $a \in b$ takes the value 1 if a is a member of b, and takes the value 0 if a is not a member of b. It is convenient to introduce the characteristic function f corresponding to b. We put

$$f(x) = 1 \quad \text{if} \quad x \in b$$

$$f(x) = 0 \quad \text{if} \quad \sim x \in b.$$

Then we may say that $a \in b$ takes the value $f(a)$. Indeed, we can dispense with b altogether, replacing it by f. Thus, instead of a set b with members and nonmembers, we have a function f whose values are either 1 or 0. We then interpret $a \in f$ as a statement with the truth value $f(a)$.

In this formulation the generalization to a Boolean valued logic is quite evident. A "set" will be a function f whose values are elements of the Boolean algebra. Thus, if for a "set" f and some a we conceive that certainly a is a member of f, then we assign

$f(a) = 1$; if we conceive that certainly a is not a member of f, then we assign $f(a) = 0$; if we think there is a fifty percent chance that a is a member of f, then we assign $f(a) = B_1$; and so on.

Certainly the value $\|a \in f\|$ to be attached to the statement $a \in f$ will be $f(a)$. That is, we set

$$\|a \in f\| = f(a).$$

(This will be (3.32) in our formal treatment.)

What about equality? We simply parallel the classical definition. That is, for $a = b$ we take

$$(x) \,.\, x \in a \equiv x \in b.$$

That is, by (3.3)

$$\prod_{x \in V} \|x \in a \equiv x \in b\|$$

will be the value of $a = b$. That is, by (3.6)

$$\|a = b\| = \prod_{x \in V} \{a(x) \Leftrightarrow b(x)\}.$$

This is essentially (3.29) except for a minor difficulty which we must now elucidate.

It is not practicable to introduce all our "sets" at once. Thus, when we introduce a new "set" f, we can define $f(a)$ for those a's which have already been introduced. For other a's, we must leave $f(a)$ undefined. Then in defining $f = g$ to be

$$(x) \,.\, x \in f \equiv x \in g,$$

one should restrict the quantifier x to the domain of f and g. If f and g have different domains, further complications arise whose resolution had best be postponed to the formal treatment. However, the complications can be resolved (see Theorem 3.4), so that $f = g$ can be defined satisfactorily. Then we assign a value to $a \in f$ when a is not in the domain of definition of f by saying that it is

$$(Ex) \,.\, a = x \,.\, x \in f,$$

where we restrict the quantifier x to the domain of f. (This is (3.28).)

With this general picture in mind, let us turn to the precise definitions of the universe V and the predicates $\in$ and $=$ over V. We define by induction on the ordinal α a subuniverse V_α and then define

$$V = \bigcup \{V_\alpha \mid \mathrm{Od}(\alpha)\}. \tag{3.13}$$

We are here using $\mathrm{Od}(\alpha)$ to mean that α is an ordinal. This is the notation of Bernays and Fraenkel [1, Chapter III]. The definition of V_α will be so phrased that

$$V_\beta \subseteq V_\alpha \qquad \text{if} \qquad \beta \leq \alpha. \tag{3.14}$$

We shall wish $\in$ and $=$ to satisfy the laws of equality, including extensionality. Namely, we will frame the definitions so that for a, b, and c in V we have

$$\vDash a = a \tag{3.15}$$

$$\vDash a = b \supset b = a \tag{3.16}$$

$$\vDash a = b \,.\, b = c \,.\supset.\, a = c \tag{3.17}$$

$$\vDash a = b \,.\, b \in c \,.\supset.\, a \in c \tag{3.18}$$

$$\vDash a \in b \,.\, b = c \,.\supset.\, a \in c. \tag{3.19}$$

Not only will we define $\|a \in b\|$ and $\|a = b\|$ for each a and b in V, but for each $G \in \mathscr{G}$ we will extend G to V in such a way that for $a, b \in V$

$$G(\|a \in b\|) = \|G(a) \in G(b)\| \tag{3.20}$$

$$G(\|a = b\|) = \|G(a) = G(b)\|. \tag{3.21}$$

Moreover, these extensions will preserve the group properties, in that if $a \in V$ and $G, H \in \mathscr{G}$, then

$$G(G^{-1}(a)) = G^{-1}(G(a)) = a \tag{3.22}$$

$$(GH)(a) = G(H(a)). \tag{3.23}$$

Furthermore, the extensions of members of $\mathscr{G}$ to V will be related to the filter Γ by the condition that the relation

$$\{G \mid G \in \mathscr{G} \,.\, \|G(a) = a\| = 1\} \in \Gamma \tag{3.24}$$

shall hold for each a in V. In the most common case, where Γ is taken to be the set of all subgroups of $\mathscr{G}$, (3.24) holds trivially by (3.22) and (3.23).

The elements to be added to V_α to produce $V_{\alpha+1}$ will be functions whose domain is V_α and whose range is a subset of the elements of the Boolean algebra. We shall use $D(a)$ to denote the domain of a. We start with

$$V_0 = \Lambda. \tag{3.25}$$

Then clearly

$$V_1 = \{\Lambda\}. \tag{3.26}$$

If α is a limit ordinal, then we set

$$V_\alpha = \bigcup \{V_\beta \mid \beta < \alpha\}. \tag{3.27}$$

Let us now look with care at the step from V_α to $V_{\alpha+1}$. We assume that the members of V_α have been specified, that (3.14) holds, that for $a, b \in V_\alpha$ we have

$$\|a \in b\| = \sum_{x \in D(b)} \|x \in b \,.\, a = x\| \tag{3.28}$$

$$\|a = b\| = \left\{\prod_{x \in D(a)} \|x \in a \supset x \in b\|\right\} \wedge \left\{\prod_{x \in D(b)} \|x \in b \supset x \in a\|\right\} \tag{3.29}$$

and that for $a, b, c \in V_\alpha$ and for $G, H \in \mathscr{G}$ each of (3.15)–(3.24), inclusive, holds. Also, if $a \in V_\alpha$, then $G(a)$ has been defined and is in V_α. Indeed, generally:

$$\text{if} \quad a \in V_\beta \quad \text{and} \quad \beta \le \alpha, \qquad \text{then} \quad G(a) \in V_\beta. \tag{3.30}$$

We further assume that every member of V_α is a function whose values are elements of the Boolean algebra. Moreover:

$$\text{if} \quad a \in V_{\beta+1}, \quad {\sim}a \in V_\beta, \quad \text{and} \quad \beta < \alpha, \qquad \text{then} \quad D(a) = V_\beta; \tag{3.31}$$

$$\text{if} \quad a \in V_\alpha \quad \text{and} \quad x \in D(a), \qquad \text{then} \quad \|x \in a\| = a(x). \tag{3.32}$$

Finally, every member of V_α is extensional, by which we mean:

$$\text{if} \quad x, y \in D(a), \qquad \text{then} \quad a(x) \wedge \|x = y\| \le a(y). \tag{3.33}$$

We first put into $V_{\alpha+1}$ each member of V_α. We next generate each function a from V_α to A. Certain of these will be chosen and adjoined to V_α to make up $V_{\alpha+1}$. Whatever our choice, we have already ensured that (3.14) and (3.31) hold for $\alpha + 1$. As $D(a) = V_\alpha$ for each new a, the value of $\|x = y\|$ has already been determined for each $x, y \in D(a)$. Hence for each $x, y \in D(a)$, it is determinate if $a(x) \wedge \|x = y\| \leq a(y)$. So it is determinate which new a's are extensional. We restrict our choice of a's to those that are extensional, thereby ensuring that (3.33) holds for $\alpha + 1$.

We define $G(a)$ by

$$G(a)(G(x)) = G(a(x)) \tag{3.34}$$

for each $x \in V_\alpha$. If $y \in V_\alpha$ and $G \in \mathscr{G}$, then $G^{-1} \in \mathscr{G}$, and so by (3.30) $G^{-1}(y) \in V_\alpha$. So by (3.34) and (3.22)

$$G(a)(y) = G(a)(G(G^{-1}(y))) = G(a(G^{-1}(y))).$$

So indeed, $G(a)$ is a function from V_α to A. Moreover, it is extensional, for since $a(x) \wedge \|x = y\| \leq a(y)$ for $x, y \in V_\alpha$, we have

$$a(G^{-1}(x)) \wedge \|G^{-1}(x) = G^{-1}(y)\| \leq a(G^{-1}(y)).$$

So by (2.81) and (2.74)

$$G(a(G^{-1}(x))) \wedge G(\|G^{-1}(x) = G^{-1}(y)\|) \leq G(a(G^{-1}(y))).$$

Then by (3.21) and (3.34)

$$G(a)(G(G^{-1}(x))) \wedge \|G(G^{-1}(x)) = G(G^{-1}(y))\| \leq G(a)(G(G^{-1}(y))).$$

So by (3.22)

$$G(a)(x) \wedge \|x = y\| \leq G(a)(y).$$

So by restricting our choice to extensional a's, we have not invalidated (3.30) for $\alpha + 1$.

For $x \in V_\alpha$, we define $\|x \in a\|$ to be $a(x)$ for each new a. This verifies (3.32) for $\alpha + 1$. We now define $\|a = b\|$ by (3.29). If $a, b \in V_\alpha$, this merely duplicates the known result (3.29). If $a \in V_\alpha$ and $b \in V_{\alpha+1}$ but $\sim b \in V_\alpha$, this is still an acceptable definition, since $D(a) \subseteq V_\alpha$ and $D(b) = V_\alpha$, and hence $\|x \in a\|$ is determined by (3.28) and $\|x \in b\|$ is determined by (3.32), so that

$\|x \in a \supset x \in b\|$ and $\|x \in b \supset x \in a\|$ are both determined. If $b \in V_\alpha$ and $a \in V_{\alpha+1}$ but $\sim a \in V_\alpha$, we proceed similarly; likewise if $a, b \in V_{\alpha+1}$ but both a and b are not in V_α. So (3.29) holds for $\alpha + 1$. Now, if $\sim a \in D(b)$, and $b \in V_{\alpha+1}$ and $\sim b \in V_\alpha$, we define

$$\|a \in b\| = \sum_{x \in D(b)} \|x \in b \,.\, a = x\|.$$

This is an acceptable definition since, for each $x \in D(b)$,

$$\|x \in b \,.\, a = x\|$$

is determined by (3.32) and (3.29). We now wish to verify that (3.28) holds for $\alpha + 1$. The only case where we have specified something different is when $b \in V_{\alpha+1}$, $\sim b \in V_\alpha$, and $a \in D(b)$, in which case we used (3.32). But in this case $D(b) = V_\alpha$, so that $a \in V_\alpha$. Then by (3.15)

$$\|a \in b\| = \|a \in b \,.\, a = a\| \leq \sum_{x \in D(b)} \|x \in b \,.\, a = x\|. \quad (3.35)$$

Now take $x \in D(b) = V_\alpha$. Then by (3.32) and (3.16)

$$\|x \in b \,.\, a = x\| \leq b(x) \wedge \|x = a\|.$$

So by (3.33) and (3.32)

$$\|x \in b \,.\, a = x\| \leq b(a) = \|a \in b\|.$$

Summing on x on the left gives

$$\sum_{x \in D(b)} \|x \in b \,.\, a = x\| \leq \|a \in b\|.$$

Then by (3.35) we infer that (3.28) holds for $\alpha + 1$.

We wish to verify (3.20) and (3.21) for $\alpha + 1$. We first verify (3.20) for $a \in V_\alpha$. If also $b \in V_\alpha$, then we have the case of (3.20) for α, which was assumed. If $b \in V_{\alpha+1}$ but $\sim b \in V_\alpha$, then $D(b) = V_\alpha$, so that $a \in D(b)$. Then we use (3.32) together with (3.34), using the fact that $D(b) = D(G(b))$ which follows by (3.30). We also have $D(b) = D(G(b))$ for $b \in V_\alpha$, by (3.30) and (3.31). So we now conclude (3.21) by means of (3.29), since $x \in a$ and $x \in b$ occur in it only if $x \in V_\alpha$, in which case we have verified (3.20). Finally, as we have verified (3.21) for $\alpha + 1$, we complete the verification of (3.20) for $\alpha + 1$ by means of (3.28).

We easily verify (3.22) and (3.23) for $\alpha + 1$ by use of (3.34). We ensure that (3.24) shall hold for $\alpha + 1$ by excluding from $V_{\alpha+1}$ all a's for which if fails. It is convenient to introduce the abbreviation

$$\mathcal{G}_a = \{G \mid G \in \mathcal{G} \,.\, \|G(a) = a\| = 1\}. \qquad (3.36)$$

Then (3.24) takes the form $\mathcal{G}_a \in \Gamma$. It is clear by (3.22) and (3.23) that $\mathcal{G}_a$ is a subgroup of Γ for each a. So in those cases in which Γ consists of all subgroups of $\mathcal{G}$, the restriction (3.24) excludes no a's. In a more special case it may do so, and then we must verify that (3.30) is not violated. Let $H \in \mathcal{G}_a$ and $G \in \mathcal{G}$. Then by (3.36), $H \in \mathcal{G}$ and $\|H(a) = a\| = 1$. So by (2.78) and (3.21), $\|G(H(a)) = G(a)\| = 1$. Then by (3.22) and (3.23), $\|(GHG^{-1})(G(a)) = G(a)\| = 1$. So $GHG^{-1} \in \mathcal{G}_{G(a)}$ by (3.36). Conversely, if $GHG^{-1} \in \mathcal{G}_{G(a)}$, then $H \in \mathcal{G}_a$. So $\mathcal{G}_{G(a)} = G\mathcal{G}_a G^{-1}$. So by (2.88), $\mathcal{G}_a \in \Gamma$ iff $\mathcal{G}_{G(a)} \in \Gamma$. Thus we complete the verification of (3.30) for $\alpha + 1$.

It remains to verify (3.15)–(3.19) for $\alpha + 1$. By (3.29), we conclude (3.15), since $\|x \in a \supset x \in a\| = 1$. Also (3.29) trivially gives (3.16).

Lemma A. If $x \in D(b)$, then

$$\|x \in b\| \wedge \| b = c \| \leq \| x \in c\|. \qquad (3.37)$$

PROOF. By (3.5), (2.37), and (2.35)

$$\|x \in b\| \wedge \|x \in b \supset x \in c\| = \|x \in b\| \wedge \|x \in c\|.$$

So by (2.46)

$$\|x \in b\| \wedge \|x \in b \supset x \in c\| \leq \|x \in c\|.$$

Since $\prod$ is the infimum, we have by (2.44)

$$\|x \in b\| \wedge \prod_{x \in D(b)} \|x \in b \supset x \in c\| \leq \|x \in c\|$$

if $x \in D(b)$. So by (3.29) our lemma follows.

Lemma B. If $a, b \in V_\alpha$ and $c \in V_{\alpha+1}$, then (3.19) holds.

PROOF. If $c \in V_\alpha$, then we appeal to the assumption that (3.19) holds for α. Therefore let $\sim c \in V_\alpha$. Then $D(c) = V_\alpha$. So by (3.14) and (3.31), $D(b) \subseteq D(c)$. Let $x \in D(b)$. Then by Lemma A

$$\|x \in b \,.\, a = x\| \wedge \|b = c\| \leq \|x \in c \,.\, a = x\|.$$

Summing on x over $D(b)$ and using (3.28) and Theorem 2.22, we obtain

$$\|a \in b\| \wedge \|b = c\| \leq \sum_{x \in D(b)} \|x \in c \,.\, a = x\|.$$

However, as $D(b) \subseteq D(c)$, we have

$$\sum_{x \in D(b)} \|x \in c \,.\, a = x\| \leq \sum_{x \in D(c)} \|x \in c \,.\, a = x\|.$$

By (3.28), the right side of this is $\|a \in c\|$. So by combining the two inequalities just above, we obtain

$$\|a \in b \,.\, b = c\| \leq \|a \in c\|,$$

which gives (3.19).

We now verify (3.17) for $a + 1$. Let $x \in D(a)$. Then, by Lemma A, we have

$$\|x \in a\| \wedge \|a = b\| \leq \|x \in b\|.$$

So

$$\|a = b \,.\, b = c\| \wedge \|x \in a\| \leq \|x \in b\| \wedge \|b = c\|. \tag{3.38}$$

Case 1. $b \in V_\alpha$. Then by Lemma B

$$\|x \in b\| \wedge \|b = c\| \leq \|x \in c\|. \tag{3.39}$$

Case 2. $\sim b \in V_\alpha$. Then $D(b) = V_\alpha$, so that $x \in D(b)$. Then by Lemma A we again conclude (3.39).

Therefore (3.39) holds in both cases. By (3.38) and (3.39), we obtain

$$\|a = b \,.\, b = c\| \wedge \|x \in a\| \leq \|x \in c\|.$$

So by (2.45), (2.37), and (2.35)

$$\|a = b \,.\, b = c\| \vee \|x \in a\|' \leq \|x \in a\| \Rightarrow \|x \in c\|.$$

So by (2.46) and (3.5)

$$\|a = b \,.\, b = c\| \leq \|x \in a \supset x \in c\|.$$

Multiplying on the right over all $x \in D(a)$ gives

$$\|a = b \,.\, b = c\| \leq \prod_{x \in D(a)} \|x \in a \supset x \in c\|. \tag{3.40}$$

One can start with $x \in D(c)$ and go through a similar argument to obtain

$$\|c = b \,.\, b = a\| \leq \prod_{x \in D(c)} \|x \in c \supset x \in a\|. \tag{3.41}$$

Then by (3.16) and (3.29), we can combine (3.40) and (3.41) to obtain

$$\|a = b \,.\, b = c\| \leq \|a = c\|,$$

which gives (3.17).

We next verify (3.18) for $\alpha + 1$. Let $x \in D(c)$. By (3.17), we obtain

$$\|a = b \,.\, b = x\| \leq \|a = x\|.$$

Therefore

$$\|a = b\| \wedge \|x \in c \,.\, b = x\| \leq \|x \in c \,.\, a = x\|.$$

Summing both sides over $x \in D(c)$ and using Theorem 2.22, we get (3.18) by (3.28).

Finally, we verify (3.19) for $\alpha + 1$. Let $x \in D(b)$. By Lemma A

$$\|x \in b\| \wedge \|b = c\| \leq \|x \in c\|.$$

Therefore

$$\|x \in b \,.\, a = x\| \wedge \|b = c\| \leq \|a = x \,.\, x \in c\|.$$

Then by (3.18)

$$\|x \in b \,.\, a = x\| \wedge \|b = c\| \leq \|a \in c\|.$$

Sum on the left over $x \in D(b)$ and use Theorem 2.22. Then we obtain (3.19) by (3.28).

Theorem 3.4. If $a, b \in V$, then

$$\vdash a = b \,.\, \equiv \,.\, (x) \,.\, x \in a \equiv x \in b.$$

PROOF. By (3.19) and (3.16)

$$\|a = b\| \leq \|x \in a \equiv x \in b\|.$$

As this is true for each $x \in V$, we can multiply on x and use (3.3) to obtain

$$\|a = b\| \leq \|(x) \,.\, x \in a \equiv x \in b\|.$$

Then by (3.5) and (2.48)

$$\vdash a = b \,.\supset.\, (x) \,.\, x \in a \equiv x \in b.$$

Conversely, we have by the restricted predicate calculus

$$\vdash (x) \,.\, x \in a \equiv x \in b :\supset: (x) \,.\, x \in a \supset x \in b : (x) \,.\, x \in b \supset x \in a.$$

However

$$\|(x) \,.\, x \in a \supset x \in b\| = \prod_{x \in V} \|x \in a \supset x \in b\|$$
$$\leq \prod_{x \in D(a)} \|x \in a \supset x \in b\|.$$

Similarly

$$\|(x) \,.\, x \in b \supset x \in a\| \leq \prod_{x \in D(b)} \|x \in b \supset x \in a\|.$$

So by (3.29)

$$\|(x) \,.\, x \in a \equiv x \in b\| \leq \|a = b\|.$$

Corollary.

$$\vdash (y, z) : y = z \,.\equiv.\, (x) \,.\, x \in y \equiv x \in z.$$

This makes available the definition of equality given by Rosser [7, p. 211]. Also, by (3.16) and (3.18), we have available Axiom 7 given by Rosser [7, p. 213]. So we can parallel the proof of his Theorem IX.2.4 [7, p. 214] to obtain:

Theorem 3.5. Let $F(x)$ be a statement containing certain free occurrences of x, and let $F(y)$ be the result of replacing these free occurrences of x by (free) occurrences of y. Then

$$\vdash (x, y) : x = y \,.\supset.\, F(x) \equiv F(y).$$

Thus we have the equality axioms of Chapter VII of Rosser [7], and can infer $\models X$ if $\vdash X$ is proved in Chapter VII.

Theorem 3.6.

$$\models(c, x, b) :: c \subseteq b \,.\, x \subseteq b : (y) : y \in b \,.$$
$$\supset . \, y \in c \equiv y \in x \,.: \supset :. \, c = x.$$

PROOF. As we mentioned earlier, we are entitled to use the proof procedures of the restricted predicate calculus. Therefore, assume

(i) $c \subseteq b \,.\, x \subseteq b$

(ii) $(y) : y \in b \,.\supset.\, y \in c \equiv y \in x$

(iii) $w \in c.$

Then by (i) and (iii), $w \in b$. So by (ii), $w \in c \equiv w \in x$. So by (iii), $w \in x$. Hence

$$\text{(i), (ii)} \ \vdash w \in c \supset w \in x.$$

Thus by Rule G (see Rosser [7, p. 124])

$$\text{(i), (ii)} \ \vdash (w) \,.\, w \in c \supset w \in x.$$

Similarly

$$\text{(i), (ii)} \ \vdash (w) \,.\, w \in x \supset w \in c.$$

So

$$\text{(i), (ii)} \ \vdash (w) \,.\, w \in c \equiv w \in x.$$

Then by Theorem 3.4.

$$\text{(i), (ii)} \ \vdash c = x.$$

So our theorem follows.

C. Methods for Defining Members of V

Various of the axioms of set theory require the definition of special sets; that is, special members of V. In preparation, we consider some general principles for defining members of V.

For example, the axiom of the power set requires that for each set b we can produce a set a such that

$$\vDash (x) : x \in a \,.\equiv.\, x \subseteq b.$$

Similarly, the axiom of choice requires (ultimately) that for each set b we can produce a set a which well-orders b, and so on. Essentially, we succeed in verifying all such axioms because in constructing V we were very generous in putting in members, so that indeed the various a's required were put in.

However, we did not engage in totally unbridled liberality in introducing members of V. Thus, when we undertook to form $V_{\alpha+1}$, we first generated *each* function a from V_α to A, but we promptly excluded all which were not extensional. (Had we not done so, (3.18) would have been violated.) We further excluded all a's which did not satisfy the relation (3.24). (The purpose of this will indeed be to exclude the a which well-orders b when we are proving AxC to be independent. However, if Γ is the filter of all subgroups of $\mathscr{G}$, then (3.24) imposes no restriction, and then we do admit the a which well-orders b, so that AxC holds in the model in this case.) Thus it is not a complete triviality to show that we have indeed admitted all the sets required by the various axioms of set theory. We shall show this in the next section, but first in the present section we present some general principles about what sorts of sets have been admitted.

A crucial principle (Theorem 3.10) says in effect that we have admitted each set which can be defined by a statement. Since the power set a of b can be defined by the statement

$$(x) : x \in a \,.\equiv.\, x \subseteq b$$

we will be able to verify the axiom of the power set. Similarly for the axiom of the null set, the axiom of unordered pairs, the axiom of the sum set, etc. One cannot define the set a which well-orders b by a statement. Indeed, by a proper choice of Γ (see Chapter 6), such a's are excluded from V. However, for other choices of Γ, such a's are admitted to V. This will be the function of Theorem 3.9. It will turn out that we have admitted equivalents for all the intuitive sets (see Theorems 3.18–3.24).

Thus we will be able to verify the axiom of infinity by citing the equivalent of the intuitive set of natural integers. Similarly, we can verify other cardinality results, for which we will cite the equivalent of an intuitive one-to-one correspondence.

Theorem 3.7. Let $F(x_1, \ldots, x_n)$ be a statement containing no constants and no free variables other than $x_1, \ldots, x_n$. Let $G \in \mathscr{G}$. Then for $a_1, \ldots, a_n \in V$

$$G(\|F(a_1, \ldots, a_n)\|) = \|F(G(a_1), \ldots, G(a_n))\|.$$

PROOF. We prove Theorem 3.7 by induction on the number of symbols in $F(x_1, \ldots, x_n)$. We start the induction by appealing to (3.20) and (3.21). The only part of the induction that is not trivial is handled as follows. Suppose that for each $a \in V$

$$G(\|F(a, a_1, \ldots, a_n)\|) = \|F(G(a), G(a_1), \ldots, G(a_n))\|.$$

Then by (2.83)

$$\begin{aligned} G(\|(x)F(x, a_1, \ldots, a_n)\|) &= \prod_{a \in V} G(\|F(a, a_1, \ldots, a_n)\|) \\ &= \prod_{a \in V} \|F(G(a), G(a_1), \ldots, G(a_n))\|. \end{aligned}$$

However, as G merely permutes the elements of V, by (3.30), we have

$$\begin{aligned} \prod_{a \in V} \|F(G(a), G(a_1), \ldots, G(a_n))\| &= \prod_{a \in V} \|F(a, G(a_1), \ldots, G(a_n))\| \\ &= \|(x)F(x, G(a_1), \ldots, G(a_n))\|. \end{aligned}$$

Until we come to Theorem 3.15, whenever we write $F(x, x_1, \ldots, x_n)$ it shall denote a statement containing no constants and no free variables other than $x, x_1, \ldots, x_n$.

Let $a_1, \ldots, a_n$ be elements of V. Then, for each $a \in V$, the statement $F(a, a_1, \ldots, a_n)$ determines an element of the Boolean algebra, namely $\|F(a, a_1, \ldots, a_n)\|$. However, not every relationship which, for each $a \in V$, determines an element of the Boolean algebra can be so defined. Specifically, since $F(x, x_1, \ldots, x_n)$ is a statement, it is understood that it is built from variables by means of $\in$, $=$, $\sim$, &, and quantifiers. This is implicit in the proofs of

Theorems 3.5 and 3.7. We may wish to define more general predicates, and consider formulas containing them; we may wish to be even more general. When we wish to consider a more general relationship, we shall write $\Phi(a)$ for the element of the Boolean algebra which is determined by the relationship for $a \in V$.

Definition 3.1. We say that Φ is extensional iff for each a and b in V

$$\Phi(a) \wedge \|a = b\| \le \Phi(b). \tag{3.42}$$

Theorem 3.8. If for $a_1, \ldots, a_n \in V$,

$$\Phi(a) = \|F(a, a_1, \ldots, a_n)\| \tag{3.43}$$

then Φ is extensional.

PROOF. Use Theorem 3.5.

Theorem 3.9. Let Φ be extensional. Define a with $D(a) = V_\alpha$ by the condition that if $x \in V_\alpha$, then

$$a(x) = \Phi(x). \tag{3.44}$$

Then (3.33) holds for a, so that a is extensional. Moreover, if $a \in V$ then for each $b \in V$

$$\|b \in a\| \le \Phi(b). \tag{3.45}$$

If Γ is the set of all subgroups of $\mathscr{G}$, then $a \in V_{\alpha+1}$, so that indeed (3.45) holds.

PROOF. Let $x \in D(a)$. Then by (3.44) and (3.42)

$$a(x) \wedge \|x = b\| \le \Phi(b). \tag{3.46}$$

If $y \in V_\alpha$, we can put it for b in (3.46), and then conclude (3.33) by (3.44). If $a \in V$, we can sum the left side of (3.45) for $x \in D(a)$, and so conclude (3.45) by (3.28). If Γ is the set of all subgroups of $\mathscr{G}$, then (3.24) is satisfied trivially, so that $a \in V_{\alpha+1}$.

Theorem 3.10. For a fixed $a_1, \ldots, a_n \in V$, let a with $D(a) = V_\alpha$ be defined by

$$a(x) = \|F(x, a_1, \ldots, a_n)\|. \tag{3.47}$$

Then $a \in V_{\alpha+1}$ and

$$\vDash (y) \,.\, y \in a \supset F(y, a_1, \ldots, a_n).$$

PROOF. This amounts to defining Φ by (3.43) and then a by (3.44). So by Theorems 3.8 and 3.9, a is extensional and (3.45) holds if $a \in V$. As we now have no assumption on Γ, we must show that (3.24) is satisfied if we are to conclude $a \in V$. As $a_i \in V$ for $1 \leq i \leq n$, we obtain

$$\mathscr{G}_{a_i} \in \Gamma, \qquad 1 \leq i \leq n, \tag{3.48}$$

by (3.24) and (3.36). Then by (2.86)

$$\mathscr{G}_{a_1} \cap \cdots \cap \mathscr{G}_{a_n} \in \Gamma. \tag{3.49}$$

Take

$$G \in \mathscr{G}_{a_1} \cap \cdots \cap \mathscr{G}_{a_n}. \tag{3.50}$$

Then $\|G(a_i) = a_i\| = 1$ for $1 \leq i \leq n$ by (3.48). So, if $x \in V$, then by Theorem 3.5, (3.6), and (2.49)

$$\|F(x, a_1, \ldots, a_n)\| = \|F(x, G(a_1), \ldots, G(a_n)\|.$$

Then by (3.47), Theorem 3.7, and (3.34)

$$\begin{aligned} a(x) &= \|F(x, a_1, \ldots, a_n)\| \\ &= \|F(G(G^{-1}(x)), G(a_1), \ldots, G(a_n))\| \\ &= G(\|F(G^{-1}(x), a_1, \ldots, a_n)\|) \\ &= G(a(G^{-1}(x))) \\ &= G(a)(x) \end{aligned}$$

for each $x \in V_\alpha$. So a and $G(a)$ are identical functions, and $\|G(a) = a\| = 1$ by (3.15). So $G \in \mathscr{G}_a$ by (3.36). Thus by (3.50)

$$\mathscr{G}_{a_1} \cap \cdots \cap \mathscr{G}_{a_n} \subseteq \mathscr{G}_a.$$

So by (3.49) and (2.87), $\mathscr{G}_a \in \Gamma$. So a satisfies (3.24), and hence $a \in V_{\alpha+1}$. Then indeed $a \in V$.

By (3.47) and (3.45)

$$\|y \in a\| \leq \|F(y, a_1, \ldots, a_n)\|.$$

So

$$\|y \in a \supset F(y, a_1, \ldots, a_n)\| = 1$$

for each $y \in V$. Hence the conclusion of our theorem holds.

If $F(x, a_1, \ldots, a_n)$ "defines a set," then one will in general be able to verify

$$\vdash (y) \,.\, y \in a \equiv F(y, a_1, \ldots, a_n)$$

provided one has chosen α large enough so that V_α contains "the set defined by $F(x, a_1, \ldots, a_n)$." However, $F(x, a_1, \ldots, a_n)$ may define a class rather than a set, and then the result displayed above will fail no matter how large α is taken. For example, this would be the case if $n = 0$ and $F(x, a_1, \ldots, a_n)$ is $x = x$.

Theorem 3.11. There are ordinals α and β such that if $\gamma \geq \alpha$, then

$$\prod_{a \in V} \Phi(a) = \prod_{a \in V_\gamma} \Phi(a) \tag{3.51}$$

and if $\gamma \geq \beta$, then

$$\sum_{a \in V} \Phi(a) = \sum_{a \in V_\gamma} \Phi(a) \tag{3.52}$$

PROOF. Put

$$P_\gamma = \prod_{a \in V_\gamma} \Phi(a).$$

Clearly, if $\gamma \geq \alpha$, then $P_\gamma \leq P_\alpha$. Now for each element P of the Boolean algebra, define $\theta(P)$ to be the least γ for which

$$P_\gamma \leq P \qquad \text{and} \qquad P_\gamma \neq P$$

if there is such a γ; otherwise set $\theta(P) = 0$. Take

$$\alpha = \sum_{p \in A} \theta(P).$$

As A is a set, α is an ordinal, by 2.3 on p. 87 of Bernays and Fraenkel [1]. By the definition of α, there cannot be a $\gamma > \alpha$ for which $P_\gamma \leq P_\alpha$ and $P_\gamma \neq P_\alpha$. However, for each $\gamma \geq \alpha$ we have $P_\gamma \leq P_\alpha$. Therefore, for each $\gamma \geq \alpha$ we must have $P_\gamma = P_\alpha$. So (3.51) holds for this α, since

$$V = \sum_{\gamma \geq \alpha} V_\gamma.$$

The proof of (3.52) follows by applying (3.51) to $(\Phi(a))'$.

If (3.43) holds, then (3.51) and (3.52) say that if $\gamma \geq \alpha$, then

$$\|(x)F(x, a_1, \ldots, a_n)\| = \prod_{a \in V_\gamma} \|F(a, a_1, \ldots, a_n)\|$$

and if $\gamma \geq \beta$, then

$$\|(Ex)F(x, a_1, \ldots, a_n)\| = \sum_{a \in V_\gamma} \|F(a, a_1, \ldots, a_n)\|.$$

One can describe this situation by saying that the unbounded quantifiers (x) and (Ex) are equivalent to bounded quantifiers. It is possible to prove a stronger result which says in effect that all quantifiers appearing in $(x)F(x, a_1, \ldots, a_n)$ or $(Ex)F(x, a_1, \ldots, a_n)$ are replaceable by bounded quantifiers. Indeed something analogous to this is done in the forcing arguments (see Cohen [3, p. 124], for instance). However, we do not need the stronger result.

Theorem 3.12. Let Γ be the set of all subgroups of $\mathscr{G}$. Let Φ be extensional. Then there is a $c \in V$ such that

$$\prod_{x, y \in V} (\Phi(x) \wedge \Phi(y) \Rightarrow \|x = y\|) \leq \Phi(c) \Leftrightarrow \sum_{x \in V} \Phi(x). \quad (3.53)$$

PROOF. Choose β so that for $\gamma \geq \beta$ (3.52) holds. Define c with $D(c) = V_\beta$ by the condition that for $z \in \dot{V}_\beta$

$$c(z) = \sum_{x \in V} \Phi(x) \wedge \|z \in x\|. \quad (3.54)$$

We have by (3.18)

$$(\Phi(x) \wedge \|z \in x\|) \wedge \|z = y\| \leq \Phi(x) \wedge \|y \in x\|.$$

Summing both sides on x and using Theorem 2.22 gives

$$\Big(\sum_{x \in V} \Phi(x) \wedge \|z \in x\|\Big) \wedge \|z = y\| \leq \sum_{x \in V} \Phi(x) \wedge \|y \in x\|.$$

Thus by Theorem 3.9 we conclude $c \in V_{\beta+1}$ and so get

$$\Phi(c) \leq \sum_{x \in V} \Phi(x).$$

So

$$\Phi(c) \Rightarrow \sum_{x \in V} \Phi(x) = 1. \quad (3.55)$$

Let

$$a \in V_\beta . \tag{3.56}$$

Let $z \in D(a)$. Then by (3.31) and (3.14), $z \in V_\beta$. So by (3.54)

$$\Phi(a) \wedge \|z \in a\| \leq c(z).$$

Then by (3.32)

$$\Phi(a) \wedge \|z \in a\| \leq \|z \in c\|.$$

So by (2.35), (2.37), and (3.5)

$$\Phi(a) \leq \Phi(a) \vee \|z \in a\|' \leq \|z \in a \supset z \in c\|.$$

Multiplying the right side over $z \in D(a)$ gives

$$\Phi(a) \leq \prod_{z \in D(a)} \|z \in a \supset z \in c\|. \tag{3.57}$$

Write

$$R = \prod_{x,\, y \in V} (\Phi(x) \wedge \Phi(y) \Rightarrow \|x = y\|). \tag{3.58}$$

Clearly

$$\Phi(x) \wedge \Phi(a) \wedge R \leq \|x = a\|.$$

Take $z \in V_\beta$. Then by (3.19)

$$\Phi(a) \wedge R \wedge (\Phi(x) \wedge \|z \in x\|) \leq \|z \in a\|.$$

Summing on the left over x and using (3.54) gives

$$\Phi(a) \wedge R \wedge c(z) \leq \|z \in a\|.$$

So by (3.32)

$$\Phi(a) \wedge R \leq \|z \in c \supset z \in a\|.$$

Hence

$$\Phi(a) \wedge R \leq \prod_{z \in D(c)} \|z \in c \supset z \in a\|.$$

Then by (3.57) and (3.29)

$$\Phi(a) \wedge R \leq \|a = c\|.$$

Therefore

$$\Phi(a) \wedge R \leq \Phi(a) \wedge \|a = c\|.$$

As Φ is extensional, we obtain

$$\Phi(a) \wedge R \leq \Phi(c).$$

Since this holds for each $a \in V_\beta$ (note (3.56)), we can sum on the left over $a \in V_\beta$ and obtain

$$R \wedge \sum_{a \in V_\beta} \Phi(a) \leq \Phi(c).$$

So by (3.52)

$$R \wedge \sum_{x \in V} \Phi(x) \leq \Phi(c).$$

That is

$$R \leq \left(\sum_{x \in V} \Phi(x) \right) \Rightarrow \Phi(c).$$

Then by (3.55) and (2.38)

$$R \leq \Phi(c) \Leftrightarrow \sum_{x \in V} \Phi(x).$$

By (3.58), this is our theorem.

Theorem 3.13. For each $a_1, \ldots, a_n$ in V there is a $c \in V$ such that

$$\vDash (x, y) : F(x, a_1, \ldots, a_n) . F(y, a_1, \ldots, a_n) . \supset . x = y . :$$
$$\supset : . F(c, a_1, \ldots, a_n) \equiv (Ex)F(x, a_1, \ldots, a_n).$$

PROOF. We simply parallel the proof of Theorem 3.12.

Definition 3.2. We say that a function $a^{(S)}$ is a Scott core of a and that $SD(a)$ is the corresponding Scott domain of a iff

$$SD(a) = D(a^{(S)}) \subseteq D(a), \tag{3.59}$$

and for $x \in D(a)$,

$$a(x) = \sum_{y \in SD(a)} a^{(S)}(y) \wedge \|x = y\|. \tag{3.60}$$

Theorem 3.14. One Scott core of a is a itself, with $D(a)$ as the corresponding Scott domain.

PROOF. By (3.32) and (3.28), if $x \in D(a)$, then

$$a(x) = \|x \in a\| = \sum_{y \in D(a)} \|y \in a \,.\, x = y\|$$
$$= \sum_{y \in D(a)} a(y) \wedge \|x = y\|.$$

Theorem 3.15. If $a \in V$ and $a^{(S)}$ is a Scott core of a and $SD(a)$ is the corresponding Scott domain, then

$$\|(x) \,.\, x \in a \supset F(x)\| = \prod_{x \in SD(a)} a^{(S)}(x) \Rightarrow \|F(x)\|, \tag{3.61}$$
$$\|(Ex) \,.\, x \in a \,.\, F(x)\| = \sum_{x \in SD(a)} a^{(S)}(x) \wedge \|F(x)\|. \tag{3.62}$$

PROOF. We have returned essentially to the conventions stated by Rosser [7, p. 95]. These permit $F(x)$ to have other variables occurring free besides x, and in addition we allow $F(x)$ to contain constant terms. However, for the Boolean values appearing in (3.61) and (3.62) to have the right interpretations, we must require that $F(x)$ contain no free occurrences of variables other than x. We first prove (3.62). Let $x \in SD(a)$. Then $x \in D(a)$. Also

$$a^{(S)}(x) = a^{(S)}(x) \wedge \|x = x\|$$
$$\leq \sum_{y \in SD(a)} a^{(S)}(y) \wedge \|x = y\|.$$

So by (3.60) and (3.32)

$$a^{(S)}(x) \wedge \|F(x)\| \leq \|x \in a \,.\, F(x)\|$$
$$\leq \|(Ex) \,.\, x \in a \,.\, F(x)\|.$$

Summing the left over $x \in SD(a)$ gives

$$\sum_{x \in SD(a)} a^{(S)}(x) \wedge \|F(x)\| \leq \|(Ex) \,.\, x \in a \,.\, F(x)\|. \tag{3.63}$$

Now take $x \in V$, $y \in D(a)$, and $z \in SD(a)$. Then by (3.17) and Theorem 3.5

$$\|x = y \,.\, y = z\| \wedge a^{(S)}(z) \wedge \|F(x)\|$$
$$\leq a^{(S)}(z) \wedge \|F(z)\|$$
$$\leq \sum_{x \in SD(a)} a^{(S)}(x) \wedge \|F(x)\|.$$

Summing the left over $z \in SD(a)$ and using (3.60) and (3.32) gives

$$\|x = y\| \wedge \|y \in a\| \wedge \|F(x)\| \leq \sum_{x \in SD(a)} a^{(S)}(x) \wedge \|F(x)\|.$$

Summing the left over $y \in D(a)$ and using (3.28) gives

$$\|x \in a \,.\, F(x)\| \leq \sum_{x \in SD(a)} a^{(S)}(x) \wedge \|F(x)\|.$$

Summing the left over $x \in V$ gives

$$\|(Ex) \,.\, x \in a \,.\, F(x)\| \leq \sum_{x \in SD(a)} a^{(S)}(x) \wedge \|F(x)\|.$$

Combining this with (3.63) gives (3.62).

If we now replace $F(x)$ by $\sim F(x)$ in (3.62) and take the prime of both sides, we get (3.61).

Corollary. If $a \in V$, then

$$\|(x) \,.\, x \in a \supset F(x)\| = \prod_{x \in D(a)} a(x) \Rightarrow \|F(x)\|, \tag{3.64}$$

$$\|(Ex) \,.\, x \in a \,.\, F(x)\| = \sum_{x \in D(a)} a(x) \wedge \|F(x)\|, \tag{3.65}$$

$$\|(x) \,.\, x \in a \supset F(x)\| = \prod_{x \in D(a)} \|x \in a \supset F(x)\|, \tag{3.66}$$

$$\|(Ex) \,.\, x \in a \,.\, F(x)\| = \sum_{x \in D(a)} \|x \in a \,.\, F(x)\|. \tag{3.67}$$

PROOF. We get (3.64) and (3.65) by Theorem 3.14, and then (3.66) and (3.67) follow by (3.32).

Theorem 3.16. If $a, x \in V$ and $a^{(S)}$ is a Scott core of a and $SD(a)$ is the corresponding Scott domain, then

$$\|x \in a\| = \sum_{y \in SD(a)} a^{(S)}(y) \wedge \|x = y\|.$$

PROOF. By a standard theorem

$$\vdash x \in a \,.\equiv.\, (Ey) \,.\, y \in a \,.\, x = y$$

(see Theorem VII.1.5, Part I, p. 166 of Rosser [7]). But by (3.62)

$$\|(Ey) \,.\, y \in a \,.\, x = y\| = \sum_{y \in SD(a)} a^{(S)}(y) \wedge \|x = y\|.$$

Theorem 3.17. Suppose we start with a function b from a subset of V to the Boolean algebra. Choose α so that $D(b) \subseteq V_\alpha$. Define a with $D(a) = V_\alpha$ by the condition that if $x \in V_\alpha$ then

$$a(x) = \sum_{y \in D(b)} b(y) \wedge \|x = y\|. \tag{3.68}$$

Then a is extensional. If also $\mathcal{G}_a \in \Gamma$, then $a \in V_{\alpha+1}$ and b is a Scott core of a and $D(b)$ is the corresponding Scott domain.

PROOF. Let $x, z \in V_\alpha$. Then

$$b(y) \wedge \|x = y\| \wedge \|x = z\| \leq b(y) \wedge \|z = y\|.$$

Summing both sides over $y \in D(b)$ and using (3.68) gives

$$a(x) \wedge \|x = z\| \leq a(z),$$

verifying (3.33). The rest of the theorem is trivial.

Definition 3.3. For intuitive sets s we define the image of s, Img(s), in V by induction on the rank of s. (See Cohen [3, pp. 68–69] for a discussion of rank.) We shall usually write $\check{s}$ for Img(s). Suppose $\check{t}$ defined for all t of rank less than s. Let μ be the rank of s. Define $\check{s}$ with $D(\check{s}) = V_\mu$ by the condition that if $x \in V_\mu$ then

$$\check{s}(x) = \sum_{t \in s} \|x = \check{t}\|. \tag{3.69}$$

Theorem 3.18. If s is an intuitive set of rank μ and $G \in \mathcal{G}$, then $\check{s} \in V_{\mu+1}$ and $G(\check{s}) = \check{s}$.

PROOF. We use induction on μ. Clearly $\check{\Lambda}$ is the null function. By (3.26), $\check{\Lambda} \in V_1$. Clearly $G(\check{\Lambda}) = \check{\Lambda}$ by (3.34). So let s be of rank μ, and assume that $\check{t} \in V_{\eta+1}$ and $G(\check{t}) = \check{t}$ for each t of rank η where $\eta < \mu$. Then for each $t \in s$, we have $\check{t} \in V_\mu$. So (3.69) is a special case of Theorem 3.17 in which we take

$$D(b) = \{\check{t} \mid t \in s\}$$

and put $b(y) = 1$ for each $y \in D(b)$. So $\check{s}$ is extensional. Now

$$\begin{aligned}\check{s}(x) &= \sum_{t \in s} \|x = \check{t}\| \\ &= \sum_{t \in s} \|G(G^{-1}(x)) = G(\check{t})\| \\ &= G\Big(\sum_{t \in s} \|G^{-1}(x) = \check{t}\|\Big) \\ &= G(\check{s}(G^{-1}(x)) \\ &= G(\check{s})(x)\end{aligned}$$

by (3.34). So $G(\check{s}) = \check{s}$. Thus $\mathscr{G}\check{s} = \mathscr{G}$, and so $\mathscr{G}\check{s} \in \Gamma$ by (2.85). Hence $\check{s} \in V_{\mu+1}$.

Theorem 3.19. For s an intuitive set and $x \in V$

$$\|x \in \check{s}\| = \sum_{t \in s} \|x = \check{t}\|.$$

PROOF. In Theorem 3.16, we take

$$SD(\check{s}) = \{\check{t} \mid t \in s\}$$

and $\check{s}^{(S)}$ to be the function defined by $\check{s}^{(S)}(x) = 1$ for $x \in SD(\check{s})$.

Theorem 3.20. For s an intuitive set

$$\|(x) \, . \, x \in \check{s} \supset F(x)\| = \prod_{t \in s} \|F(\check{t})\|,$$

$$\|(Ex) \, . \, x \in \check{s} \, . \, F(x)\| = \sum_{t \in s} \|F(\check{t})\|.$$

PROOF. We apply Theorem 3.15 in the same way we applied Theorem 3.16 to prove Theorem 3.19.

Theorem 3.21. If $t \in s$, then $\models \check{t} \in \check{s}$.

PROOF. Take x to be $\check{t}$ in Theorem 3.19 and use (3.15).

Theorem 3.22. Suppose that for some ordinal η and for each $x \in V_\eta$ we have $\|x = \check{s}\| = 0$ for each intuitive set s of rank $\geq \eta$. Then for this ordinal η and for each $y \in V_{\eta+1}$ we have $\|\check{s} \in y\| = 0$ for each intuitive set s of rank $\geq \eta$.

PROOF. Let $y \in V_{\eta+1}$. Then $D(y) \subseteq V_\eta$. So

$$\begin{aligned}\|\check{s} \in y\| &= \sum_{x \in D(y)} \|x \in y \,.\, \check{s} = x\| \\ &\leq \sum_{x \in V_\eta} \|x \in y\| \wedge \|\check{s} = x\| \\ &\leq \sum_{x \in V_\eta} \|\check{s} = x\|.\end{aligned}$$

However, by hypothesis, $\|\check{s} = x\| = 0$ for each $x \in V_\eta$. So our theorem follows by Theorem 2.25.

Theorem 3.23. For each ordinal η and for each $x \in V_\eta$ we have $\|x = \check{s}\| = 0$ for each intuitive set s of rank $\geq \eta$.

PROOF. The theorem is vacuously true for $\eta = 0$. Assume it for η. Let $x \in V_{\eta+1}$ and let $\eta + 1 \leq$ the rank of s. Then s must have a member t of rank at least η. Then by Theorem 3.21, $\|\check{t} \in \check{s}\| = 1$. Hence

$$\|x = \check{s}\| = \|x = \check{s} \,.\, \check{t} \in \check{s}\| \leq \|\check{t} \in x\|.$$

However $\|\check{t} \in x\| = 0$ by Theorem 3.22, so that $\|x = \check{s}\| = 0$.

Let σ be a limit ordinal, and suppose that the theorem holds for each $\eta < \sigma$. Let $x \in V_\sigma$ and $\sigma \leq \text{rank}(s)$. Then there is an $\eta < \sigma$ such that $x \in V_\eta$. So $\|x = \check{s}\| = 0$.

Corollary. For each ordinal η and for each $x \in V_{\eta+1}$ we have $\|\check{s} \in x\| = 0$ for each intuitive set s of rank $\geq \eta$.

Theorem 3.24. If t and s are intuitive sets, then $\|\check{t} \in \check{s}\| = 1$ if $t \in s$, $\|\check{t} \in \check{s}\| = 0$ if $\sim t \in s$, $\|\check{t} = \check{s}\| = 1$ if $t = s$, and $\|\check{t} = \check{s}\| = 0$ if $t \neq s$.

PROOF. If $t \in s$, then $\|\check{t} \in \check{s}\| = 1$ by Theorem 3.21, and if $t = s$, then $\|\check{t} = \check{s}\| = 1$ by (3.15). We now prove the rest of the theorem by induction on the rank of s. Assume it for all intuitive sets of rank less than rank(s). Now let $\sim t \in s$. Then for each $u \in s$, we have $t \neq u$. Also, each such u has rank less than rank(s), so that by hypothesis $\|\check{t} = \check{u}\| = 0$. But by Theorem 3.19

$$\|\check{t} \in \check{s}\| = \sum_{u \in s} \|\check{t} = \check{u}\|,$$

so that $\|\check{t} \in \check{s}\| = 0$. Now suppose $t \neq s$. By Theorem 3.23 and Theorem 3.18, we need only consider the case where rank(t) $\leq$ rank(s). Now, as $t \neq s$. there must be a u with $u \in s \,.\, {\sim} u \in t$ or $u \in t \,.\, {\sim} u \in s$. The argument is the same in both cases, and we give only the former. By the argument in the earlier part of the proof, we have

$$\|\check{u} \in \check{s} \,.\, {\sim}\check{u} \in \check{t}\| = 1.$$

But

$$\|\check{u} \in \check{s} \,.\, {\sim}\check{u} \in \check{t}\| \leq \|(Ex) \,.\, x \in \check{s} \,.\, {\sim} x \in \check{t}\|.$$

However by Theorem 3.4

$$\|(Ex) \,.\, x \in \check{s} \,.\, {\sim} x \in \check{t}\| \leq \|\check{s} \neq \check{t}\|.$$

So $\|\check{s} \neq \check{t}\| = 1$.

D. The Basic Set Theory Axioms

We proceed to prove $\models X$, where we successively take X to be the basic axioms of set theory.

Theorem 3.25. The axiom of extensionality holds in the model.

PROOF. We need to show

$$\models (y, z) :. (x) \,.\, x \in y \equiv x \in z : \supset : y = z,$$

which follows trivially from the corollary to Theorem 3.4.

Actually, in some treatments of set theory, $=$ is not taken as primitive, but $y = z$ is defined to be

$$(x) \,.\, x \in y \equiv x \in z.$$

In such cases, the axiom of extensionality is a tautology. However, in all cases one needs to assume the axioms of equality. In some cases this is implicit, as in Cohen [3] and Gödel [5]. In other cases it is explicit (see E1 p. 52 of Bernays and Fraenkel [1]). In any case, the axioms of equality hold for our model by (3.15) and Theorem 3.5.

Theorem 3.26. The axiom of the null set holds in the model.

PROOF. As noted earlier, $\check{\Lambda}$ is the null function, and by (3.26) $\check{\Lambda} \in V_1$, so that $\check{\Lambda} \in V$. Then by (3.28) and (2.51)

$$\vDash \sim a \in \check{\Lambda} \tag{3.70}$$

holds for each $a \in V$. Thence

$$\vDash (x) \,.\, \sim x \in \check{\Lambda}$$

and

$$\vDash (Ew)(x) \,.\, \sim x \in w,$$

the latter being the axiom of the null set.

Theorem 3.27. The axiom of unordered pairs holds in the model.

PROOF. Let $b, c \in V$. Choose the least ordinal α such that b, $c \in V_\alpha$. Define a with $D(a) = V_\alpha$ by the condition that if $x \in V_\alpha$ then

$$a(x) = \|x = b \vee x = c\|.$$

Then by Theorem 3.10, $a \in V_{\alpha+1}$ and

$$\vDash (y) : y \in a \,.\, \supset \,.\, y = b \vee y = c.$$

As $b \in V_\alpha = D(a)$, we have $a(b) = 1$ by (3.15); therefore $\vDash b \in a$ by (3.32). Therefore

$$\vDash y = b \supset y \in a$$

by (3.18). Similarly, we have

$$\vDash y = c \supset y \in a.$$

So finally

$$\vDash (y) : y \in a \,.\, \equiv \,.\, y = b \vee y = c.$$

We will write this as

$$\vDash (y) : y \in \{b, c\} \,.\, \equiv \,.\, y = b \vee y = c. \tag{3.71}$$

Generally, we shall denote by $\{b, c\}$ the a described above, and call it the unordered pair consisting of b and c. From (3.71), we get

$$\vDash(u, v)(Ew)(y) : y \in w \,.\equiv .\, y = u \vee y = v,$$

which is the axiom of unordered pairs.

Theorem 3.28. The axiom of the sum set holds in the model.

PROOF. Let $b \in V$. Choose the least ordinal α such that $D(b) \subseteq V_\alpha$.

Define a with $D(a) = V_\alpha$ by the condition that if $x \in V_\alpha$, then

$$a(x) = \|(Ez) \,.\, x \in z \,.\, z \in b\|.$$

Then by Theorem 3.10, $a \in V_{\alpha+1}$ and

$$\vDash(y) : y \in a \,.\supset .\, (Ez) \,.\, y \in z \,.\, z \in b.$$

Let $z \in D(b)$ and $y \in D(z)$. Then $D(z) \subseteq V_\alpha$, so that $y \in V_\alpha$. Hence

$$\|y \in z \,.\, z \in b\| \leq \|(Ez) \,.\, y \in z \,.\, z \in b\| = a(y).$$

Therefore

$$\|z \in b\| \wedge \|y \in z\| \leq \|y \in a\|$$

and hence

$$\|z \in b\| \leq \|y \in z \supset y \in a\|.$$

Then multiplying on the right gives

$$\|z \in b\| \leq \prod_{y \in D(z)} \|y \in z \supset y \in a\|.$$

So by (3.66)

$$\|z \in b\| \leq \|(y) \,.\, y \in z \supset y \in a\|.$$

Therefore

$$\|z \in b \,.\supset .\, (y) \,.\, y \in z \supset y \in a\| = 1$$

so that

$$\prod_{z \in D(b)} \|z \in b \,.\supset .\, (y) \,.\, y \in z \supset y \in a\| = 1.$$

Appealing again to (3.66), we have finally

$$\vDash(z) : z \in b \,.\supset .\, (y) \,.\, y \in z \supset y \in a.$$

Standard transformations of the restricted predicate calculus yield successively

$$\vDash(y)(z) : z \in b \,.\supset .\, y \in z \supset y \in a,$$
$$\vDash(y)(z) : y \in z \,.\, z \in b \,.\supset .\, y \in a,$$
$$\vDash(y) :.\, (Ez) \,.\, y \in z \,.\, z \in b : \supset : y \in a.$$

So altogether we conclude

$$\vDash(y) : y \in a \,.\equiv .\, (Ez) \,.\, y \in z \,.\, z \in b.$$

We will write this as

$$\vDash(y) : y \in \bigcup b \,.\equiv .\, (Ez) \,.\, y \in z \,.\, z \in b. \tag{3.72}$$

Generally, we shall denote by $\bigcup b$ the a described above and call it the sum set of b. From (3.72), we get

$$\vDash(u)(Ew)(y) : y \in w \,.\equiv .\, (Ez) \,.\, y \in z \,.\, z \in u,$$

which is the axiom of the sum set.

We shall follow standard logical practice in defining

$$\{a\} = \{a, a\},$$
$$\langle a, b\rangle = \{\{a\}, \{a, b\}\},$$
$$a \cup b = \bigcup \{a, b\},$$

and use (3.71) and (3.72) to prove the familiar properties

$$\vDash(u, x) : x \in \{u\} \,.\equiv .\, x = u,$$
$$\vDash(u, v, x, y) : \langle u, v\rangle = \langle x, y\rangle \,.\equiv .\, u = x \,.\, v = y,$$
$$\vDash(u, v, x) : x \in u \cup v \,.\equiv .\, x \in u \vee x \in v.$$

Theorem 3.29. If μ is an ordinal, then $\vDash\text{Trans}(\check{\mu})$.

PROOF. We are using the notation of Bernays and Fraenkel [1, p. 80], and so are to prove

$$\vDash(x) : x \in \check{\mu} \,.\supset .\, x \subseteq \check{\mu}.$$

Let $\sigma < \eta < \mu$. So $\sigma < \mu$. Recall that this is the same as $\sigma \in \mu$ (see Bernays and Fraenkel [1, Chapter III]). So by Theorem 3.21

$$\|\check{\sigma} \in \check{\mu}\| = 1.$$

Then by Theorem 2.25

$$\prod_{\sigma \in \eta} \|\check{\sigma} \in \check{\mu}\| = 1.$$

By Theorem 3.20, this is the same as

$$\|(x) \, . \, x \in \check{\eta} \supset x \in \check{\mu}\| = 1.$$

That is,

$$\|\check{\eta} \subseteq \check{\mu}\| = 1.$$

So by Theorem 2.25

$$\prod_{\eta \in \mu} \|\check{\eta} \subseteq \check{\mu}\| = 1.$$

By Theorem 3.20, this is the same as

$$\|(x) : x \in \check{\mu} \, . \supset . \, x \subseteq \check{\mu}\| = 1.$$

This gives our theorem.

Theorem 3.30. The axiom of infinity holds in the model.

PROOF. Let σ and η be ordinals. Since $\sigma < \eta$ is the same as $\sigma \in \eta$, we see that if $\sigma < \eta + 1$, then $\sigma \in \eta$ or $\sigma = \eta$, so that by Theorem 3.21

$$\models \check{\sigma} \in \check{\eta} \cup \{\check{\eta}\}.$$

Hence by Theorem 2.25

$$\prod_{\sigma \in \eta + 1} \|\check{\sigma} \in \check{\eta} \cup \{\check{\eta}\}\| = 1.$$

So by Theorem 3.20

$$\|(x) : x \in \mathrm{Img}(\eta + 1) \, . \supset . \, x \in \check{\eta} \cup \{\check{\eta}\}\| = 1.$$

That is

$$\models \mathrm{Img}(\eta + 1) \subseteq \check{\eta} \cup \{\check{\eta}\}. \tag{3.73}$$

Since $\eta \in \eta + 1$, Theorem 3.21 gives

$$\models \check{\eta} \in \mathrm{Img}(\eta + 1).$$

So by Theorem 3.29

$$\models \check{\eta} \subseteq \mathrm{Img}(\eta + 1).$$

In addition, we have

$$\models \{\check{\eta}\} \subseteq \mathrm{Img}(\eta + 1).$$

These last two give

$$\models \check{\eta} \cup \{\check{\eta}\} \subseteq \mathrm{Img}(\eta + 1).$$

With (3.73), we have

$$\models \mathrm{Img}(\eta + 1) = \check{\eta} \cup \{\check{\eta}\}. \tag{3.74}$$

If $\eta \in \omega$, then $\eta + 1 \in \omega$, so that by Theorem 3.21

$$\models \mathrm{Img}(\eta + 1) \in \check{\omega}.$$

So by (3.74)

$$\prod_{\eta \in \omega} \|\check{\eta} \cup \{\check{\eta}\} \in \check{\omega}\| = 1.$$

Then by Theorem 3.20

$$\models (y) : y \in \check{\omega} \,.\, \supset \,.\, y \cup \{y\} \in \check{\omega}. \tag{3.75}$$

As $\Lambda \in \omega$, we have by Theorem 3.21

$$\models \check{\Lambda} \in \check{\omega}. \tag{3.76}$$

We saw in the proof of Theorem 3.26 that $\check{\Lambda}$ is the null class of the model. Hence, (3.75) and (3.76) together imply the axiom of infinity, namely

$$\models (Ew) :: \varnothing \in w :. (y) : y \in w \,.\, \supset \,.\, y \cup \{y\} \in w.$$

Theorem 3.31. Let $F(x, y)$ be a statement containing no free variables other than x and y. Let $b \in V$. Then there is an $a \in V$ such that

$$\models (x)(E_1 y)F(x, y) : \supset : (y) : y \in a \,.\, \equiv \,.\, (Ex) \,.\, x \in b \,.\, F(x, y).$$

PROOF. $F(x, y)$ may contain constants. We have not indicated them explicitly, but this does not debar us from using Theorem 3.13. In particular, for each $x \in D(b)$ we are assured of a y_x such that

$$\vDash (y, z) : F(x, y) \,.\, F(x, z) \,.\, \supset . \, y = z \,.:\supset :.\, F(x, y_x) \equiv (Ey)F(x, y).$$

Thus for each $x \in D(b)$

$$\vDash (x)(E_1 y)F(x, y) \,.\supset .\, F(x, y_x).$$

Write

$$R = \|(x)(E_1 y)F(x, y)\|.$$

So for each $x \in D(b)$

$$R \leq \|F(x, y_x)\|. \tag{3.77}$$

For each $x \in D(b)$, let α_x be the least α such that $y_x \in V_\alpha$. Take

$$\alpha = \sum_{x \in D(b)} \alpha_x .$$

So for each $x \in D(b)$, we have $y_x \in V_\alpha$. Define a with $D(a) = V_\alpha$ by the condition that if $y \in V_\alpha$, then

$$a(y) = \|(Ex) \,.\, x \in b \,.\, F(x, y)\|.$$

Then by Theorem 3.10, $a \in V_{\alpha+1}$ and

$$\vDash (y) : y \in a \,.\supset.\, (Ex) \,.\, x \in b \,.\, F(x, y).$$

Now let $x \in D(b)$. Then by (3.77)

$$R \wedge \|x \in b\| \leq \|x \in b \,.\, F(x, y_x)\| \leq \|y_x \in a\|.$$

However, by (3.77)

$$R \wedge \|F(x, y)\| \leq R \wedge \|F(x, y) \,.\, F(x, y_x)\| \leq \|y = y_x\|.$$

So

$$R \wedge \|x \in b \,.\, F(x, y)\| \leq \|y \in a\|.$$

Summing over x on the left gives

$$R \wedge \sum_{x \in D(b)} \|x \in b \,.\, F(x, y)\| \leq \|y \in a\|.$$

So by (3.67)

$$R \leq \| (Ex) \,.\, x \in b \,.\, F(x, y) : \supset : y \in a \| .$$

We then conclude our theorem without difficulty.

Corollary.

$$\vdash (u) :: (x) : x \in u \,.\supset.\, (E_1 y) F(x, y) \,.:\, \supset :.\, (Ew)(y) : y \in w \,.\equiv.\, (Ex) \,.\, x \in u \,.\, F(x, y).$$

PROOF. Let $b \in V$. Define $G(x, y)$ to be

$$x \in b \,.\, F(x, y) \,.\vee.\, {\sim} x \in b \,.\, y = \check{\Lambda}.$$

Then by the restricted predicate calculus and (3.16) and (3.17)

$$\vdash (x) : x \in b \,.\supset.\, (E_1 y) F(x, y) \,.:\supset:.\, (x)(E_1 y) G(x, y).$$

By our theorem there is an a such that

$$\vdash (x)(E_1 y) G(x, y) : \supset : (y) : y \in a \,.\equiv.\, (Ex) \,.\, x \in b \,.\, G(x, y).$$

However by the definition of $G(x, y)$

$$\vdash (Ex) \,.\, x \in b \,.\, G(x, y) : \equiv : (Ex) \,.\, x \in b \,.\, F(x, y).$$

Combining the last three formulas gives

$$\vdash (x) : x \in b \,.\supset.\, (E_1 y) F(x, y) \,.:\, \supset :.\, (y) : y \in a \,.\equiv.\, (Ex) \,.\, x \in b \,.\, F(x, y).$$

As we can do this for each $b \in V$, our corollary holds.

Theorem 3.32. The axiom of replacement holds in the model.

PROOF. As the corollary to Theorem 3.31 holds for each choice of the constants appearing (but not indicated) in $F(x\ y)$, we infer

$$\vdash (z_1, \ldots, z_n)(u) :: (x) : x \in u \,.\supset.\, (E_1 y) F(x, y, z_1, \ldots, z_n) \,.:\supset:.\, (Ew)(y) : y \in w \,.\equiv.\, (Ex) \,.\, x \in u \,.\, F(x, y, z_1, \ldots, z_n).$$

This is the axiom of replacement.

Theorem 3.33. The axiom of the power set holds in the model.

PROOF. Let $b \in V$. By (3.31), we can choose an ordinal α such that $D(b) = V_\alpha$. Define a with $D(a) = V_{\alpha+1}$ by the condition that if $x \in V_{\alpha+1}$ then

$$a(x) = \|x \subseteq b\|.$$

Then by Theorem 3.10, $a \in V_{\alpha+2}$ and

$$\vDash (x) : x \in a \,.\supset.\, x \subseteq b. \tag{3.78}$$

Take $x \in V$. Define c with $D(c) = V_\alpha$ by the condition that if $y \in V_\alpha$ then

$$c(y) = \|y \in x\|.$$

So by Theorem 3.10, $c \in V_{\alpha+1}$ and

$$\vDash (y) : y \in c \,.\supset.\, y \in x.$$

That is

$$\vDash c \subseteq x.$$

Then

$$\vDash x \subseteq b \,.\supset.\, c \subseteq b. \tag{3.79}$$

Now for $y \in D(b)$

$$\|y \in c\| = c(y) = \|y \in x\|.$$

Therefore

$$\|y \in c \equiv y \in x\| = 1$$

so that

$$\|y \in b \,.\supset.\, y \in c \equiv y \in x\| = 1.$$

Therefore

$$\prod_{y \in D(b)} \|y \in b \,.\supset.\, y \in c \equiv y \in x\| = 1.$$

Then by (3.66)

$$\vDash (y) : y \in b \,.\supset.\, y \in c \equiv y \in x. \tag{3.80}$$

By (3.79),

$$\vDash x \subseteq b \,.\supset.\, c \subseteq b \,.\, x \subseteq b.$$

By this, (3.80), and Theorem 3.6

$$\vDash x \subseteq b \,.\supset .\, c = x.$$

However, since $c \in D(a)$, we obtain by (3.79) that

$$\|x \subseteq b\| \le \|c \subseteq b\| = a(c) = \|c \in a\|.$$

That is,

$$\vDash x \subseteq b \,.\supset .\, c \in a.$$

Therefore

$$\vDash x \subseteq b \,.\supset .\, c = x \,.\, c \in a.$$

Hence

$$\vDash x \subseteq b \,.\supset .\, x \in a.$$

So by (3.78)

$$\vDash (x) : x \in a \,.\equiv .\, x \subseteq b.$$

We will write this as

$$\vDash (x) : x \in SC(b) \,.\equiv .\, x \subseteq b. \tag{3.81}$$

Generally, we shall denote by $SC(b)$ the a described above, and call it the power set of b. From (3.81), we get

$$\vDash (u)(Ew)(x) : x \in w \,.\equiv .\, x \subseteq u,$$

which is the axiom of the power set.

Other notations for $SC(b)$ which appear in the literature are $\pi(b)$ (Bernays and Fraenkel [1]), $P(b)$ (Cohen [3]), and $\mathscr{P}(b)$ (Halmos [6]).

Theorem 3.34. The axiom of regularity holds in the model.

PROOF. We need to prove

$$\vDash (x) :. (y) \,.\, y \in x \supset F(y) : \supset : F(x) :: \supset :: (x)F(x).$$

We prove by induction on α that

$$\vDash X \supset F(b) \tag{3.82}$$

holds for each $b \in V_\alpha$, where we have written X for

$$(x) :. (y) . y \in x \supset F(y) : \supset : F(x).$$

It is clear that (3.82) holds vacuously when $\alpha = 0$. Assume that (3.82) holds for α. Let $b \in V_{\alpha+1}$. If $b \in V_\alpha$, then we have (3.82) by our hypothesis of induction. So let $\sim b \in V_\alpha$. Then $D(b) = V_\alpha$. So for $y \in D(b)$

$$\models X \supset F(y)$$

and hence

$$\models y \in b . \supset . X \supset F(y).$$

Then

$$\prod_{y \in D(b)} \|y \in b . \supset . X \supset F(y)\| = 1.$$

So by (3.66)

$$\models (y) : y \in b . \supset . X \supset F(y).$$

Standard transformations of the restricted predicate calculus give

$$\models X : \supset : (y) . y \in b \supset F(y).$$

But by Theorem 3.3

$$\models X .: \supset :. (y) . y \in b \supset F(y) : \supset : F(b).$$

So (3.82) holds for b.

E. Ordinals and Cardinals in the Model

We have now verified in the model all the axioms of set theory that are assumed by Bernays and Fraenkel [1] previous to their p. 130. Indeed we have done more than that, inasmuch as they do not assume either the axiom of the power set or the axiom of regularity before their p. 130. Thus we can state that even if the axioms of the power set or regularity had not been verified, it would still be the case that if $\vdash X$ is a theorem in the first 129 pages of Bernays and Fraenkel [1] then we may conclude $\models X$. This observation will be of the utmost importance in Chapter 9, where the proof that the axiom of the power set holds presents great difficulty; its proof will succeed only because the remaining developments of the present chapter do not depend upon the fact that the axiom of the power set has been verified. Hence we shall carefully refrain throughout the rest of this chapter from appealing to the fact that the axioms of the power set and regularity hold in the model. Nevertheless, as we noted above, this entitles us to use results from the first 129 pages of Bernays and Fraenkel [1]. We shall take advantage of the fact that these pages include extensive developments of the theory of ordinals and cardinals.

Theorem 3.35. If μ is an ordinal, then $\models \mathrm{Od}(\check{\mu})$.

Proof by Induction on μ. The theorem is certainly true when $\mu = 0$. Now assume $\models \mathrm{Od}(\check{\eta})$ for $\eta < \mu$. Then by Theorem 3.20

$$\models (x) : x \in \check{\mu} \,.\supset .\, \mathrm{Od}(x).$$

By means of this, Theorem 3.29, and 1.13 on p. 85 of Bernays and Fraenkel [1], we infer our theorem.

Theorem 3.36. If $a \in V_\alpha$, then $\|\mathrm{Od}(a)\| = \sum_{\eta < a} \|a = \check{\eta}\|$.

Proof. By Theorems 3.5 and 3.35,

$$\|a = \check{\eta}\| \leq \|\mathrm{Od}(a)\|.$$

So

$$\sum_{\eta<\alpha} \|a = \check{\eta}\| \leq \|\mathrm{Od}(a)\|.$$

As $a \in V_\alpha$, we have also $a \in V_{\alpha+1}$. So by Theorem 3.23 and its corollary, $\|a = \check{\alpha}\| = 0$ and $\|\check{\alpha} \in a\| = 0$. But by 1.11 on p. 84 of Bernays and Fraenkel [1],

$$\|\mathrm{Od}(a)\| \wedge \|\mathrm{Od}(\check{\alpha})\| \leq \|a = \check{\alpha}\| \vee \|a \in \check{\alpha}\| \vee \|\check{\alpha} \in a\|.$$

However, $\|\mathrm{Od}(\check{\alpha})\| = 1$ by Theorem 3.35, So

$$\|\mathrm{Od}(a)\| \leq \|a \in \check{\alpha}\|.$$

Our theorem follows by Theorem 3.19.

Corollary. If $a \in V$, then $\|\mathrm{Od}(a)\| = \sum_{\eta} \|a = \check{\eta}\|$.

PROOF. By the theorem

$$\|\mathrm{Od}(a)\| = \sum_{\eta<\alpha} \|a = \check{\eta}\| \leq \sum_{\eta} \|a = \check{\eta}\|.$$

However, as in the proof of the theorem,

$$\|a = \check{\eta}\| \leq \|\mathrm{Od}(a)\|$$

so that

$$\sum_{\eta} \|a = \check{\eta}\| \leq \|\mathrm{Od}(a)\|.$$

We now investigate the cardinality relations in the model.

Theorem 3.37.

$$\vDash F(\check{0}) : (x) : x \in \check{\omega} \,.\, F(x) \,.\supset .\, F(x \cup \{x\}) \,.:\supset:.\, (x) \,.\, x \in \check{\omega} \supset F(x).$$

PROOF. One easily proves by induction on η that for $\eta < \omega$

$$\|F(\check{0})\| \wedge \|(x) : x \in \check{\omega} \,.\, F(x) \,.\supset .\, F(x \cup \{x\})\| \leq \|F(\check{\eta})\|$$

by appealing to (3.74). So

$$\|F(\check{0})\| \wedge \|(x) : x \in \check{\omega} \,.\, F(x) \,.\supset .\, F(x \cup \{x\})\| \leq \prod_{\eta<\omega} \|F(\check{\eta})\|.$$

Since

$$\prod_{\eta<\omega} \|F(\check{\eta})\| = \|(x) \,.\, x \in \check{\omega} \supset F(x)\|$$

by Theorem 3.20, our theorem follows.

If we take $F(x)$ to be $\mathrm{Fin}(x)$ in Theorem 3.37, we get:

Theorem 3.38. $\vDash (x) \,.\, x \in \check{\omega} \supset \mathrm{Fin}(x)$.

That is, every member of $\check{\omega}$ is finite. One can define $\mathrm{Fin}(x)$ in any of various suitable fashions. See, for instance, Bernays and Fraenkel [1, p. 97].

One also has no trouble in proving:

Theorem 3.39. $\vDash \sim \mathrm{Fin}(\check{\omega})$.

So $\check{\omega}$ is the first infinite ordinal. That is:

Theorem 3.40. $\vDash \check{\omega} = \omega_0$.

Theorem 3.41. $\vDash \check{\omega} = \aleph_0$.

Suppose $\aleph_\alpha \leq \eta < \aleph_{\alpha+1}$. Then there is an intuitive one-to-one correspondence C between the members of $\aleph_\alpha$ and η. Then $\check{C}$ is a formal one-to-one correspondence between $\mathrm{Img}(\aleph_\alpha)$ and $\check{\eta}$. So we infer the theorem:

Theorem 3.42. If $\aleph_\alpha \leq \eta < \aleph_{\alpha+1}$, then

$$\vDash \aleph(\mathrm{Img}(\aleph_\alpha)) = \aleph(\check{\eta}).$$

We are following Bernays and Fraenkel [1] in using $\aleph(a)$ to denote the cardinality of a [1, p. 139, Definition 3.1]. Translating the definition of $\aleph(a)$ into the formal model, we see that we must prove that the least ordinal in one-to-one correspondence with $\mathrm{Img}(\aleph_\alpha)$ is also the least ordinal in one-to-one correspondence with $\check{\eta}$. To show this, it suffices to show that $\mathrm{Img}(\aleph_\alpha)$ and $\check{\eta}$ are in one-to-one correspondence, which is shown by use of $\check{C}$.

One does not find it so easy to prove

$$\vDash \aleph(\mathrm{Img}(\aleph_\alpha)) \neq \aleph(\mathrm{Img}(\aleph_{\alpha+1})),$$

which is the formal equivalent of the statement that $\aleph_\alpha$ and $\aleph_{\alpha+1}$ have different cardinalities. Many peculiar objects have been admitted to V, particularly if the Boolean algebra is very complex. It is by no means clear that we may not have admitted an object which formally sets up a one-to-one correspondence between $\mathrm{Img}(\aleph_\alpha)$ and $\mathrm{Img}(\aleph_{\alpha+1})$. Indeed, we need a special assumption about the Boolean algebra to be sure this has not happened. However, we first note that by the same arguments used in the proof of Theorem 3.42 one can prove:

Theorem 3.43. If $\aleph(\eta) \leq \aleph(\mu)$, then $\vDash \aleph(\check{\eta}) \leq \aleph(\check{\mu})$.

Throughout the next few theorems, we shall use "If CCC" as an abbreviation for "If the Boolean algebra satisfies the countable chain condition."

Theorem 3.44. If CCC and $\aleph(\eta) < \aleph(\mu)$, then

$$\vDash \aleph(\check{\eta}) < \aleph(\check{\mu}).$$

PROOF. The case where $\aleph(\mu) \leq \aleph_0$ is handled by Theorems 3.38 and 3.39. So let $\aleph(\mu) \geq \aleph_1$ and let $\aleph(\eta) < \aleph(\mu)$. Write $F(x, y, f)$ for

$$(u) : u \in x \,.\supset.\, (E_1 v) \,.\, v \in y \,.\, \langle u, v \rangle \in f :.$$
$$(v) : v \in y \,.\supset.\, (E_1 u) \,.\, u \in x \,.\, \langle u, v \rangle \in f.$$

Suppose

$$\|(Ef)F(\check{\eta}, \check{\mu}, f)\| \neq 0.$$

Then by Theorem 2.25 there must be an $f \in V$ for which

$$\|F(\check{\eta}, \check{\mu}, f)\| \neq 0.$$

Put $P = \|F(\check{\eta}, \check{\mu}, f)\|$. Take $\sigma < \mu$. Then by Theorem 3.21

$$P \leq \|(E_1 u) \,.\, u \in \check{\eta} \,.\, \langle u, \check{\sigma} \rangle \in f\|.$$

So

$$P \leq \|(Eu) \,.\, u \in \check{\eta} \,.\, \langle u, \check{\sigma} \rangle \in f\|.$$

So

$$P \wedge \|(Eu) \,.\, u \in \check{\eta} \,.\, \langle u, \check{\sigma} \rangle \in f\| \neq 0.$$

Then by Theorems 3.20 and 2.22 there is a $\tau < \eta$ for which

$$P \wedge \|\langle \check{\tau}, \check{\sigma} \rangle \in f\| \neq 0.$$

For each $\tau < \eta$, set

$$\theta(\tau) = \{\sigma \mid P \wedge \|\langle \check{\tau}, \check{\sigma} \rangle \in f\| \neq 0\}.$$

As each $\sigma < \mu$ is in some $\theta(\tau)$, and $\aleph(\eta) < \aleph(\mu)$ and $\aleph(\mu) \geq \aleph_1$, there must be a $\tau_0 < \eta$ for which $\theta(\tau_0)$ is noncountable. But if σ_1 and σ_2 are in μ, then

$$P \wedge \|\langle \check{\tau}_0, \check{\sigma}_1 \rangle \in f\| \wedge \|\langle \check{\tau}_0, \check{\sigma}_2 \rangle \in f\| \leq \|\check{\sigma}_1 = \check{\sigma}_2\|$$

by Theorem 3.21 and the definition of $F(x, y, f)$. But if $\sigma_1 \neq \sigma_2$, then $\|\check{\sigma}_1 = \check{\sigma}_2\| = 0$ by Theorem 3.24. So

$$\{P \wedge \|\langle \check{\tau}_0, \check{\sigma}_1 \rangle \in f\|\} \wedge \{P \wedge \|\langle \check{\tau}_0, \check{\sigma}_2 \rangle \in f\|\} = 0$$

if $\sigma_1 \neq \sigma_2$. Thus

$$\{P \wedge \|\langle \check{\tau}_0, \check{\sigma} \rangle \in f\| \mid \sigma \in \theta(\tau_0)\}$$

is a noncountable disjoint set of nonzero elements. So we have contradicted the countable chain condition.

Theorem 3.45. If CCC and α is an ordinal, then

$$\models \aleph(\mathrm{Img}(\aleph_\alpha)) = \mathrm{Img}(\aleph_\alpha).$$

PROOF. By Theorem 3.44, we have

$$\models \aleph(\check{\eta}) < \aleph(\mathrm{Img}(\aleph_\alpha))$$

for each $\eta < \aleph_\alpha$. So by Theorem 3.20

$$\models (x) : x < \mathrm{Img}(\aleph_\alpha) \,.\supset.\, \aleph(x) < \aleph(\mathrm{Img}(\aleph_\alpha)).$$

From this, our theorem follows.

Theorem 3.46. If CCC and $\alpha < \beta$, then

$$\models \mathrm{Img}(\aleph_\alpha) < \mathrm{Img}(\aleph_\beta).$$

PROOF. Use Theorems 3.44 and 3.45.

Theorem 3.47. If CCC and α is an ordinal, then

$$\models \mathrm{Img}(\aleph_\alpha) = \aleph_{\check{\alpha}}.$$

PROOF. This result is to be interpreted as follows. Let f be defined as on p. 107 of Bernays and Fraenkel [1] by the conditions:

$f(0) = \check{\omega}$;
$f(\alpha') =$ the least ordinal of greater cardinality than $f(\alpha)$;
if β is a limit ordinal, then $f(\beta) = \sum_{\alpha<\beta} f(\alpha)$.

Then we write $\aleph_\alpha$ for $f(\alpha)$, so that the result to be proved is

$$\models \mathrm{Img}(\aleph_\alpha) = f(\check{\alpha}).$$

The proof proceeds by intuitive induction on α.

F. The Axiom of Choice

Clearly the axiom of choice will not hold in all Boolean models, else we would not be able to prove the independence of AxC from the other axioms of a suitable choice of the Boolean algebra However, it holds whenever Γ is the filter of all subsets of $\mathcal{G}$, as we shall now proceed to show.

We mentioned very early that we are considering our "intuitive" logic to be set theory with AxC and GCH added. The developments which will now follow will proceed under the assumption that $V = L$ has also been added (see p. 38 and Chapter VIII of Gödel [5]). However, they could proceed well enough under the weaker assumption AxC by assuming that the ξ_η which will be introduced is a well-ordering of V_α for some sufficiently high α. The value of α needed will vary from theorem to theorem, but as long as we use a finite number of instances of theorems at a time, we can find a value of α high enough to take care of all at once.

Let ξ_η be an ordering of V, in that ξ_η runs through all members of V as η runs through all ordinals; one could arrange that it do so without repetitions, but this is not needed.

Definition 3.4. We define the predicate Ord(x, y) by

$$\|\mathrm{Ord}(x, y)\| = \sum_\eta \|x = \check{\eta} \,.\, y = \xi_\eta\|.$$

Theorem 3.48. The predicate Ord(x, y) is extensional. Specifically

$$\vDash (x, y, u, v) : x = u \,.\, y = v \,.\, \mathrm{Ord}(x, y) \,.\supset .\, \mathrm{Ord}(u, v).$$

PROOF. Clearly

$$\|x = u \,.\, y = v \,.\, x = \check{\eta} \,.\, y = \xi_\eta\| \leq \|u = \check{\eta} \,.\, v = \xi_\eta\|.$$

Summing on η gives the theorem.

Let us now consider formulas which may involve Ord(x, y) as a constituent. By Theorem 3.48, we can conclude that Theorem 3.5 holds for such formulas. Also, if Γ is the filter of all subgroups of $\mathcal{G}$, then Theorems 3.10 and 3.13 both hold for such formulas.

Thus, we shall wish to make this assumption about Γ in certain key theorems of this section. We make the following definition.

Definition 3.5. Hyp(Γ) is the hypothesis that Γ is the filter of all subgroups of $\mathscr{G}$.

Theorem 3.49.

$$\vDash (x, y, z) : \mathrm{Ord}(x, y) \,.\, \mathrm{Ord}(x, z) \,.\, \supset \,.\, y = z.$$

PROOF. Let $x, y, z \in V$. We first undertake to show that

$$\| x = \check{\eta} \,.\, y = \xi_\eta \,.\, x = \check{\sigma} \,.\, z = \xi_\sigma \| \leq \| y = z \|.$$

Case 1. $\eta \neq \sigma$. Then $\| \check{\eta} = \check{\sigma} \| = 0$ by Theorem 3.24. But by (3.17) and (3.16)

$$\| x = \check{\eta} \,.\, x = \check{\sigma} \| \leq \| \check{\eta} = \check{\sigma} \|.$$

Case 2. $\eta = \sigma$. Then $\xi_\eta = \xi_\sigma$, so that

$$\| y = \xi_\eta \,.\, z = \xi_\sigma \| \leq \| y = z \|.$$

This proves the stated result, and our theorem follows by summing over η and σ.

Theorem 3.50.

$$\vDash (y)(Ex) \,.\, \mathrm{Od}(x) \,.\, \mathrm{Ord}(x, y).$$

PROOF. Let $y \in V$. Then there is an η such that $y = \xi_\eta$. So by (3.15) and Theorem 3.35

$$\vDash \mathrm{Od}(\check{\eta}) \,.\, \mathrm{Ord}(\check{\eta}, y).$$

Theorem 3.51.

$$\vDash (x, y) \,.\, \mathrm{Ord}(x, y) \supset \mathrm{Od}(x).$$

PROOF. This is obvious by Theorems 3.5 and 3.35.

In view of this, Theorem 3.50 would be just as strong if the factor Od(x) were omitted. However, it was put in for emphasis.

The predicate Ord(x, y) reflects formally the intuitive ordering

ξ_η of V. Indeed, we may read Ord(x, y) as "x is the order of y." Even if ξ_η orders V without repetitions, Ord(x, y) will not do so, since we can find η and σ with $\xi_\eta \neq \xi_\sigma$ but

$$\vdash \xi_\eta = \xi_\sigma .$$

So we wish to introduce a predicate which formally well-orders V without repetitions.

Definition 3.6. We write Mord(x, y) for

$$\mathrm{Ord}(x, y) : (w) . \mathrm{Ord}(w, y) \supset x \leq w.$$

We may read Mord(x, y) as "x is the minimal order of y."

Theorem 3.52.

$$\vdash (x, y, z) : \mathrm{Mord}(x, y) . \mathrm{Mord}(z, y) . \supset . x = z.$$

PROOF. If $x, y, z \in V$, then by Definition 3.6.

$$\vdash \mathrm{Mord}(x, y) . \mathrm{Mord}(z, y) . \supset . x \leq z . z \leq x.$$

But by [1] on p. 81 and 1.11 on p. 84 of Bernays and Fraenkel [1],

$$\vdash \mathrm{Od}(x) . \mathrm{Od}(z) . x \leq z . z \leq x . \supset . x = z.$$

Our theorem now follows by use of Theorem 3.51.

As we have previously emphasized, only variables, constants, $\in$, $=$, $\sim$, &, and quantifiers are used in building up statements. If more general predicates, such as Ord(x, y) are used, we refer to the result as a formula. By Theorem 3.48, Ord(x, y) is extensional. If it is the only unorthodox predicate used, then the resulting formula will be extensional. However, there may be formulas which are not extensional. Hence we have had to insert in the next two theorems the hypothesis (3.83) to the effect that $F(x)$ is extensional.

Theorem 3.53. Let $F(x)$ be a formula containing no free variables other than x, and such that

$$\vdash (x, y) : x = y . F(x) . \supset . F(y). \tag{3.83}$$

If Hyp(Γ), then there are $a, b \in V$ such that

$$\vDash (Ex)F(x) :: \supset :: \mathrm{Ord}(a, b) \,.\, F(b) :.$$
$$(z, w) : \mathrm{Ord}(w, z) \,.\, F(z) \,.\supset .\, a \leq w.$$

Proof. By requiring only that $F(x)$ be a formula, we permit it to contain predicates such as $\mathrm{Ord}(x, y)$, or other predicates that we may wish to introduce later. If $F(x)$ is a statement, then the hypothesis (3.83) holds by Theorem 3.5, It is permitted that $F(z)$ contain constants. To commence the proof, we note that by Theorem 3.11 there is an α such that

$$\|(Ex)F(x)\| = \sum_{x \in V_\alpha} \|F(x)\|. \tag{3.84}$$

Take σ large enough so that each $x \in V_\alpha$ is a ξ_η for some $\eta < \sigma$. Take β large enough so that $\xi_\eta \in V_\beta$ for each $\eta < \sigma$. Define U_β with $D(U_\beta) = V_\beta$ by the condition that if $x \in V_\beta$, then

$$U_\beta(x) = 1.$$

Then by Theorem 3.9, $U_\beta \in V_{\beta+1}$. Also for each $x \in V_\beta$

$$\vDash x \in U_\beta .$$

So for $\eta < \sigma$

$$\|F(\xi_\eta)\| \leq \|(Ex, z) \,.\, x < \check{\sigma} \,.\, z \in U_\beta \,.\, \mathrm{Ord}(x, z) \,.\, F(z)\|$$

follows by taking x to be $\check{\eta}$ and z to be ξ_η. Summing on η and using (3.84) gives

$$\|(Ex)F(x)\| \leq \|(Ex, z) \,.\, x < \check{\sigma} \,.\, z \in U_\beta \,.\, \mathrm{Ord}(x, z) \,.\, F(z)\|.$$

Then one easily concludes

$$\vDash (Ex)F(x) : \supset : (Ex, z) \,.\, x < \check{\sigma} \,.\, z \in U_\beta \,.\, \mathrm{Ord}(x, z) \,.\, F(z). \tag{3.85}$$

Define c with $D(c) = V_\sigma$ by the condition that if $x \in V_\sigma$ then

$$c(x) = \|x < \check{\sigma} : (Ez) \,.\, z \in U_\beta \,.\, \mathrm{Ord}(x, z) \,.\, F(z)\|.$$

Then, as we are assuming (3.83) and Hyp(Γ), we can conclude by Theorem 3.9 that $c \in V_{\sigma+1}$ and

$$\vDash (x) :. x \in c : \supset : x < \check{\sigma} : (Ez) \,.\, z \in U_\beta \,.\, \mathrm{Ord}(x, z) \,.\, F(z). \tag{3.86}$$

Let $\eta < \sigma$. Then $\check{\eta} \in V_\sigma = D(c)$. So by the definition of c, we have

$$\|\check{\eta} < \check{\sigma} : (Ez) . z \in U_\beta . \mathrm{Ord}(\check{\eta}, z) . F(z) : \supset : \check{\eta} \in c\| = 1.$$

Taking the product over $\eta < \sigma$ and using Theorem 3.20 gives

$$\vDash (x) :: x < \check{\sigma} .: \supset :. x < \check{\sigma} : (Ez) . z \in U_\beta . \mathrm{Ord}(x, z) . F(z) : \supset : x \in c.$$

So by (3.86)

$$\vDash (x) :. x \in c : \equiv : x < \check{\sigma} : (Ez) . z \in U_\beta . \mathrm{Ord}(x, z) . F(z). \quad (3.87)$$

By 1.12 on p. 84 of Bernays and Fraenkel [1]

$$\vDash (Ex) . \mathrm{Od}(x) . x \in c .: \supset :. (Ex) :. \mathrm{Od}(x) . x \in c : (w) : \mathrm{Od}(w) . w \in c . \supset . x \leq w.$$

By reasoning as in the proof of Theorem 3.52, we get

$$\vDash (Ex) . \mathrm{Od}(x) . x \in c .: \supset :. (E_1x) .: \mathrm{Od}(x) . x \in c : (w) : \mathrm{Od}(w) . w \in c . \supset . x \leq w.$$

Hence by Theorem 3.13 there is an $a \in V$ such that

$$\vDash (Ex) . \mathrm{Od}(x) . x \in c .: \supset :. \mathrm{Od}(a) . a \in c : (w) : \mathrm{Od}(w) . w \in c . \supset . a \leq w. \quad (3.88)$$

By (3.87) and Theorem 3.51,

$$\vDash (x) : x \in c . \supset . \mathrm{Od}(x) . x \in c.$$

But by (3.85) and (3.87)

$$\vDash (Ex)F(x) . \supset . (Ex) . x \in c.$$

So by (3.88)

$$\vDash (Ex)F(x) .: \supset :. \mathrm{Od}(a) . a \in c : (w) : \mathrm{Od}(w) . w \in c . \supset . a \leq w.$$

Then (3.87) and Theorem 3.51 give

$$\vDash (Ex)F(x) :: \supset :: a < \check{\sigma} :. (Ez) . z \in U_\beta . \mathrm{Ord}(a, z) . F(z) :. (z, w) : w < \check{\sigma} . z \in U_\beta . \mathrm{Ord}(w, z) . F(z) . \supset . a \leq w. \quad (3.89)$$

By Theorems 3.13 and 3.49, there is a $b \in V$ such that

$$\vDash (Ez) \,.\, z \in U_\beta \,.\, \mathrm{Ord}(a, z) \,.\, F(z) : \supset : \mathrm{Ord}(a, b) \,.\, F(b). \quad (3.90)$$

Lemma.

$$\vDash (a) :: a < \check{\sigma} : (z, w) : w < \check{\sigma} \,.\, z \in U_\beta \,.\, \mathrm{Ord}(w, z) \,.\, F(z) \,.$$
$$\supset \,.\, a \leq w \,.: \supset :.\, (z, w) : \mathrm{Ord}(w, z) \,.\, F(z) \,.\supset .\, a \leq w.$$

PROOF. By 1.5 on p. 82 of Bernays and Fraenkel [1] and Theorem 3.35

$$\vDash a < \check{\sigma} \,.\supset .\, \mathrm{Od}(a).$$

Also by Theorems 3.35 and 3.51, and by 1.11 on p. 84 of Bernays and Fraenkel [1],

$$\vDash \mathrm{Ord}(w, z) \,.\supset .\, w < \check{\sigma} \,.\vee .\, \check{\sigma} \leq w.$$

Then

$$\vDash a < \check{\sigma} \,.\, \mathrm{Ord}(w, z) \,.\supset .\, w < \check{\sigma} \,.\vee .\, a \leq w. \quad (3.91)$$

Let $\nu < \sigma$. Then

$$\|\check{\nu} = \check{\eta} \,.\, z = \xi_\eta\| \leq \|z \in U_\beta\|.$$

Case 1. $\nu = \eta$. Then $\xi_\eta \in V_\beta$, so that $\vDash \xi_\eta \in U_\beta$. Hence

$$\|z = \xi_\eta\| \leq \|z \in U_\beta\|.$$

Case 2. $\nu \neq \eta$. Then $\|\check{\nu} = \check{\eta}\| = 0$, so that our result holds. Summing over η gives

$$\|\mathrm{Ord}(\check{\nu}, z)\| \leq \|z \in U_\beta\|.$$

That is

$$\|\mathrm{Ord}(\check{\nu}, z) \supset z \in U_\beta\| = 1.$$

Therefore

$$\prod_{\nu < \sigma} \|\mathrm{Ord}(\check{\nu}, z) \supset z \in U_\beta\| = 1.$$

So by Theorem 3.20

$$\vDash (w) :.\, w < \check{\sigma} : \supset : \mathrm{Ord}(w, z) \,.\supset .\, z \in U_\beta \,.$$

So by (3.91)

$$\vDash a < \check{\sigma} \,.\, \mathrm{Ord}(w, z) \,.\supset .\, w < \check{\sigma} \,.\, z \in U_\beta \,.\, \mathrm{Ord}(w, z) \,.\vee.\, a \leq w.$$

Then our lemma follows.

By (3.89), (3.90), and our lemma, we get our theorem.

The theorem says in effect that if there is an x such that $F(x)$, then there is a "first" such x in the sense of the ordering implied by $\mathrm{Ord}(x, y)$. This gives the key to two very useful results, which we now present.

Theorem 3.54. Let $F(x)$ be a formula containing no free variables other than x, and such that

$$\vDash (x, y) : x = y \,.\, F(x) \,.\supset .\, F(y).$$

If $\mathrm{Hyp}(\Gamma)$, then there is a $b \in V$ such that

$$\vDash (Ex)F(x) \,.\equiv .\, F(b).$$

PROOF. With the b of Theorem 3.53 we readily infer

$$\vDash (Ex)F(x) \,.\supset .\, F(b)$$

from the conclusion of that theorem. However, the reverse implication presents no difficulty.

Theorem 3.55. If $\mathrm{Hyp}(\Gamma)$ and $c \in V$, then there is a $a \in V$ such that

$$\vDash \mathrm{Mord}(a, c).$$

PROOF. In Theorem 3.53, take $F(x)$ to be $x = c$. We have $\vDash (Ex)F(x)$ of course, and so conclude

$$\vDash \mathrm{Ord}(a, b) \,.\, b = c :.\, (z, w) : \mathrm{Ord}(w, z) \,.\, z = c \,.\supset .\, a \leq w.$$

From this, our theorem follows easily.

Theorem 3.56. If $\mathrm{Hyp}(\Gamma)$, then

$$\vDash (y)(E_1 x) \,.\, \mathrm{Mord}(x, y).$$

PROOF. Use Theorems 3.55 and 3.52.

This is a very strong well-ordering principle, in that it says that the well-ordering Mord embraces all elements of V. Thus there is a single well-ordering of all of V. In effect, this gives us the strong Axiom E of Gödel [5, p. 6]. This depends on assuming a strong well-ordering principle in the external logic. If only AxC were assumed, one would define Ord(x, y) and Mord(x, y) so as to well-order all elements of V_β, for some given β. Then the various theorems we have proved about Ord(x, y) and Mord(x, y) would have to have hypotheses $y \in U_\beta$ added in some cases. Naturally the definitions of Ord(x, y) and Mord(x, y) would change as β changes. This would still suffice to derive standard versions of the axiom of choice in the model. We will merely sketch the derivation.

Theorems 3.50 and 3.56 will require the additional hypothesis $y \in U_\beta$. If now $D(c) \subseteq V_\beta$, then by Theorem 3.31 there will be an $a \in V$ such that

$$\vDash (x) : x \in a \,.\equiv.\, (Ey)\,.\, y \in c\,.\,\mathrm{Mord}(x, y).$$

That is, a is the set of the "orders" of the members of c. If $\vDash c \neq \Lambda$, then $\vDash a \neq \Lambda$, and by 1.12 on p. 84 of Bernays and Fraenkel [1], there is a least member of a, and indeed a unique least one. By Theorem 3.49, there will be a unique member of c which has this "least order." It is definable by a formula involving Mord(x, y), and is unique. That is, we can write a formula $F(x, y)$ which says that y is the "first" member of x. Using this as the $F(x, y)$ in Theorem 3.31 will enable us to define the set of "first" members of members of b.

A classic form of the axiom of choice (see Rosser [7, p. 492]) is as follows.

If λ is a set of nonempty, nonoverlapping sets, then there is a set γ which has exactly one member in common with each member of λ.

To show this, we appeal to the corollary of Theorem 3.31. We take u to be λ, and take $F(x, y)$ to be the statement that y is the unique element of "least order" in x. Then the w whose existence is affirmed by the corollary will be the desired γ.

CHAPTER FOUR

The Independence of $V = L$

A. Preliminaries

If $V = L$ can be proved, then one can write a statement without constants which will well-order the set of real numbers (see Chapter VIII of Gödel [5]). Now one can certainly well-order the real numbers with a formula. Indeed, we saw just at the end of the previous chapter that with the help of the predicate $\mathrm{Ord}(x, y)$ one can well-order any set. However, formulas containing $\mathrm{Ord}(x, y)$ are not statements.

We will construct a model in which AxC and GCH both hold, but in which there is no statement without constants which well-orders the real numbers. Hence in this model we must have $\models V \neq L$.

How is this to be done? First we define X by (2.24) with $I = \omega$, and with basis sets defined by (2.26), and then define the Boolean algebra by Definition 2.9. We take $\mathscr{G}$ to be the entire group of automorphisms of the Boolean algebra. By Theorem 2.29, 0 and 1 are the only elements of the Boolean algebra which are invariant under all automorphisms of $\mathscr{G}$. We take Γ to be the set of all subgroups of $\mathscr{G}$. Then by Theorem 3.56, we have $\models$AxC. Moreover, we have $\models$GCH, as we will show in the next section.

We note that the real numbers can be put into one-to-one correspondence with $SC(\omega)$, the power class of ω. This is indeed the content of Theorem XI.5.5 on p. 446 of Rosser [7]. The proof of this theorem can be carried out in set theory. Hence in our model we can identify the question of well-ordering the real numbers with that of well-ordering $SC(\check{\omega})$.

Suppose $F(x, y)$ is a statement containing no constants and no free variables other than x and y. Consider the statement that $F(x,y)$ well orders $SC(\check{\omega})$, From this one can conclude that $F(x, y)$ will choose a unique "first" member of any nonempty subset of $SC(\check{\omega})$. One can construct a member q of $SC(\check{\omega}) - \mathrm{Img}(SC(\omega))$. So in terms of $F(x, y)$, one can describe a "first" member of this set. In this description the only constants that appear are $\check{\omega}$ and $\mathrm{Img}(SC(\omega))$. (The constant q was used to prove

$$\vDash (Ex) \,.\, x \in SC(\check{\omega}) - \mathrm{Img}(SC(\omega)),$$

but does not appear in this statement, and hence does not appear in the description of the "first" member of $SC(\check{\omega}) - \mathrm{Img}(SC(\omega))$.) So by Theorems 3.7 and 3.18, the value of the description must be invariant under all automorphisms of $\mathscr{G}$. So if c is the "first" member of $SC(\check{\omega}) - \mathrm{Img}(SC(\omega))$ chosen by $F(x, y)$ (see Theorem 3.54), then c must be invariant also. So $c(\check{\eta})$ must be invariant also for each $\eta < \omega$, by Theorem 3.18. Then $c(\check{\eta})$ must be either 0 or 1 for each $\eta < \omega$, by Theorem 2.29. But then $\vDash c \in \mathrm{Img}(SC(\omega))$, contrary to its definition. Hence no such $F(x, y)$ can exist.

B. Proof of GCH

We show:

Theorem 4.1. $\vDash$GCH.

PROOF. By (3.74) and Theorem 3.47, it suffices to show that for each ordinal α

$$\vDash \mathrm{Img}(\aleph_{\alpha+1}) = \aleph(SC(\aleph_{\check{\alpha}})).$$

To do this, we first note that Cantor's theorem gives

$$\vDash \aleph_{\check{\alpha}} < \aleph(SC(\aleph_{\check{\alpha}}))$$

(see Bernays and Fraenkel [1, p. 117]). So by (3.74) and Theorem 3.47

$$\vDash \mathrm{Img}(\aleph_{\alpha+1}) \leq \aleph(SC(\aleph_{\check{\alpha}})). \tag{4.1}$$

So it suffices to prove

$$\|\mathrm{Img}(\aleph_{\alpha+2}) \leq \aleph(SC(\aleph_{\check{\alpha}}))\| = 0.$$

Suppose this is not so. Then by Theorems 3.7, 3.18, and 2.29

$$\|\mathrm{Img}(\aleph_{\alpha+2}) \leq \aleph(SC(\aleph_{\check{\alpha}}))\| = 1.$$

Put μ for $\aleph_\alpha$, ν for $\aleph_{\alpha+2}$ and $G(x, y, f)$ for

$$(u) : u \subseteq x \,.\supset.\, (E_1 v) \,.\, v \in y \,.\, \langle u, v\rangle \in f :.$$
$$(v) : v \in y \,.\supset.\, (Eu) \,.\, u \subseteq x \,.\, \langle u, v\rangle \in f.$$

Therefore

$$\|(Ef)G(\check{\mu}, \check{\nu}, f)\| = 1.$$

So by Theorem 3.54, there is an $f \in V$ such that

$$\|G(\check{\mu}, \check{\nu}, f)\| = 1. \tag{4.2}$$

So for $\sigma \in \nu$ we have

$$\|(Eu) \,.\, u \subseteq \check{\mu} \,.\, \langle u, \check{\sigma}\rangle \in f\| = 1.$$

Applying Theorem 3.54 again, we see that there is an $a \in V$ such that

$$\|a \subseteq \check{\mu} \,.\, < a, \check{\sigma} > \in f\| = 1. \tag{4.3}$$

Call this a_σ. If for $\eta < \mu$ we put

$$g(\eta) = \|\check{\eta} \in a_\sigma\|, \tag{4.4}$$

then g is a function from μ to A. However there are at most $\aleph_{\alpha+1}$ functions from μ to A, as one can see by the following argument. By (2.26) the basis sets are denumerable. Hence there are $\aleph_1$ open sets, and so at most $\aleph_1$ regular open sets. So the number of functions from $\mu = \aleph_\alpha$ to A is at most

$$(\aleph_1)^{\aleph_\alpha} = (2^{\aleph_0})^{\aleph_\alpha} = 2^{\aleph_0 \times \aleph_\alpha} = 2^{\aleph_\alpha} = \aleph_{\alpha+1}$$

since we are assuming the GCH externally to our model. So there must be at least one g which results from two distinct ordinals. So there are distinct σ and τ with $\sigma < \nu$ and $\tau < \nu$ such that

$$\|\check{\eta} \in a_\sigma\| = \|\check{\eta} \in a_\tau\|$$

for each $\eta < \mu$. Therefore

$$\prod_{\eta \in \mu} \|\check{\eta} \in a_\sigma \equiv \check{\eta} \in a_\tau\| = 1.$$

Then by Theorem 3.20

$$\models (y) : y \in \check{\mu} \,.\supset.\, y \in a_\sigma \equiv y \in a_\tau \,.$$

So by (4.3) and Theorem 3.6

$$\models a_\sigma = a_\tau \,.$$

However, by (4.3)

$$\models \langle a_\sigma, \check{\sigma} \rangle \in f$$

$$\models \langle a_\tau, \check{\tau} \rangle \in f.$$

Therefore

$$\models \langle a_\sigma, \check{\tau} \rangle \in f.$$

However, by $\models a_\sigma \subseteq \check{\mu}$ and (4.2) we have

$$\models (E_1 v) \,.\, v \in \check{\nu} \,.\, \langle a_\sigma, v \rangle \in f.$$

So $\models \check{\sigma} = \check{\tau}$, which violates Theorem 3.24.

C. Subsets of $\check{\omega}$

We now develop the results referred to earlier.

Theorem 4.2. $\models \mathrm{Img}(SC(\omega)) \subseteq SC(\check{\omega})$.

PROOF. Let $a \subseteq \omega$. Then for each $t \in a$ we have $\models \check{t} \in \check{\omega}$ by Theorem 3.21. So

$$\prod_{t \in a} \|\check{t} \in \check{\omega}\| = 1.$$

So by Theorem 3.20

$$\models (x) \,.\, x \in \check{a} \supset x \in \check{\omega}.$$

That is, $\models \check{a} \subseteq \check{\omega}$. Since this holds for each $a \in SC(\omega)$, we can use Theorem 3.20 again to get

$$\models (x) : x \in \operatorname{Img}(SC(\omega)) \,.\supset.\, x \subseteq \check{\omega}.$$

From this, our theorem follows.

Definition 4.1. Define q with $D(q) = V_\omega$ by the condition that if $x \in V_\omega$ then

$$q(x) = \sum_{\eta<\omega} B_\eta^{\ 1} \wedge \|x = \check{\eta}\|, \tag{4.5}$$

where $B_\eta^{\ 1}$ is as in (2.25).

Theorem 4.3. We have $q \in V_{\omega+1}$. Also

$$\models q \subseteq \check{\omega}. \tag{4.6}$$

PROOF. To show $q \in V_{\omega+1}$ we use Theorem 3.9, which also gives for each $x \in V$

$$\|x \in q\| \leq \sum_{\eta<\omega} B_\eta^{\ 1} \wedge \|x = \check{\eta}\|. \tag{4.7}$$

Since $\models \check{\eta} \in \check{\omega}$ for $\eta < \omega$ by Theorem 3.21, we get

$$\|x = \check{\eta}\| \leq \|x \in \check{\omega}\|,$$

and hence

$$B_\eta^{\ 1} \wedge \|x = \check{\eta}\| \leq \|x \in \check{\omega}\|.$$

Summing over $\eta < \omega$ and using (4.7) gives

$$\|x \in q\| \leq \|x \in \check{\omega}\|.$$

Therefore

$$\models (x) \,.\, x \in q \supset x \in \check{\omega},$$

which is (4.6).

Naturally, $\mathrm{Img}(SC(\omega))$ is the image of the intuitive set of all the subsets of ω. We shall show that q is not a member of $\mathrm{Img}(SC(\omega))$. Thus, one may think of q as a queer subset of $\check{\omega}$. This is why we have denoted it by "q."

Theorem 4.4. $\vDash \sim q \in \mathrm{Img}(SC(\omega))$.

PROOF. We have to show

$$\|q \in \mathrm{Img}(SC(\omega))\| = 0.$$

As $q \in D(\mathrm{Img}(SC(\omega)))$ by Definition 3.3, we have to show

$$\sum_{b \subseteq \omega} \|q = \check{b}\| = 0,$$

because of (3.69). So let $b \subseteq \omega$, and let g be its characteristic function. That is, for $\eta < \omega$

$$g(\eta) = \begin{cases} 1 & \text{if} \quad \eta \in b \\ 0 & \text{if} \quad \sim\eta \in b. \end{cases}$$

Now, $B_\eta{}^1$ is a Scott core for q by (4.5) and g is a Scott core for $\check{b}$ by (3.69), where now one interprets $g(\eta)$ as the Boolean value 0 or 1 rather than the integer 0 or 1. For both q and $\check{b}$, the corresponding Scott domains are

$$\{\check{\eta} \mid \eta < \omega\}.$$

Hence by Theorem 3.15

$$\|q \subseteq \check{b}\| = \prod_{\eta<\omega} B_\eta{}^1 \Rightarrow \|\check{\eta} \in \check{b}\|$$

$$\|\check{b} \subseteq q\| = \prod_{\eta<\omega} g(\eta) \Rightarrow \|\check{\eta} \in q\|.$$

However, by Theorem 3.24

$$\|\check{\eta} \in \check{b}\| = g(\eta),$$

and by (4.5) and Theorem 3.24,

$$\|\check{\eta} \in q\| = B_\eta{}^1.$$

So by Theorem 2.23

$$\|q \subseteq \check{b}\| \wedge \|\check{b} \subseteq q\| = \prod_{\eta<\omega} B_\eta{}^1 \Leftrightarrow g(\eta).$$

So by Theorem 3.4

$$\|q = \check{b}\| = \prod_{\eta<\omega} B_\eta{}^1 \Leftrightarrow g(\eta).$$

Since $g(\eta) = 0$ or 1, one easily verifies that

$$B_\eta{}^1 \Leftrightarrow g(\eta) = B_\eta^{g(\eta)},$$

where we interpret the $g(\eta)$ in the superscript as being again the integer 0 or 1. So finally, we must show

$$\prod_{\eta<\omega} B_\eta^{g(\eta)} = 0, \tag{4.8}$$

which follows by Theorem 2.30.

We are now ready for our key result. By standard manipulations of set theory, one can write a statement which sets up a one-to-one correspondence between the real numbers and $SC(\check{\omega})$. As noted earlier, one can do this by paralleling the proof of Theorem XI.5.5 on p. 446 of Rosser [7]. So one can write a statement which well-orders the real numbers if and only if one can write a statement which well-orders $SC(\check{\omega})$. We shall show that the latter is impossible without constants.

Theorem 4.5. Let $F(x, y)$ be a statement containing no constants and no free variables other than x and y. Then

$$\begin{aligned}\vDash \sim[(x, y) : x, y \in SC(\check{\omega}) . \supset . F(x, y) \vee x = y \vee F(y, x)::\\ (z) :. z \subseteq SC(\check{\omega}) . z \neq \Lambda : \supset : (Ey) : y \in z :\\ (x) . F(x, y) \supset \sim x \in z].\end{aligned}$$

PROOF. By theorems 3.7 and 3.18, we conclude that the value of the statement in question in invariant under all automorphisms of $\mathcal{G}$. So by Theorem 2.29, it must be 0 or 1. We shall assume it to be 0, from which we will derive a contradiction. Assuming it to be 0 gives

$$\vDash (x, y) : x, y \in SC(\check{\omega}) . \supset . F(x, y) \vee x = y \vee F(y, x) \tag{4.9}$$

and

$$\begin{aligned}\vDash (z) :. z \subseteq SC(\check{\omega}) . z \neq \Lambda : \supset : (Ey) : y \in z :\\ (x) . F(x, y) \supset \sim x \in z.\end{aligned} \tag{4.10}$$

Write $G(z, y)$ for

$$y \in z : (x) \,.\, F(x, y) \supset \sim x \in z.$$

Then (4.10) can be written as

$$\models (z) : z \subseteq SC(\check{\omega}) \,.\, z \neq \Lambda \,.\supset.\, (Ey) \,.\, G(z, y). \tag{4.11}$$

By (4.9), we get

$$\models (z) :. z \subseteq SC(\check{\omega}) : \supset : (x, y) : G(z, x) \,.\, G(z, y) \,.\supset.\, x = y. \tag{4.12}$$

Write Q for $SC(\check{\omega}) - \mathrm{Img}(SC(\omega))$. By Theorems 4.3 and 4.4

$$\models q \in Q.$$

Therefore

$$\models Q \subseteq SC(\check{\omega}) \,.\, Q \neq \Lambda.$$

So by (4.11)

$$\models (Ey) \,.\, G(Q, y).$$

So by (4.12) and Theorem 3.13 there is a $c \in V$ such that

$$\models G(Q, c). \tag{4.13}$$

Then from (4.12)

$$\vdash (x) : x \in c \,.\equiv\cdot\, (Ey) \,.\, x \in y \,.\, G(Q, y)$$

follows by simple manipulations of set theory. So for η an ordinal

$$\|\check{\eta} \in c\| = \|(Ey) \,.\, \check{\eta} \in y \,.\, G(Q, y)\|. \tag{4.14}$$

However, by Theorems 3.7 and 3.18, the right side of (4.14) is invariant under each automorphism of $\mathscr{G}$. So by Theorem 2.29

$$\|\check{\eta} \in c\| = 0 \quad \text{or} \quad 1.$$

Define a subset b of ω by

$$b = \{\eta \mid \eta \in \omega \,.\, \|\check{\eta} \in c\| = 1\}.$$

Then by Theorem 3.21, $\models \check{b} \in \mathrm{Img}(SC(\omega))$. So by Theorem 4.2

$$\models \check{b} \subseteq \check{\omega}. \tag{4.15}$$

By (4.13), $\models c \in Q$. Hence

$$\models c \subseteq \check{\omega}. \tag{4.16}$$

By Theorem 3.24, we have for $\eta < \omega$

$$\|\check{\eta} \in c\| = \|\check{\eta} \in \check{b}\|.$$

So by Theorem 3.20

$$\models (x) : x \in \check{\omega} \,.\, \supset \,.\, x \in c \equiv x \in \check{b}.$$

So by (4.15), (4.16), and Theorem 3.6,

$$\models c = \check{b}.$$

We had $\models \check{b} \in \mathrm{Img}(SC(\omega))$. Therefore $\models c \in \mathrm{Img}(SC(\omega))$. In view of the definitions of Q and $G(z, y)$, this contradicts (4.13).

If we have $\models V = L$, then we could construct an $F(x, y)$ that would well-order $SC(\check{\omega})$. (See Chapter VIII of Gödel [5].) However, by Theorem 4.5, there is no such $F(x, y)$. So $\|V = L\| \neq 1$. But $\|V = L\|$ is invariant under every transformation of $\mathscr{G}$. So we conclude:

Theorem 4.6. $\models V \neq L$.

In summary, we have shown that even if we add AxC and GCH to the axioms of set theory, we cannot prove $V = L$.

We should not close the chapter without assuring that there can be no misunderstanding on one fundamental point. In Theorem 4.5 we showed that $SC(\check{\omega})$ cannot be well-ordered by a statement with no free variables and no constants. If $\models V = L$, then such a statement could be constructed; hence we conclude Theorem 4.6. However, this does not mean that there is not a statement which well-orders $SC(\check{\omega})$. Indeed there is such a statement, and we shall show how to construct one.

First let us construct a formula which well-orders $SC(\check{\omega})$. This can be done by defining $G(x, y)$ to be

$$(Eu, v) \,.\, u < v \,.\, \mathrm{Mord}(u, x) \,.\, \mathrm{Mord}(v, y).$$

In view of Theorems 3.52 and 3.56 we can prove

$$\vDash(x, y) \,.\, G(x, y) \vee x = y \vee G(y, x) \tag{4.17}$$

$$\vDash(x, y, z) :.\, z \neq \Lambda : \supset : (Ey) : y \in z : (x) \,.\, G(x, y) \supset \sim x \in z. \tag{4.18}$$

In proving (4.18), it would be helpful to appeal to Theorem 3.53 with $F(x)$ taken to be $x \in z$. Now define c with $D(c) = V_{\omega+3}$ by the condition that if $w \in V_{\omega+3}$ then

$$c(w) = \|(Ex, y) \,.\, w = \langle x, y\rangle \,.\, G(x, y)\|. \tag{4.19}$$

Then one proves easily that

$$\vDash(x, y) : x, y \in SC(\check{\omega}) \,.\supset.\, G(x, y) \equiv \langle x, y\rangle \in c. \tag{4.20}$$

So if we take $F(x, y)$ to be $\langle x, y\rangle \in c$, then (4.9) and (4.10) hold. Thus $F(x, y)$ well-orders $SC(\check{\omega})$, and $F(x, y)$ is a statement.

If the c used above were invariant under all automorphisms, then the reasoning in the proof of Theorem 4.5 could be applied to conclude that $\langle x, y\rangle \in c$ could not well-order $SC(\check{\omega})$. So c cannot be invariant under all automorphisms. This shows that although c was defined by means of a formula, it cannot be defined by means of a statement with no constants or free variables.

It can be defined by means of a statement involving a constant. Thus, choose σ large enough so that for each $x \in V_{\omega+1}$ there is an $\eta < \sigma$ such that $\vDash\text{Ord}(\check{\eta}, x)$. Define b with $D(b) = V_{\sigma+2}$ by the condition that if $w \in V_{\sigma+2}$ then

$$b(w) = \|(Ex, y) \,.\, w = \langle x, y\rangle \,.\, \text{Mord}(x, y)\|.$$

Then we can replace (4.19) by

$$c(w) = \|(Ex, y, u, v) \,.\, w = \langle x, y\rangle \,.\, u < v \,.\, \langle u, x\rangle \in b \,.\, \langle v, y\rangle \in b\|.$$

Then (4.20) will hold.

Of course, b will not be invariant under all automorphisms, else c would be invariant also.

CHAPTER FIVE

Analogies with Forcing

A. Comparison of Specific Proofs

The material of this chapter is not used elsewhere in the present text, and can be omitted. It is inserted for the benefit of the reader who has some acquaintance with forcing and who would like to compare the forcing method with the use of Boolean algebra.

The notion of forcing was first presented by Cohen [2], and a definitive treatment is given by Cohen [3]. In the simplest case, corresponding to our treatment in the preceding chapter, Cohen introduces a generic set, a, which is a subset of ω. No complete description of a is ever given, but an analysis is made of the consequences of various "conditions" that one might impose on a. For each condition there are various statements which it "forces." As a particularly simple example, the condition that "$3 \in a$ and $\sim 4 \in a$" forces "$a \neq \{4\}$," "$3 \in a \vee Y$," "$\sim(4 \in a \;\&\; Y)$," "$(Ex) \,.\, x \in a$," etc. Each condition is taken to be a specification, for some finite subset s of ω, of which members of s lie in a and which do not.

Taking I to be ω in (2.24), as we did in the previous chapter, we can set up an exact correspondence between conditions and basis sets. Specifically, take B as in (2.26) and assume $B \neq 0$. Then take s to be the support of B. That is, by Definition 2.15,

$$s = \{f(j) \mid 1 \leq j \leq N\}.$$

Then s is a finite subset of ω. Then we let B correspond to the condition which specifies that $f(j) \in a$ if $g(j) = 1$ and $\sim f(j) \in a$ if $g(j) = 0$. Because $B \neq 0$, we shall not have a case where $f(j) = f(k)$ but $g(j) \neq g(k)$, so that we do indeed specify which members of s lie in a and which do not. It is clear that from a condition P we can conversely define a unique basis set B_P by (2.26).

Now let X be a statement without free variables. Some set of conditions (perhaps null) may force X and another set (perhaps null) may force $\sim X$. If a condition P forces X and P corresponds to the basis set B_P, then $B_P \subseteq \|X\|$. If P forces $\sim X$, then $B_P \subseteq \|\sim X\|$. The converse is not entirely true. If $B_P \subseteq \|\sim X\|$, then P forces $\sim X$, but if $B_P \subseteq \|X\|$, the most we can conclude is that P forces $\sim\sim X$. In view of the definition given by Cohen [3, p. 139], we can say that P weakly forces X if and only if $B_P \subseteq \|X\|$.

We now get a parallelism of properties of forcing and properties of the Boolean algebra. We list the main ones. This will include parallels of three of the clauses of the definition of forcing, as given by Cohen [3,p .118]. The other clauses do not have simple parallels because of the fact that $B_P \subseteq \|X\|$ corresponds to P weakly forcing X rather than P forcing X.

We note first that $Q \supseteq P$ corresponds to $B_Q \subseteq B_P$, since $Q \supseteq P$ means that the specifications of Q include all those of P, and perhaps others besides. We note further that in our subsequent remarks the statements mentioned must be without free variables; our special treatment of statements with free variables has no parallel in forcing.

Let us first consider Lemma 1 on p. 118 of Cohen [3].

(a) "For all P and A we do not have both P forces A and P forces $\sim A$."

The parallel of this is that if B_P is a basis set, then we cannot have both $B_P \subseteq \|X\|$ and $B_P \subseteq \|\sim X\|$. Since $B_P \neq 0$, this follows by (3.1) and (2.16).

Consider next Clause 3 on p. 118 of Cohen [3].

(b) "P forces $\sim B$ if for all $Q \supseteq P$, Q does not force B."

The parallel of this is that $B_P \subseteq \|\sim X\|$ iff for each $B_Q \subseteq B_P$

it is not true that $B_Q \subseteq \|X\|$. First let $B_P \subseteq \|\sim X\|$. If $B_Q \subseteq B_P$, then $B_Q \subseteq \|\sim X\|$, and so by (a) we cannot have $B_Q \subseteq \|X\|$. Conversely, let $B_P \subseteq \|\sim X\|$ fail. But then $B_P \wedge \|X\| \neq 0$; for suppose not. Then by Definition 2.3, $B_P \wedge \mathrm{Cl}(\|X\|) = 0$, so that $B_P \subseteq \mathrm{Cc}(\|X\|)$. Then by (2.8) and (3.1), $B_P \subseteq \|\sim X\|$. So let $x \in B_P \wedge \|X\|$. As $\|X\|$ is an open set, there is a basis set B such that $x \in B$ and $B \subseteq \|X\|$. Then by Axiom 2.2 there is a B_Q with $x \in B_Q$ and $B_Q \subseteq B_P$ and $B_Q \subseteq B \subseteq \|X\|$.

Consider next Clause 2 on p. 118 of Cohen [3].

(c) "P forces $\forall x B(x)$ if for all $c \in S$, $Q \supseteq P$, Q does not force $\sim B(c)$."

The parallel of this is that $B_P \subseteq \|(x)F(x)\|$ iff for each $c \in V$ and each $B_Q \subseteq B_P$ we do not have $B_Q \subseteq \|\sim F(c)\|$. By (b) this is the same as $B_P \subseteq \|(x)F(x)\|$ iff for each $c \in V$ we have $B_P \subseteq \|\sim \sim F(c)\|$. Since $\|\sim \sim F(c)\| = \|F(c)\|$ by (3.1) and (2.17), this just embodies (3.3).

Consider next clause 4 on p. 118 of Cohen [3].

(d) "P forces B & C if P forces B and P forces C."

The parallel of this is that $B_P \subseteq \|X \,\&\, Y\|$ iff $B_P \subseteq \|X\|$ and $B_P \subseteq \|Y\|$. This follows trivially from (3.2).

Consider next Lemma 2 on p. 118 of Cohen [3].

(e) "If P forces A and $Q \supseteq P$, then Q forces A."

The parallel of this is that if $B_P \subseteq \|X\|$ and $B_Q \subseteq B_P$, then $B_Q \subseteq \|X\|$, which is a triviality.

Consider next Lemma 3 on p. 119 of Cohen [3].

(f) "For all P and A there is a $Q \supseteq P$ such that either Q forces A or Q forces $\sim A$."

The parallel of this is that for each basis set B_P and statement X there is a basis set B_Q such that $B_Q \subseteq B_P$ and either $B_Q \subseteq \|X\|$ or $B_Q \subseteq \|\sim X\|$; to prove this, we appeal to Theorem 2.27, as follows. Since $\|X\| \vee \|\sim X\| = \|X\| \vee \|X\|' = 1$, and $B_P \neq 0$, we have

$$B_P \wedge (\|X\| \vee \|\sim X\|) \neq 0.$$

We take $Q_1 = \|X\|$ and $Q_2 = \|\sim X\|$ and $I = \{1, 2\}$ in Theorem 2.27 to conclude our result.

Cohen [3, p. 117] makes two different cases for the forcing of $c_1 \in c_2$, according as the rank of c_1 is less than that of c_2 or not. Clause 9 on p. 117 of Cohen [3] treats the case when the rank of c_1 is less than that of c_2 in a manner quite similar to (3.32), while Clause 10 handles the other case in a manner quite similar to (3.28).

There is nothing in the Boolean algebra treatment that quite corresponds to the complete sequence $\{P_n\}$ for forcing conditions defined by Cohen [3, p. 119]. One can achieve much the same result by choosing an ultra-filter Δ of the Boolean algebra and then saying that X is true if $\|X\| \in \Delta$ and X is false otherwise. In this way, a two valued model results. This approach is taken by Sochor [9] and Vopěnka [11,12]. This refinement produces some interesting models, but is not needed for the independence proofs. This raises the question of whether one can get an independence proof by forcing methods without introducing a complete sequence $\{P_n\}$ of forcing conditions. At the top of p. 148 of Cohen [3], it appears that Cohen is saying that indeed this was the case in his original approach to forcing arguments.

B. Replacing Boolean Algebra by Forcing in Proofs?

At the American Mathematical Society Summer Institute on Axiomatic Set Theory, University of California at Los Angeles, 1967, Azriel Lévy pointed out a method for translating forcing arguments into Boolean algebra arguments. This proceeds as follows. Take the ramified language (see Cohen [3, pp. 115–117]) and let $\|X\|$ be the class of all statements Y for which $X \equiv Y$ is forced by the null condition. Take $0 = \|X \& \sim X\|$, $1 = \|X \vee \sim X\|$, $\|X\| \vee \|Y\| = \|X \vee Y\|$, $\|X\| \wedge \|Y\| = \|X \& Y\|$, and $\|X\|' = \|\sim X\|$. Then it is easily verified that the set of elements $\|X\|$ for all X forms a Boolean algebra (the Lindenbaum algebra of the ramified language). Moreover, if P is a condition

$$\begin{array}{lll} n \in a & \text{for} & n \in t \\ \sim n \in a & \text{for} & n \in s - t, \end{array} \tag{5.1}$$

where s and t are finite subsets of ω, and

$$B_P \text{ is } \|X_1 \ \&\ X_2 \ \&\cdots\&\ X_m\|,$$

where

$$X_i = \begin{cases} n_i \in a & \text{for} \quad n_i \in t \\ \sim n_i \in a & \text{for} \quad n_i \in s - t \end{cases} \tag{5.2}$$

and where n_i runs through all members of s and t as i goes from 1 to m inclusive, then P weakly forces X if and only if $B_P \subseteq \|X\|$.

This method of translating forcing arguments into Boolean algebra arguments has been credited to Solovay, and is reported to have been the inspiration for the appreciably different Boolean algebra approach which we are using.

In fact, this method of translating forcing arguments into Boolean algebra arguments is likely to be an empty formalism in most cases, since the defintion of the Boolean algebra is tied so closely to the forcing argument that the only means apparent for proving any statement relative to the Boolean algebra is to translate it back into a statement relative to forcing and then prove it by a forcing argument. Still, in some sense, this translation lets us replace a forcing treatment by a Boolean algebra treatment.

Can we say conversely that each Boolean algebra treatment can be transformed into the familiar type of forcing treatment? No argument for this seems apparent. Indeed, note that for the developments of the preceding chapter, the universe V of the model is not denumerable. In fact, it is a class rather than a set. Therefore it cannot be identified readily with one of the ramified languages used in forcing arguments, since these are customarily taken to be denumerable.

However, we can extract a subset of V which will correspond very well to the universe of a ramified language of a forcing argument. Specifically, let us identify the subset q of $\check{\omega}$ defined in Definition 4.1 with Cohen's generic set a. If now we take P to be as in (5.1), then the corresponding B_P (under the parallelism we described early in this chapter) is indeed $\|X_1 \ \&\ X_2 \ \&\cdots\&\ X_m\|$ with X_i defined as in (5.2), but with q in place of a. If now we start with the single term q, and successively introduce other constants by means of Theorem 3.54, we will extract a denumerable model. The language using only these constants can be identified closely with the ramified language based on the generic set a. Moreover, the condition P will weakly force X if and only if $B_P \subseteq \|X\|$. Then the choice of a complete sequence of forcing conditions is equivalent to choosing an ultra-filter with respect to which supremums are preserved. By the Rasiowa–Sikorski Lemma, this can be done, since we now have only a denumerable number of supremums to preserve.

CHAPTER SIX

The Independence of AxC

A. The Key Idea of the Proof

Let us review the key idea of Chapter 4. There we showed that if $F(x, y)$ is a statement with no constants, then it cannot be a well-ordering relation for $SC(\check{\omega})$. We noted that $SC(\check{\omega})$ is invariant under all automorphisms of $\mathscr{G}$. Then we removed from $SC(\check{\omega})$ each member which was invariant, obtaining

$$Q = SC(\check{\omega}) - \operatorname{Img}(SC(\omega)).$$

We showed that Q is not empty. Therefore if $F(x, y)$ well-orders $SC(\check{\omega})$, it must choose a first member of Q. As Q is invariant and $F(x, y)$ is a statement with no constants, this first element of Q must be invariant, which it cannot be since Q was formed by removing all invariant elements from $SC(\check{\omega})$.

If we are to show the independence of AxC we must show for each $a \in V$ that the statement $\langle x, y \rangle \in a$ cannot be a well-ordering relation for $SC(\check{\omega})$. It turns out that we can do this by much the same argument. Instead of working with invariance under all automorphisms of $\mathscr{G}$, we work with invariance under all automorphisms of $\mathscr{G}_a$. By (3.36), this is the set of all automorphisms which leave a invariant. By the restriction (3.24), we have required that $\mathscr{G}_a$ be a member of the filter Γ .The trick is to choose Γ so that $\mathscr{G}_a$ has certain significant properties. Then we are able to proceed in a manner strictly analogous to that used in Chapter 4. First we remove from $SC(\check{\omega})$ all elements which are invariant under each automorphism of $\mathcal{G}_a$. Then, by using the special properties of Γ, we show that the resulting set t is not empty. So if $\langle x, y\rangle \in a$ well-orders $SC(\check{\omega})$, it must choose a first member of t. Since this first member is defined in terms of a and $SC(\check{\omega})$, it must be invariant under each automorphism of $\mathcal{G}_a$, which it cannot be since t was formed by removing all invariant elements from $SC(\check{\omega})$.

Therefore there is no $a \in V$ which well-orders $SC(\check{\omega})$. Hence there is no $a \in V$ which well-orders the real numbers. Hence AxC must fail to hold in the model.

We remark that GCH must also fail to hold, since in set theory GCH implies AxC (see Section 12 of Chapter IV of Cohen [3]; specifically, p. 148–150).

B. The Choice of Γ

As we saw in Chapter 3, ⊨AxC holds in the model if Γ consists of every subgroup of $\mathcal{G}$. Therefore we must introduce a restricted Γ. We wish to do this in such a way that the restriction (3.24) will exclude the well-ordering relations over the real numbers.

To accomplish this, we first define X by (2.24) with $I = \omega \times \omega$, and with basis sets defined by (2.26), and then define the Boolean algebra by Definition 2.9. It is convenient to identify elements of I by two coordinates; indeed a typical element of I is an ordered pair $\langle i, j\rangle$ with $i, j \in \omega$. Then the points of X can be considered as functions x such that for $i, j \in \omega$ the value $x(i, j)$ is either 0 or 1. Analogous to (2.25), we can write

$$B_{i,j}^{n} = \{x \mid x(i, j) = n\}. \tag{6.1}$$

We call J the support of a product

$$\bigcap \{B_{i,j}^{g(i,j)} \mid < i, j > \in J\}. \tag{6.2}$$

The basis sets are those (nonempty) products of the form (6.2) with a finite support.

If for a specific j and k we interchange $B_{i,j}^{n}$ with $B_{i,k}^{n}$ for each i and n, we will induce an automorphism of the Boolean algebra. We take $\mathcal{G}$ to be the set of finite products, each factor of which is one of these automorphisms.

For a subset J of ω we define $\mathscr{G}_J$ to be the subgroup consisting of all automorphisms which leave $B^n_{i,j}$ fixed for each $j \in J$. We take Γ to consist of every subgroup $\mathscr{H}$ of $\mathscr{G}$ which includes some $\mathscr{G}_J$ for a finite J. Since $\mathscr{G}_J$ will contain an automorphism induced by interchanging $B^n_{i,j}$ and $B^n_{i,k}$ for all i and n unless one of j or k is in J, we can see that $B^n_{i,j}$ is fixed under every automorphism of $\mathscr{G}_J$ if and only if $j \in J$. Thus $\mathscr{H}$ is a member of Γ only if there are at most a finite number of j's for which $B^n_{i,j}$ is fixed under every automorphism of $\mathscr{H}$. As $\mathscr{G}_J = \mathscr{G}$ when J is the null set, we verify (2.85). We easily verify (2.86)–(2.88) also.

By (3.24) and (3.36) we admit an element a to V only if there is a finite J such that

$$\mathscr{G}_J \subseteq \mathscr{G}_a.$$

Consequently, there must be at most a finite number of j's for which $B^n_{i,j}$ is fixed under every automorphism which carries a into itself.

We will define a set of distinct subsets q_j of $\check{\omega}$, one for each $j \in \omega$, such that q_j and q_k are interchanged by the automorphism induced by interchanging $B^n_{i,k}$ with $B^n_{i,j}$ for all i and n.

Suppose that there could be an $a \in V$ which would well-order $SC(\check{\omega})$. Then there must be a finite J such that $\mathscr{G}_J \subseteq \mathscr{G}_a$. There are an infinite number of j's with $j \in \omega$ and $\sim j \in J$. Now a must well-order the q_j for such j's. In particular, it must pick a first and second, say q_{j_1} and q_{j_2}. Since $\sim j_1 \in J$ and $\sim j_2 \in J$, there is an automorphism in $\mathscr{G}_J$ which interchanges j_1 and j_2, and hence interchanges q_{j_1} and q_{j_2}. But since $\mathscr{G}_J \subseteq \mathscr{G}_a$, this automorphism must leave a unchanged (by (3.36)). As q_{j_1} and q_{j_2} have been interchanged, this would require that now the unchanged a must choose q_{j_2} as first and q_{j_1} as second, contrary to its initial choice. Hence there cannot be any such a.

C. Subsets of $\check{\omega}$

Let g be a function defined over ω, whose values are elements of the Boolean algebra. If we define b with $D(b) = V_\omega$ by the condition that if $x \in V_\omega$ then

$$b(x) = \sum_{\eta < \omega} g(\eta) \wedge \|x = \check{\eta}\|, \tag{6.3}$$

then by Theorem 3.17 we see that b is extensional. However, to assure that $b \in V$, we must also require that b satisfy (3.24). By (3.36), this is equivalent to requiring that there be a finite J such that

$$\mathscr{G}_J \subseteq \mathscr{G}_b. \tag{6.4}$$

Then indeed we will have $b \in V_{\omega+1}$.

Definition 6.1. Let $a \in V$. We denote by S_a the set of all b's defined by (6.3) for which

$$\mathscr{G}_a \subseteq \mathscr{G}_b. \tag{6.5}$$

Theorem 6.1. If $a \in V$ and $b \in S_a$, then $b \in V_{\omega+1}$ and

$$\models b \subseteq \check{\omega}, \tag{6.6}$$

PROOF. Since $a \in V$, we must have $\mathscr{G}_a \in \Gamma$. So there is a finite J such that

$$\mathscr{G}_J \subseteq \mathscr{G}_a. \tag{6.7}$$

Then we conclude (6.4) by means of (6.5). Therefore $b \in V_{\omega+1}$. The proof of (6.6) proceeds like the proof of (4.6) in Theorem 4.3.

Definition 6.2. Let $a \in V$. Define s_a with $D(s_a) = V_{\omega+1}$ by the condition that if $x \in V_{\omega+1}$ then

$$s_a(x) = \sum_{b \in S_a} \|x = b\|. \tag{6.8}$$

Theorem 6.2. Let $a \in V$. Then $s_a \in V_{\omega+2}$. Moreover

$$\mathscr{G}_a \subseteq \mathscr{G}_{s_a}, \tag{6.9}$$

$$\models s_a \subseteq SC(\check{\omega}), \tag{6.10}$$

and for $b \in S_a$

$$\models b \in s_a. \tag{6.11}$$

PROOF. That s_a is extensional follows from Theorem 3.17. Now let $G \in \mathscr{G}_a$. Then by (6.5), $G \in \mathscr{G}_b$ for each $b \in S_a$. Then

$$\begin{aligned} s_a(x) &= \sum_{b \in S_a} \|x = b\| \\ &= \sum_{b \in S_a} \|G(G^{-1}(x)) = G(b)\| \\ &= G\Big(\sum_{b \in S_a} \|G^{-1}(x) = b\|\Big) \\ &= G(s_a(G^{-1}(x))) \\ &= G(s_a)(x). \end{aligned}$$

Therefore $\|G(s_a) = s_a\| = 1$. Hence $G \in \mathscr{G}_{s_a}$. Thus we conclude (6.9).

Since $a \in V$, there is a finite J such that (6.7) holds. So by (6.9), we have $\mathscr{G}_J \subseteq \mathscr{G}_{s_a}$. Therefore $s_a \in V_{\omega+2}$. To prove (6.11), we note that if $b \in S_a$, then $b \in D(s_a)$. So we can use (3.15) and (3.32). To prove (6.10), let $b \in S_a$ and $x \in D(s_a)$. Then by (6.6)

$$\|x = b\| \leq \|x \in SC(\check{\omega})\|.$$

Summing over $b \in S_a$ gives

$$s_a(x) \leq \|x \in SC(\check{\omega})\|.$$

So

$$s_a(x) \Rightarrow \|x \in SC(\check{\omega})\| = 1.$$

Hence

$$\prod_{x \in D(s_a)} s_a(x) \Rightarrow \|x \in SC(\check{\omega})\| = 1.$$

Then (6.10) follows by (3.64).

Definition 6.3. For $\mu < \omega$ define q_μ with $D(q_\mu) = V_\omega$ by the condition that if $x \in V_\omega$ then

$$q_\mu(x) = \sum_{\eta < \omega} B^1_{\eta, \mu} \wedge \|x = \check{\eta}\|. \tag{6.12}$$

Theorem 6.3. For $\mu < \omega$ we have $q_\mu \in V_{\omega+1}$. Also

$$\vDash q_\mu \subseteq \check{\omega}. \tag{6.13}$$

PROOF. Clearly

$$\mathscr{G}_{\{\mu\}} \subseteq \mathscr{G}_{q_\mu}.$$

So $q_\mu \in V_{\omega+1}$. The proof of (6.13) proceeds like the proof of (4.6) in Theorem 4.3.

Theorem 6.4. If $\sigma < \mu < \omega$, then

$$\models q_\sigma \neq q_\mu .$$

PROOF. $B^1_{\eta,\sigma}$ and $B^1_{\eta,\mu}$ are Scott cores for q_σ and q_μ, respectively, and the corresponding Scott domains are both

$$\{\check{\eta} \mid \eta < \omega\}.$$

Hence by Theorem 3.15

$$\|q_\sigma \subseteq q_\mu\| = \prod_{\eta<\omega} B^1_{\eta,\sigma} \Rightarrow \|\check{\eta} \in q_\mu\|$$

$$\|q_\mu \subseteq q_\sigma\| = \prod_{\eta<\omega} B^1_{\eta,\mu} \Rightarrow \|\check{\eta} \in q_\sigma\|.$$

So by (6.12)

$$\|q_\sigma = q_\mu\| = \prod_{\eta<\omega} B^1_{\eta,\sigma} \Leftrightarrow B^1_{\eta,\mu} .$$

So we must show that

$$\prod_{\eta<\omega} B^1_{\eta,\sigma} \Leftrightarrow B^1_{\eta,\mu} \qquad (6.14)$$

is 0. Suppose not. Then there must be a basis set included in (6.14). We can choose η^* large enough so that neither $\langle \eta^*, \sigma\rangle$ nor $\langle \eta^*, \mu\rangle$ is included in the support of the basis set. So some point x with

$$x(\eta^*, \sigma) = 1$$
$$x(\eta^*, \mu) = 0$$

will be in the basis set. However, no such point can be in (6.14).

Theorem 6.5. If $a \in V$ then there is a $\mu < \omega$ such that

$$\models \sim q_\mu \in s_a . \qquad (6.15)$$

PROOF. As $a \in V$, we have (6.7) for some finite J. Choose μ not in J. Then $q_\mu \in D(s_a)$, so that by (6.8) it suffices to prove that

$$\|q_\mu = b\| \qquad (6.16)$$

is 0 for each b in S_a. Suppose there is a b for which (6.16) is not 0. Then, by Definition 2.2, (6.16) is a nonempty sum of basis sets. As in the proof of Theorem 2.26 we conclude that (6.16) is indeed the supremum of this set of basis sets. We wish to show that it is the supremum of a set of basis sets whose supports are subsets of $\omega \times (J \cup \{\mu\})$. For this, we generalize the proof of Theorem 2.31. Let B be one of the basis sets of which (6.16) is the supremum. Suppose there is a $\sigma < \omega$ with σ not in $J \cup \{\mu\}$ such that

$$B = Q \cap \prod_{j=1}^{M} B_{f(j),\sigma}^{g(j)}$$

where $M \geq 1$ and no factor of Q has σ as its second subscript. Choose a $\tau < \omega$ such that τ is different from σ and τ is not in $J \cup \{\mu\}$ and τ does not occur as the second subscript of any factor of Q. There will be an infinity of such τ's. Now consider the G induced by interchanging $B_{i,\sigma}^{n}$ with $B_{i,\tau}^{n}$ for each i and n. For this G we have $\|G(b) = b\| = 1$ by (6.7) and (6.5). Also $\|G(q_\mu) = q_\mu\| = 1$ by (6.12). So by (3.17)

$$\|G(q_\mu) = G(b)\| = \|q_\mu = b\|.$$

So by (3.22)

$$G(\|q_\mu = b\|) = \|q_\mu = b\|.$$

Therefore (6.16) is invariant under G. As in the proof of Theorem 2.31 we conclude

$$Q \wedge \left(\left\{\prod_{j=1}^{M} B_{f(j),\sigma}^{g(j)}\right\} \vee \left\{\prod_{j=1}^{M} B_{f(j),\tau}^{g(j)}\right\}\right) \leq \|q_\mu = b\|.$$

Indeed, as in the proof of Theorem 2.31, we conclude

$$Q \wedge \sum_{\tau} \prod_{j=1}^{M} B_{f(j),\tau}^{g(j)} \leq \|q_\mu = b\|.$$

So we wish to show that

$$\sum_{\tau} \prod_{j=1}^{M} B_{f(j),\tau}^{g(j)} = 1.$$

Suppose not. Then there must be a basis set B_1 with

$$B_1 \subseteq \prod_{\tau} \sum_{j=1}^{M} B_{f(j),\tau}^{1-g(j)}.$$

Choose a τ which appears in the product but is not the second subscript of any factor of B_1. Then an x with

$$x(f(j), \tau) = g(j), \qquad 1 \leq j \leq M,$$

will lie in B_1 but not in the product.

So we conclude that

$$Q \leq \|q_\mu = b\|.$$

We repeat this process as often as needed, and finally conclude that (6.16) is the supremum of a set of basis sets whose supports are subsets of $\omega \times (J \cup \{\mu\})$. This set must be nonempty, as we are assuming that (6.16) is not zero. Let one of these basis sets be

$$B \wedge B_\mu$$

where the support of B is a subset of $\omega \times J$ and all factors of B_μ have μ as their second subscript. (It could be the case that B_μ has null support, so that $B_\mu = 1$, but this will not invalidate the argument.) Now, for a σ with $\sigma \neq \mu$ and $\sim\sigma \in J$, consider the G induced by interchanging $B^n_{i,\mu}$ with $B^n_{i,\sigma}$ for each i and n. Then since

$$B \wedge B_\mu \leq \|q_\mu = b\|,$$

we have

$$G(B \wedge B_\mu) \leq G(\|q_\mu = b\|).$$

That is

$$B \wedge B_\sigma \leq \|q_\sigma = b\|,$$

where B_σ is obtained from B_μ by changing the second subscript of each factor from μ to σ.

Therefore

$$B \wedge B_\mu \wedge B_\sigma \leq \|q_\mu = b\| \wedge \|q_\sigma = b\|.$$

This gives

$$B \wedge B_\mu \wedge B_\sigma \leq \|q_\mu = q_\sigma\|. \tag{6.17}$$

However, the left side of (6.17) is not 0, whereas by Theorem 6.4 the right side is 0. This cannot be.

D. The Real Numbers Are Not Well-Ordered

Clearly it suffices to prove that there is no well-ordering of $SC(\check{\omega})$, and this we now do.

Theorem 6.6.

$$\models \sim(Ea)\{(x, y) :. x, y \in SC(\check{\omega}) : \supset : < \langle x, y\rangle \in a . \vee . x = y. \vee . \langle y, x\rangle \in a :: (z) :. z \subseteq SC(\check{\omega}) . z \neq \Lambda : \supset : (Ey) : y \in z : (x) . \langle x, y\rangle \in a \supset \sim x \in z\}.$$

PROOF. If this were not so, then there would have to be an $a \in V$ for which the formula in the braces does not have the value 0. For this a, choose a μ for which (6.15) holds. Then

$$\models SC(\check{\omega}) - s_a \subseteq SC(\check{\omega}) . SC(\check{\omega}) - s_a \neq \Lambda \tag{6.18}$$

by Theorems 6.3 and 6.5. We make the following abbreviations: t for $SC(\check{\omega}) - s_a$, $F(a)$ for

$$(x, y) :. x, y \in SC(\check{\omega}) : \supset : \langle x, y\rangle \in a . \vee . x = y . \vee . \langle y, x\rangle \in a,$$

and $H(a, z, y)$ for

$$y \in z : (x) . \langle x, y\rangle \in a \supset \sim x \in z.$$

We are assuming

$$\|F(a) :. (z) : z \subseteq SC(\check{\omega}) . z \neq \Lambda . \supset . (Ey)H(a, z, y)\| \neq 0.$$

So by (6.18)

$$\|F(a) . (Ey)H(a, t, y)\| \neq 0. \tag{6.19}$$

Moreover, in view of the fact that (6.18) gives

$$\models t \subseteq SC(\check{\omega}) \tag{6.20}$$

we have

$$\|F(a)\| \leq \|(x, y) . H(a, t, x)H(a, t, y) \supset x = y\|. \tag{6.21}$$

By going through the proof of Theorem 3.13, we see that there is a c with $D(c) = V_\beta$ defined by the condition that for $z \in V_\beta$

$$c(z) = \|(Ex) . H(a, t, x) . z \in x\| \tag{6.22}$$

such that

$$\vDash (x, y) \,.\, H(a, t, x)H(a, t, y) \supset x = y : \supset : \\ H(a, t, c) \equiv (Ex)H(a, t, x). \tag{6.23}$$

By (6.9) and (6.22), we conclude

$$\mathscr{G}_a \subseteq \mathscr{G}_c. \tag{6.24}$$

By (6.19), (6.21), and (6.23),

$$\|H(a, t, c)\| \neq 0. \tag{6.25}$$

Therefore

$$\|c \in t\| \neq 0. \tag{6.26}$$

So by the definition of t

$$\| \sim c \in s_a\| \neq 0. \tag{6.27}$$

Take $z \in D(c)$. Then by (6.20)

$$\|y = z\| \wedge \|H(a, t, x) \,.\, z \in x\| \leq \|y \in \check{\omega}\|.$$

Summing on x gives by (6.22) and (3.32)

$$\|z \in c \,.\, y = z\| \leq \|y \in \check{\omega}\|.$$

Summing over $z \in D(c)$ and using (3.28) gives

$$\|y \in c\| < \|y \in \check{\omega}\|.$$

So

$$\vDash c \subseteq \check{\omega}. \tag{6.28}$$

Define b with $D(b) = V_\omega$ by the condition that for $x \in V_\omega$

$$b(x) = \sum_{\eta < \omega} \|\check{\eta} \in c \,.\, x = \check{\eta}\|. \tag{6.29}$$

It is easily verified that

$$\mathscr{G}_c \subseteq \mathscr{G}_b. \tag{6.30}$$

As $c \in V$, there must be a finite J with $\mathscr{G}_J \subseteq \mathscr{G}_c$. So $\mathscr{G}_J \subseteq \mathscr{G}_b$. Therefore $b \in V_{\omega+1}$. We infer

$$\vDash b \subseteq \check{\omega} \tag{6.31}$$

by a proof like that of (4.6) in Theorem 4.3.

By (6.29) we have

$$\|\check{\eta} \in c\| = \|\check{\eta} \in b\|$$

for $\eta < \omega$. Therefore

$$\models (x) : x \in \check{\omega} \, . \supset . \, x \in c \equiv x \in b.$$

Then by (6.28), (6.31), and Theorem 3.6, we have

$$\models c = b.$$

So by (6.27)

$$\| \sim b \in s_a \| \neq 0. \tag{6.32}$$

However, by (6.24) and (6.30), we have $\mathscr{G}_a \subseteq \mathscr{G}_b$, so that by (6.29), (6.3), and Definition 6.1, we have $b \in S_a$. Then (6.11) contradicts (6.32).

By Theorem 6.6, we conclude:

Theorem 6.7. $\models \sim$AxC.

CHAPTER SEVEN

The Independence of the Continuum Hypothesis

A. The Key Result

By Cantor's theorem (see Bernays and Fraenkel [1, p. 117]) we have

$$\aleph_\alpha < 2^{\aleph_\alpha} \tag{7.1}$$

for each ordinal α. In particular

$$\aleph_0 < 2^{\aleph_0}. \tag{7.2}$$

Since

$$\aleph(\mathrm{SC}(\omega)) = 2^{\aleph_0},$$

and $SC(\omega)$ has the same cardinality as the real numbers, (7.2) says that the real numbers are not denumerable. That is, $\aleph_0$ is not the cardinal number of the continuum. By the axiom of choice, the real numbers can be well-ordered, and so must have a cardinal number. What then is it?

There seems no reason why it might not be the next cardinal greater than $\aleph_0$, namely $\aleph_1$. Indeed, it is shown by Gödel [5] that this assumption can be added consistently to the axioms of set theory plus AxC. This assumption, that

$$\aleph_1 = 2^{\aleph_0}, \tag{7.3}$$

is known as the continuum hypothesis. In the present chapter we shall show that it cannot be deduced from the axioms of set theory plus AxC.

The continuum hypothesis is a special case of GCH, the generalized continuum hypothesis. This states that

$$\aleph_{\alpha+1} = 2^{\aleph_\alpha} \tag{7.4}$$

for each ordinal α. Gödel [5] has shown that this is consistent with the axioms of set theory plus AxC. Our proof that (7.3) cannot be derived from the axioms of set theory plus AxC naturally entails that (7.4) cannot be derived either.

The proof proceeds by a very simple cardinality argument. If we have the countable chain condition, then we have Theorems 3.45–3.47, which say in effect that sets have the same cardinality within the model as they actually have externally. Therefore if we are going to refute (7.3), we must choose our Boolean algebra so that in fact $SC(\check{\omega})$ has more than $\aleph_1$ elements. Now suppose g is a function defined over ω, whose values are elements of the Boolean algebra, and we define b with $D(b) = V_\omega$ by the condition that if $x \in V_\omega$ then

$$b(x) = \sum_{\eta < \omega} g(\eta) \wedge \|x = \check{\eta}\|$$

(see (6.3)). Then for $\eta < \omega$ we have by Theorem 3.21

$$g(\eta) \wedge \|x = \check{\eta}\| \leq \|x = \check{\eta}\| \wedge \|\check{\eta} \in \check{\omega}\| \leq \|x \in \check{\omega}\|.$$

Summing over η gives by Theorem 3.9

$$\|x \in b\| \leq \|x \in \check{\omega}\|.$$

Hence

$$\|x \in b \supset x \in \check{\omega}\| = 1$$

so that multiplying over x gives

$$\models b \subseteq \check{\omega}.$$

Thus, if we can choose many such functions g, then we will have many subsets of $\check{\omega}$. If we take a Boolean algebra with a large number of elements, then clearly we can define a large number of different g's, and so should be able to refute (7.3).

It will be noted that this argument does not depend in any way on the group $\mathscr{G}$ or the filter Γ. This contrasts with Chapter 4 in which $\mathscr{G}$ played an important role, and with Chapter 6 in which Γ played a crucial role. In fact, for the purposes of the present chapter, namely proving the independence of the continuum hypothesis, both $\mathscr{G}$ and Γ are quite irrelevant. Indeed, had this proof been our sole aim, we should have omitted all mention of $\mathscr{G}$ and Γ, which would have eliminated the considerable bother of extending the automorphisms of $\mathscr{G}$ to members of V. This would have produced quite a streamlined proof. However, in order to get a development which could be used for a number of different independence proofs we have incorporated $\mathscr{G}$ and Γ firmly into our structure. So we must now make some disposition of them. We shall take Γ to be the set of all subgroups of $\mathscr{G}$. It really does not matter what $\mathscr{G}$ is; to illustrate this, we shall choose the simplest possible $\mathscr{G}$, namely we shall take $\mathscr{G}$ to consist solely of the identity transformation.

We define X by (2.24) with $I = \omega \times \omega_2$, and with basis sets defined by (2.26), and then define the Boolean algebra by Definition 2.9. As in Chapter 6, we identify elements of I by two coordinates. We make use of the definitions involving (6.1) and (6.2).

As in Chapter 4, $\models$AxC holds.

For $\mu < \omega_2$, we define q_μ as in Definition 6.3. Then Theorem 6.3 is valid with the modification that it holds for $\mu \omega_2 <$. Similarly Theorem 6.4 holds with the hypothesis $\sigma < \mu < \omega_2$.

***Theorem** 7.1.* $\models \mathrm{Img}(\aleph_1) \neq \aleph(SC(\check{\omega}))$.

PROOF. Because each q_μ is a subclass of $\check{\omega}$ by (6.13), and there are $\aleph_2$ distinct q_μ's by Theorem 6.4, we see that in actual fact $\aleph_1 \neq \aleph(SC(\check{\omega}))$. For this reason, we can parallel the proof of Theorem 3.44, since by Theorem 2.32 the Boolean algebra satisfies the countable chain condition. Specifically, we set $F(x, y, f)$ for

$$(u) : u \in x \,.\supset.\, (E_1 v) \,.\, v \subseteq y \,.\, \langle u, v\rangle \in f :.$$
$$(v) : v \subseteq y \,.\supset.\, (E_1 u) \,.\, u \in x \,.\, \langle u, v\rangle \in f.$$

If

$$\|(Ef)F(\check{\aleph}_1, \check{\omega}, f)\| \neq 0,$$

then we put

$$P = \|F(\aleph_1, \check{\omega}, f)\| \neq 0 \tag{7.5}$$

and obtain for $\mu < \omega_2$

$$P \wedge \|(Eu) \,.\, u \in \check{\aleph}_1 \,.\, \langle u, q_\mu \rangle \in f\| \neq 0.$$

So for each $\tau < \aleph_1$, set

$$\theta(\tau) = \{\mu \mid P \wedge \|\langle \check{\tau}, q_\mu \rangle \in f\| \neq 0\}.$$

Then there is a $\tau < \aleph_1$ for which $\theta(\tau)$ is uncountable. But if μ, $\sigma \in \theta(\tau)$ and $\mu \neq \sigma$, then

$$\{P \wedge \|\langle \check{\tau}, q_\mu \rangle \in f\|\} \wedge \{P \wedge \|\langle \check{\tau}, q_\sigma \rangle \in f\|\} = 0$$

by (7.5) and Theorem 6.4. So we contradict the countable chain condition.

Since

$$\models \aleph(SC(\check{\omega})) = 2^M$$

where M is Img($\aleph_0$), Theorem 7.1 tells us that the continuum hypothesis cannot be proved in set theory even if one adds the axiom of choice.

B. Additional Cardinality Results

Cohen [2] has shown by forcing that one can add consistently to the set theory axioms the three additional statements

$$\text{AxC} \tag{7.6}$$

$$2^{\aleph_0} = \aleph_2 \tag{7.7}$$

$$2^{\aleph_\alpha} = \aleph_{\alpha+1} \qquad \text{for} \qquad 1 \leq \alpha. \tag{7.8}$$

This settled an old question of Lusin as to whether or not one could have

$$2^{\aleph_0} = 2^{\aleph_1}.$$

We shall establish the same result that Cohen did.

***Theorem** 7.2*. Let α be an ordinal greater than or equal to 2. Then

$$\models \mathrm{Img}(\aleph_{\alpha+1}) = \aleph(SC(\aleph_{\check{\alpha}})). \tag{7.9}$$

PROOF. We parallel the proof of Theorem 4.1. We take the same definition of $G(x, y, f)$. If then we assume

$$\|\mathrm{Img}(\aleph_{\alpha+2}) \leq \aleph(SC(\aleph_{\check{\alpha}}))\| = P \neq 0,$$

we conclude

$$\|(Ef)G(\check{\mu}, \check{v}, f)\| = P,$$

and so infer that there is an f such that

$$\|G(\check{\mu}, \check{v}, f)\| = P.$$

Then for $\sigma \in v$, we have

$$\|(Eu) \,.\, u \subseteq \check{\mu} \,.\, \langle u, \check{\sigma}\rangle \in f\| = Q \geq P,$$

so that there is an $a_\sigma \in V$ such that

$$\|a_\sigma \subseteq \check{\mu} \,.\, \langle a_\sigma, \check{\sigma}\rangle \in f\| = Q.$$

Then, if $\alpha \geq 2$, there must be a g which results from two distinct ordinals. Calling them σ and τ, we get

$$\models a_\sigma = a_\tau .$$

But

$$P \leq \|\langle a_\sigma, \check{\sigma}\rangle \in f\|$$
$$P \leq \|\langle a_\tau, \check{\tau}\rangle \in f\|$$

so that

$$P \leq \|\langle a_\sigma, \check{\tau}\rangle \in f\|.$$

But also

$$P \leq \|(E_1 v) \,.\, v \in \check{v} \,.\, \langle a_\sigma, v\rangle \in f\|.$$

So

$$0 \neq P \leq \|\check{\sigma} = \check{\tau}\|,$$

which violates Theorem 3.24.

Theorem 7.2 takes care of (7.8) for $\alpha \leq 2$. We still have open (7.7) and the case $\alpha = 1$ of (7.8). To handle these, we need a somewhat stronger result than the countable chain condition. Lemma 11 of Cohen [2] is the forcing equivalent of the countable chain condition. The proof given by Cohen starts out by proving an auxiliary result, which was not given any special identification by Cohen, but which has since acquired the appellation of the "Cohen combinatorial lemma." Its Boolean analog is the stronger result which we need, and we now state and prove it.

***Theorem** 7.3.* Let W be a nonempty set of basis sets. Then there is a countable subset Π of W such that for each $P \in W$ there is a $B \in \Pi$ such that $B \wedge P \neq 0$.

PROOF. We construct Π as the sum of a denumerable sequence Π_i of finite subsets of W.

We take Π_1 to be $\{B\}$, where B is some element from W.

Suppose we have defined Π_i for $i \leq N$. Take s_N to be the sum of the supports of all the members of Π_i for $i \leq N$. Clearly s_N is finite. Take Π_{N+1}^* to consist of all basis sets R whose support is a subset of s_N. Each B in Π_i for $i \leq N$ will be such an R, but there will likely be many others. For each R in Π_{N+1}^* choose a $B \in W$ (if there is one) such that the support of R is a subset of the support of B and $B \wedge R \neq 0$. Let Π_{N+1} consist of the (finite) collection of B's so chosen.

As s_{N+1} will be the sum of the supports of all the members of Π_i for $i \leq N+1$, we clearly have $s_N \subseteq s_{N+1}$.

Now we must verify that Π has the required characteristics. Clearly it is a countable subset of W. Let $P \in W$. Let s be the support of P. As s is finite, there must be an N such that

$$s \cap s_N = s \cap s_{N+1}.$$

Then P with its support restricted to $s \cap s_N$ will be one of the R's of Π_{N+1}^*. As $P \wedge R \neq 0$, we were able to choose a $B \in W$ (for example, P) to go into Π_{N+1} such that the support of R is a subset of the support of B, and $B \wedge R \neq 0$. Then $B \wedge P \neq 0$; for suppose $B \wedge P = 0$. Then there must be a coordinate $\langle i, j \rangle$ at which $B_{i,j}^0$

and $B_{i,j}^1$ both occur as factors, one in B and the other in P. This coordinate is not in $s \cap s_N$. But it is in s_{N+1} because it is in the support of B, which is in Π_{N+1}. It is also in s. Therefore it is in $s \cap s_{N+1}$, contradicting the condition

$$s \cap s_N = s \cap s_{N+1}.$$

We note that the countable chain condition is a trivial consequence of Theorem 7.3. For let W be a disjoint set of basis elements. Choose Π by Theorem 7.3. But then W cannot contain a P which is not in Π, for if it did, then $P \wedge B = 0$ for each $B \in \Pi$ since W is disjoint. But this contradicts the properties of Π. So W and Π must coincide. Hence W is countable.

***Theorem** 7.4*. Let Q be an element of the Boolean algebra. Then there is a countable set Π of basis sets such that if P is a basis set then there is a $B \in \Pi$ such that $B \wedge P \neq 0$ and either $B \leq Q$ or $B \leq Q'$.

PROOF. We take W to be the set of basis elements B for which either $B \leq Q$ or $B \leq Q'$. As one or the other of Q or Q' is not null, W must be nonempty. So we get a countable subset Π by Theorem 7.3. Take a basis set P. In theorem 2.27, take $Q_1 = Q$, $Q_2 = Q'$, and $I = \{1, 2\}$. Then

$$\sum_{i \in I} Q_i = 1$$

so that (2.68) is satisfied. Hence there is a B^* such that

$$B^* \leq P \wedge Q \tag{7.10}$$

or

$$B^* \leq P \wedge Q'. \tag{7.11}$$

So either $B^* \leq Q$ or $B^* \leq Q'$. So $B^* \in W$. Then there is a $B \in \Pi$ such that $B \wedge B^* \neq 0$. If (7.10) holds, then

$$0 \neq B \wedge B^* \leq B \wedge P \wedge Q \leq B \wedge P.$$

Also

$$0 \neq B \wedge B^* \leq B \wedge P \wedge Q \leq Q. \tag{7.12}$$

As $B \in W$, we have either $B \leq Q$ or $B \leq Q'$. If $B \leq Q'$ could hold, we would have $B \wedge B^* \leq Q'$, so that by (7.12) and (2.44)

$$0 \neq B \wedge B^* \leq Q \wedge Q' = 0,$$

which is impossible. So $B \leq Q$. If (7.11) holds, we similarly conclude $B \wedge P \neq 0$ and $B \leq Q'$.

***Definition** 7.1.* We define Σ to be the set of all pairs $\langle \Pi, s \rangle$ such that:

(i) Π is a nonempty set of basis sets;

(ii) $\aleph(\Pi) \leq \aleph_1$;

(iii) $s \subseteq \Pi \times \aleph_1$.

***Theorem** 7.5.* $\aleph(\Sigma) = \aleph_2$.

PROOF. Each basis set has fewer than $\aleph_0$ factors, and each factor can be chosen in $\aleph_2$ ways. So there are no more basis sets than

$$\aleph_2^{\aleph_0} = (2^{\aleph_1})^{\aleph_0} = 2^{\aleph_1 \times \aleph_0} = 2^{\aleph_1} = \aleph_2 .$$

By (ii), each Π has no more than $\aleph_1$ members, and each member can be chosen in at most $\aleph_2$ ways. So there are no more Π's than

$$\aleph_2^{\aleph_1} = (2^{\aleph_1})^{\aleph_1} = 2^{\aleph_1 \times \aleph_1} = 2^{\aleph_1} = \aleph_2 .$$

By (i) and (ii), $\Pi \times \aleph_1$ has $\aleph_1$ members for each Π. So for each Π, there are $\aleph_2$ choices for s. Hence Σ has at most $\aleph_2 \times \aleph_2 = \aleph_2$ members. As there are $\aleph_2$ s's for each Π, we see that Σ has exactly $\aleph_2$ members.

***Definition** 7.2.* For each $a \in V$, we say that $\langle \Pi, s \rangle$ is a corresponding member of Σ iff:

(iv) $\langle \Pi, s \rangle \in \Sigma$;

(v) If R is a basis set and $\gamma < \aleph_1$, then there is a $B \in \Pi$ such that $B \wedge R \neq 0$ and either $B \leq \|\check{\gamma} \in a\|$ or $B \leq \|\sim \check{\gamma} \in a\|$.

(vi) $s = \{< B, \gamma > \mid B \in \Pi \,.\, \gamma < \aleph_1 \,.\, B \leq \|\check{\gamma} \in a\|\}$.

***Theorem** 7.6.* For each $a \in V$, there is a $\langle \Pi, s \rangle \in \Sigma$ which corresponds to a.

PROOF. For each $\gamma < \aleph_1$, define $\Pi^{(\gamma)}$ by taking the Π of Theorem 7.4 with Q taken to be $\|\check{\gamma} \in a\|$. Take Π to be

$$\sum_{\gamma < \aleph_1} \Pi^{(\gamma)}.$$

Then (v) is satisfied, and Π satisfies (i) and (ii). If we define s by (vi), then (vi) and (iii) are satisfied. Hence (iv) is satisfied.

***Theorem** 7.7.* If $a, b \in V$, and the same $\langle \Pi, s \rangle \in \Sigma$ corresponds to both a and b, then

$$\vdash a \subseteq \check{\aleph}_1 \,.\, b \subseteq \check{\aleph}_1 \,.\, \supset .\, a = b. \tag{7.13}$$

PROOF. Write

$$P = \|a \subseteq \check{\aleph}_1 \,.\, b \subseteq \check{\aleph}_1\|. \tag{7.14}$$

Suppose there is a $\gamma < \aleph_1$ such that

$$0 \neq P \wedge \|\check{\gamma} \in a \,.\, {\sim}\check{\gamma} \in b\|.$$

Then choose a basis set R such that

$$R \leq P \wedge \|\check{\gamma} \in a \,.\, {\sim}\check{\gamma} \in b\|. \tag{7.15}$$

By (v), we find a $B \in \Pi$ with

$$B \wedge R \neq 0 \tag{7.16}$$

and

$$B \leq \|\check{\gamma} \in a\| \tag{7.17}$$

or

$$B \leq \|{\sim}\check{\gamma} \in a\|. \tag{7.18}$$

However, if (7.18) holds, then by (7.18) we have $B \wedge R \leq \|{\sim}\check{\gamma} \in a\|$. But by (7.15), $B \wedge R \leq \|\check{\gamma} \in a\|$. This contradicts (7.16). Therefore (7.17) must hold. So by (vi) for a, $\langle B, \gamma \rangle \in s$. So by (vi) for b, $B \leq \|\check{\gamma} \in b\|$. But then $B \wedge R \leq \|\check{\gamma} \in b\|$. Since we obtain $B \wedge R \leq \|{\sim}\check{\gamma} \in b\|$ by (7.15), we contradict (7.16).

Thus we conclude that for each $\gamma < \aleph_1$

$$P \leq \|\check{\gamma} \in a \supset \check{\gamma} \in b\|.$$

Similarly

$$P \leq \|\check{\gamma} \in b \supset \check{\gamma} \in a\|.$$

Therefore

$$P \leq \|\check{\gamma} \in a \equiv \check{\gamma} \in b\|.$$

Then

$$P \leq \prod_{\gamma \in \aleph_1} \|\check{\gamma} \in a \equiv \check{\gamma} \in b\|.$$

So by Theorem 3.20

$$P \leq \|(x) : x \in \check{\aleph}_1 \,.\supset .\, x \in a \,.\equiv x \in b\|.$$

So by (7.14) and Theorem 3.6

$$\|a \subseteq \check{\aleph}_1 \,.\, b \subseteq \check{\aleph}_1\| \leq \|a = b\|.$$

This gives (7.13).

***Theorem** 7.8.* $\models \check{\aleph}_2 = \aleph(SC(\check{\aleph}_1))$.

PROOF. Because (7.1) holds in the model, we have

$$\models \aleph(SC(\check{\aleph}_1)) > \check{\aleph}_1. \tag{7.19}$$

So it suffices to prove

$$\models \sim(\aleph(SC(\check{\aleph}_1)) \geq \check{\aleph}_3). \tag{7.20}$$

Suppose this is not so. Then

$$\|\aleph(SC(\check{\aleph}_1)) \geq \check{\aleph}_3\| = P \neq 0.$$

We now parallel the proof of Theorem 4.1. We take $\mu = \aleph_1$ and $\nu = \aleph_3$, and make the same definition of $G(x, y, f)$. So

$$\|(Ef)G(\check{\mu}, \check{\nu}, f)\| = P,$$

and hence there is an f such that

$$\|G(\check{\mu}, \check{\nu}, f)\| = P. \tag{7.21}$$

So for $\sigma \in \nu$, we have

$$\|(Eu) . u \subseteq \check{\mu} . \langle u, \check{\sigma}\rangle \in f\| = Q \geq P,$$

so that there is an $a_\sigma \in V$ such that

$$\|a_\sigma \subseteq \check{\mu} . \langle a_\sigma, \check{\sigma}\rangle \in f\| = Q \geq P. \tag{7.22}$$

Now by Theorem 7.6, there is a $\langle \Pi_\sigma, s_\sigma \rangle \in \Sigma$ which corresponds to a_σ. As there are $\aleph_3$ σ's, whereas by Theorem 7.5 there are only $\aleph_2$ members of Σ, there must be a $\langle \Pi, s\rangle \in \Sigma$ which corresponds to a_σ and a_τ for $\sigma \neq \tau$ and $\sigma < \nu$ and $\tau < \nu$. Then by (7.22) and Theorem 7.7

$$P \leq \|a_\sigma = a_\tau\|.$$

Then by (7.21) we have

$$P \leq \|\check{\sigma} = \check{\tau}\|,$$

which contradicts Theorem 3.24.

Theorem 7.9. $\models \check{\aleph}_2 = \aleph(SC(\check{\aleph}_0))$.

PROOF. By Theorem 7.1, it suffices to prove

$$\models \aleph(SC(\check{\aleph}_0)) \leq \check{\aleph}_2. \tag{7.23}$$

Now

$$\models (x, y) : x \subseteq y . \supset . SC(x) \subseteq SC(y)$$

is a result of set theory (note Exercise IX.6.5(a) on p. 256 of Rosser [7]) so that

$$\models (x, y) : x \subseteq y . \supset . \aleph(SC(x)) \leq \aleph(SC(y)).$$

Hence by Theorem 7.8 we conclude (7.23) by taking x to be $\check{\aleph}_0$ and y to be $\check{\aleph}_1$.

CHAPTER EIGHT

The Generalized GCH—The Bounded Case

A. Statement of Easton's Theorem

Suppose that in the preceding chapter we had taken I to be $\omega \times \omega_n$, where n is a positive integer. Then a proof like that of Theorem 7.1 would have given

$$\vDash \mathrm{Img}(\aleph_m) \neq \aleph(SC(\check{\omega}))$$

for each $m < n$. Thence by Theorems 3.45–3.47, we conclude

$$\vDash \mathrm{Img}(\aleph_n) \leq \aleph(SC(\check{\omega})). \tag{8.1}$$

A proof like that of Theorem 7.2 gives

$$\vDash \mathrm{Img}(\aleph_{\alpha+1}) = \aleph(SC(\aleph_{\check{\alpha}})) \tag{8.2}$$

for $\alpha \geq n$. A proof like that of Theorem 7.8 gives

$$\vDash \mathrm{Img}(\aleph_n) = \aleph(SC(\mathrm{Img}(\aleph_{n-1}))). \tag{8.3}$$

Finally a proof like that of Theorem 7.9 gives

$$\vDash \mathrm{Img}(\aleph_n) = \aleph(SC(\mathrm{Img}(\aleph_m))) \tag{8.4}$$

for $0 \leq m < n$.

Suppose we should take $I = \omega \times \omega_\omega$? Analogously to (8.1) we would conclude

$$\models \mathrm{Img}(\aleph_\omega) \leq \aleph(SC(\check{\omega})). \tag{8.5}$$

Can we conclude analogously to (8.4)

$$\models \mathrm{Img}(\aleph_\omega) = \aleph(SC(\mathrm{Img}(\aleph_m)))$$

for $0 \leq m < \omega$? The answer is that we cannot. Indeed, we cannot conclude this no matter what Boolean algebra we employ, since it can be disproved in set theory. This is done by means of König's theorem. Formula 3.16 on p. 177 of Bernays and Fraenkel [1] states the generalized form of König's theorem, as given by Ph. Jourdain. In words, this takes the following form. Let J be a non-empty index set. Let f and g be functions from J to cardinal numbers such that for each $j \in J$ we have $f(j) < g(j)$. Then

$$\sum_{j \in J} f(j) < \prod_{j \in J} g(j).$$

To apply this to the case at hand, we take J to be $\omega, f(j) = \aleph_j$, and $g(j) = \aleph_\omega$. Then we have

$$\sum_{j \in \omega} \aleph_j < \prod_{j \in \omega} \aleph_\omega .$$

That is

$$\aleph_\omega < (\aleph_\omega)^{\aleph_0}.$$

Now suppose that

$$2^{\aleph_0} = \aleph_\omega .$$

Then

$$\aleph_\omega < (\aleph_\omega)^{\aleph_0} = (2^{\aleph_0})^{\aleph_0} = 2^{\aleph_0 \times \aleph_0} = 2^{\aleph_0} = \aleph_\omega ,$$

which is a contradiction.

Carrying out the above argument in our model gives

$$\models \mathrm{Img}(\aleph_\omega) \neq \aleph(SC(\check{\omega})). \tag{8.6}$$

So by (8.5)

$$\models \mathrm{Img}(\aleph_{\omega+1}) \leq \aleph(SC(\check{\omega})). \tag{8.7}$$

However a proof like that of Theorem 7.2 will give (8.2) for $\alpha \geq \omega$. Hence we conclude

$$\vDash \mathrm{Img}(\aleph_{\omega+1}) = \aleph(SC(\mathrm{Img}(\aleph_m))) \tag{8.8}$$

for $0 \leq m \leq \omega$.

Clearly one can push such results considerably farther. However the question immediately arises concerning in what other ways one can generalize GCH consistently with AxC and the set theory axioms. Can one have generally

$$2^{\aleph_\alpha} = \aleph_{\alpha+2}$$

for instance? Even more generally, for what functions E can one have

$$2^{\aleph_\alpha} = \aleph_{E(\alpha)} \tag{8.9}$$

for all ordinals α? The classical GCH says that this can be done when $E(\alpha) = \alpha + 1$. Gödel [5] has shown that GCH is consistent with AxC and the axioms of set theory.

The axioms of set theory impose certain requirements on E. Thus the argument used in the proof of Theorem 7.9 implies the following requirement.

Requirement 1. If α and β are ordinals and $\alpha \leq \beta$, then $E(\alpha) \leq E(\beta)$.

As we saw above, König's theorem implies certain additional requirements. We now formulate these in precise terms.

Definition 8.1. We write $\mathrm{Cf}(\alpha)$ for the cofinality of α, namely the least cardinal β for which there is a function f such that

$$f(\eta) < \alpha \qquad \text{if} \qquad \eta < \beta$$

$$\alpha = \sum_{\eta < \beta} f(\eta).$$

We now state our second requirement.

Requirement 2. For each ordinal α, we must have

$$\mathrm{Cf}(\aleph_{E(\alpha)}) > \aleph_\alpha. \tag{8.10}$$

To show that this is a necessary condition for (8.9), we generalize the proof of (8.6). Suppose that (8.10) is violated. Then there is a cardinal $\beta \leq \aleph_\alpha$ and a function f such that

$$f(\eta) < \aleph_{E(\alpha)} \qquad \text{if} \qquad \eta < \beta$$

$$\aleph_{E(\alpha)} = \sum_{\eta<\beta} f(\eta).$$

Then by König's theorem

$$\aleph_{E(\alpha)} = \sum_{\eta<\beta} f(\eta) < \prod_{\eta<\beta} \aleph_{E(\alpha)} = (\aleph_{E(\alpha)})^{\beta}.$$

Now suppose (8.9) holds. Then

$$2^{\aleph_\alpha} < (2^{\aleph_\alpha})^{\beta} = 2^{\aleph_\alpha \times \beta} = 2^{\aleph_\alpha}.$$

Are there any other requirements on E? The reader will note that Cantor's theorem imposes the requirement that $E(\alpha) > \alpha$. However, as $\mathrm{Cf}(\beta) \leq \beta$ when β is a cardinal, we see that Requirement 2 implies that $E(\alpha) > \alpha$.

There is a conjecture that (8.9) is consistent with the axioms of set theory plus AxC for each E which satisfies Requirements 1 and 2. The first enunciation of this conjecture has been attributed to Robert Solovay. Easton [4] has used forcing to prove a slightly weaker result.

Definition 8.2. We say that α is regular if it is a cardinal and $\mathrm{Cf}(\alpha) = \alpha$. Otherwise, we say it is singular.

Easton's Theorem. Let E satisfy Requirements 1 and 2, and also the further requirement that if $\aleph_\alpha$ is singular, then $E(\alpha)$ is the least γ such that: (i) $\gamma \geq E(\beta)$ for each $\beta < \alpha$; and (ii) $\mathrm{Cf}(\aleph_\gamma) > \aleph_\alpha$. Then it is consistent with the axioms of set theory plus AxC that

$$2^{\aleph_\alpha} = \aleph_{E(\alpha)}$$

holds for each ordinal α.

In the present chapter we shall prove a "bounded" version of Easton's theorem to the effect that Easton's theorem holds for a restricted class of E's, characterized mainly by the fact that

$E(\alpha) = \alpha + 1$ for all sufficiently large α. In the next chapter we shall prove the "unbounded" version of Easton's theorem for unrestricted E's.

In this chapter and the next, our proofs owe much to those presented by Easton [4]. Easton acknowledges a great deal of assistance from Solovay, and cites Solovay [10].

B. Specification of the Boolean Algebra

To the restrictions on E set forth in the hypothesis of Easton's theorem, let us add the "boundedness restriction," principally to the effect that the set of α's for which $E(\alpha) \neq \alpha + 1$ is bounded.

Definition 8.3. We say that E satisfies the boundedness restriction with respect to θ iff:

(i) θ is not a limiting ordinal;

(ii) $E(\theta)$ is not a limiting ordinal;

(iii) $E(\alpha) = E(\theta)$ for $\theta \leq \alpha < E(\theta)$;

(iv) $E(\alpha) = \alpha + 1$ for $E(\theta) \leq \alpha$.

Theorem 8.1. If E satisfies the restrictions of Easton's theorem and θ is a nonlimiting ordinal, then there is an E^* which satisfies the restrictions of Easton's theorem and also the boundedness restriction with respect to θ, and for which $E(\alpha) = E^*(\alpha)$ for $\alpha < \theta$.

PROOF. We define $E^*(\alpha) = E(\alpha)$ for $\alpha < \theta$, $E^*(\alpha) = E(\theta) + 1$ for $\theta \leq \alpha \leq E(\theta)$, and $E^*(\alpha) = \alpha + 1$ for $E(\theta) < \alpha$. Then the various restrictions on E^* are seen to be met.

This theorem assures us that if we are interested in making a special definition of E only for α's in a bounded set and do not care what happens outside this set, then we can do so with an E which satisfies the boundedness restriction but in which only the restrictions of Easton's theorem apply to the α's of interest.

Accordingly, throughout the rest of this chapter we shall assume that E satisfies the boundedness restriction with respect to some fixed θ. We shall not specify anything further about θ.

We define X by (2.24) with $I = \aleph_{E(\theta)}$. Our basis sets will be products of the form

$$\bigcap \{B_j^{g(j)} \mid j \in J\} \tag{8.11}$$

for each J such that

$$\aleph(J \cap \aleph_{E(\alpha)}) < \aleph_\alpha$$

for each $\alpha < E(\theta)$ for which $\aleph_\alpha$ is regular. It is clear that Axioms 2.1 and 2.2 are satisfied. We define the Boolean algebra by Definition 2.9.

Definition 8.4. If P is the product (8.11), we write $s(P)$ for J.

In accordance with Definition 2.15, we refer to $s(P)$ as the support of P. One can rephrase the definition of a basis set by saying that it is a product (8.11) with the property that

$$\aleph(s(P) \cap \aleph_{E(\alpha)}) < \aleph_\alpha \tag{8.12}$$

for each $\alpha < E(\theta)$ for which $\aleph_\alpha$ is regular.

For the present chapter the choice of $\mathscr{G}$ is quite irrelevant. For simplicity, we take $\mathscr{G}$ to be the single identity automorphism. We take Γ to be the filter of all subgroups of $\mathscr{G}$.

We readily verify that Theorems 2.29–2.31 fail, while Theorem 2.32 is no longer applicable. The theorems of Chapter 3 all hold; however, Theorems 3.44–3.47 are no longer applicable. Thus we have $\models$AxC, but must seek new proofs of the theorems on cardinality.

C. Substitutes for the Cohen Combinatorial Lemma

Not only do we not have the countable chain condition (unless $\theta = 0$), but we do not seem to have a strict generalization of the Cohen combinatorial lemma. However, we do have a generalization of Theorem 7.4, and this suffices for our needs.

Definition 8.5. If P_i $(i = 1, 2)$ are products as in (8.11) using g_i and J_i, respectively, then the agreement set of P_1 and P_2 is defined to be the set of j's in $J_1 \cap J_2$ for which $g_1(j) = g_2(j)$.

Definition 8.6. Relative to any α, we specify the α-decomposition of a product P of the form (8.11) by

$$P^L = \bigcap \{B_j^{g(j)} \mid j \in s(P) \cap \aleph_{E(\alpha)}\} \tag{8.13}$$

$$P^U = \bigcap \{B_j^{g(j)} \mid j \in s(P) - \aleph_{E(\alpha)}\}. \tag{8.14}$$

Theorem 8.2. For each α and each P of the form (8.11), we have

$$P = P^L \wedge P^U. \tag{8.15}$$

PROOF. Use (2.6).

Incidentally, we note that if $E(\alpha) \geq E(\theta)$, then $P^L = P$ and $P^U = 1$.

We shall use such abridgements of terminology as speaking of "the P^L relative to α" to indicate that we are speaking of the P^L given by (8.13).

Theorem 8.3. Suppose that either $E(\theta) \leq \alpha$ or $\alpha < E(\theta)$ and $\aleph_\alpha$ is regular. For $k \in K$, let $Q_k \in A$. Let Q be a basis set such that

$$s(Q) \cap \aleph_{E(\alpha)} = \Lambda. \tag{8.16}$$

Then there is a basis set R and a set Π of basis sets B such that:

(i) $R \leq Q$;

(ii) $s(R) \cap \aleph_{E(\alpha)} = \Lambda$;

(iii) $\aleph(\Pi) \leq \aleph_\alpha$;

(iv) if $B \in \Pi$, then $s(B) \subseteq \aleph_{E(\alpha)}$;

(v) if $B \in \Pi$, then either there is a $k \in K$ such that $B \wedge R \leq Q_k$ or else $B \wedge R \wedge Q_k = 0$ for each $k \in K$;

(vi) if P is a basis set then there is a $B \in \Pi$ such that $P \wedge B \neq 0$.

PROOF. By induction on ν, for $\nu < \aleph_\alpha$, we shall define R_ν and Π_ν so that they satisfy (i) through (v) with R_ν and Π_ν in place of R and Π; moreover, for $\mu \leq \sigma \leq \nu$

$$R_\sigma \leq R_\mu . \tag{8.17}$$

First let $\nu = 0$.

Case 1. $Q \wedge Q_k = 0$ for each $k \in K$. Then take $R_0 = Q$ and $\Pi_0 = \{1\}$.

Case 2. There is a $k \in K$ for which $Q \wedge Q_k \neq 0$. Then by Definition 2.2 there is a basis set B for which $B \leq Q \wedge Q_k$. Then take $R^0 = B^U$ and $\Pi_0 = \{B^L\}$ relative to α (that is, take B^L and B^U to be the α-decomposition of B).

Now assume that R_η and Π_η have been defined for $\eta < \nu$ so as to satisfy (i)–(v) and also (8.17). Let s_ν be the sum of the supports of all the members of Π_η for $\eta < \nu$. Then $s_\nu \subseteq \aleph_{E(\alpha)}$. Take $\Pi_\nu{}^*$ to consist of every basis set S whose support is a subset of s_ν. We first establish that $\aleph(\Pi_\nu{}^*) \leq \aleph_\alpha$.

Case 1. $\alpha = \beta + 1$ and $\alpha < E(\theta)$. Then by (8.12), each member of Π_η has fewer than $\aleph_\alpha$ members in its support. There are at most $\aleph_\alpha$ members of Π_η. So there are at most

$$\aleph_\alpha \times \aleph_\alpha \times \nu \leq \aleph_\alpha$$

members of s_ν. Now by (8.12), each possible support of an S in $\Pi_\nu{}^*$ has at most $\aleph_\beta$ members. As each member of the support of S must be a member of s_ν there are at most $\aleph_\alpha$ choices for each member of the support of S. So the possible number of supports for an S of $\Pi_\nu{}^*$ is at most

$$(\aleph_\alpha)^{\aleph_\beta} = (2^{\aleph_\beta})^{\aleph_\beta} = 2^{\aleph_\beta \times \aleph_\beta} = 2^{\aleph_\beta} = \aleph_\alpha .$$

For each possible support of an S of $\Pi_\nu{}^*$ one can find at most $2^{\aleph_\beta}$ S's with that support. So the number of S's cannot exceed

$$2^{\aleph_\beta} \times \aleph_\alpha = \aleph_\alpha \times \aleph_\alpha = \aleph_\alpha .$$

Case 2. $E(\theta) \leq \alpha$. Clearly s_ν has at most $\aleph_{E(\theta)}$ members, since in (2.24) we took $I = \aleph_{E(\theta)}$. By (8.12), each possible support of an S in $\Pi_\nu{}^*$ has fewer than $\aleph_\theta$ members, by (i) of Definition 8.3. Then by (ii) of Definition 8.3, there are at most $\aleph_{E(\theta)}$ possible supports for an S of $\Pi_\nu{}^*$. For each support, there are at most $2^{\aleph_0}$ S's with that support. So there are at most $\aleph_{E(\theta)}$ S's. That is, there are at most $\aleph_\alpha$ S's.

Case 3. $\alpha < E(\theta)$ and α a limiting ordinal. By the hypothesis of the present theorem, $\aleph_\alpha$ is regular. So we can still appeal to (8.12). So as in Case 1 there are at most $\aleph_\alpha$ members of s_ν. As $\aleph_\alpha$ is regular, we see by (8.12) that each basis set with its support included in s_ν must have its support comprised entirely within the first $\aleph_\beta$ members of s_ν for some $\beta < \alpha$. However, there are at most $\aleph_{\beta+1}$ possible basis sets with support comprised entirely within the first $\aleph_\beta$ members of s_ν. So

$$\aleph(\Pi_\nu{}^*) \leq \sum_{\beta<\alpha} \aleph_{\beta+1} = \aleph_\alpha .$$

Choose a well-ordering S_μ of $\Pi_\nu{}^*$. We now define members B_μ of Π_ν and corresponding $R_\mu{}^*$ by induction on μ. We require that (i) and (ii) hold for each $R_\mu{}^*$ and $R_\sigma{}^* \leq R_\tau{}^*$ if $\tau \leq \sigma \leq \mu$.

At the step μ we define

$$T_\mu = \Big(\prod_{\eta<\nu} R_\eta\Big) \wedge \Big(\prod_{\sigma<\mu} R_\sigma{}^*\Big).$$

Then $s(T_\eta) \cap \aleph_{E(\alpha)} = \Lambda$ by (ii). But $s(S_\mu) \subseteq \aleph_{E(\alpha)}$ by the construction of the S_μ. So $S_\mu \wedge T_\mu$ is a basis set.

Case 1. $S_\mu \wedge T_\mu \wedge Q_k = 0$ for each $k \in K$. Then take $B_\mu = S_\mu$ and $R_\mu{}^* = T_\mu$.

Case 2. There is a $k \in K$ for which $S_\mu \wedge T_\mu \wedge Q_k \neq 0$. Take a basis set B with

$$B \leq S_\mu \wedge T_\mu \wedge Q_k .$$

Then take $B_\mu = B^L$ and $R_\mu{}^* = B^U$ relative to α.

Finally, we take Π_ν to consist of all the B_μ and set

$$R_\nu = \Big(\prod_{\eta<\nu} R_\eta\Big) \wedge \Big(\prod_{\mu} R_\mu{}^*\Big).$$

Having defined Π_ν and R_ν for $\nu < \aleph_\alpha$, we put

$$\Pi = \sum_{\nu<\aleph_\alpha} \Pi_\nu \qquad \text{and} \qquad R = \prod_{\nu<\aleph_\alpha} R_\nu .$$

Clearly R and Π satisfy (i)–(v). So we must prove (vi).

Take P a basis set, and suppose if possible that $P \wedge B = 0$ for each $B \in \Pi$. By induction on ν let us choose $B_\nu \in \Pi_\nu$ in such a way that if $\mathscr{S}_\sigma$ denotes the agreement set of P and B_σ for $\sigma \leq \nu$ then for $\sigma < \eta < \nu$

$$s(P) \cap s(B_\sigma) \subseteq \mathscr{S}_\eta. \tag{8.18}$$

We take $B_0 \in \Pi_0$. Now suppose that the B_σ have been chosen for $\sigma < \nu$ in such a way as to satisfy (8.18). Take

$$\mathscr{S} = s(P) \cap \sum_{\sigma < \nu} s(B_\sigma). \tag{8.19}$$

It is clear that $\mathscr{S}$ is a subset of the s_ν introduced in the process of defining Π_ν. Then P with its support restricted to $\mathscr{S}$ will be an $S_\mu \in \Pi_\nu^*$. Corresponding to this S_μ a B_μ was chosen to go into Π_ν. It was chosen so that $s(S_\mu) \subseteq s(B_\mu)$ and $S_\mu \wedge B_\mu = B_\mu$. Hence the agreement set of B_μ and S_μ must include $s(S_\mu)$, which is just $\mathscr{S}$. Hence, since S_μ is just P with its support restricted to $\mathscr{S}$, we must have $\mathscr{S}$ included in the agreement set of B_μ and P. We pick this B_μ from Π_ν to be our B_ν. Then

$$\mathscr{S} \subseteq \mathscr{S}_\nu$$

so that by (8.19) we get

$$s(P) \cap s(B_\sigma) \subseteq \mathscr{S}_\nu \tag{8.20}$$

for each $\sigma < \nu$. Thus we have extended (8.18) to ν.

By the definition of the agreement set of P and B_σ, we have

$$\mathscr{S}_\sigma \subseteq s(P) \cap s(B_\sigma).$$

Now

$$\mathscr{S}_\sigma \neq s(P) \cap s(B_\sigma),$$

else we would have $P \wedge B_\sigma \neq 0$. So by (8.18)

$$\begin{gathered} \mathscr{S}_\sigma \subseteq \mathscr{S}_\eta \\ \mathscr{S}_\sigma \neq \mathscr{S}_\eta \end{gathered} \tag{8.21}$$

for $\sigma < \eta$.

By (iv), we have

$$\mathscr{S}_\nu \subseteq s(P) \cap \aleph_{E(\alpha)} \tag{8.22}$$

for each ν.

Case 1. $\alpha < E(\theta)$. Then by (8.12), $s(P) \cap \aleph_{E(\alpha)}$ has fewer than $\aleph_\alpha$ members. Hence by (8.21) and (8.22) we must come to a $\nu < \aleph_\alpha$ for which

$$\mathscr{S}_\nu = s(P) \cap \aleph_{E(\alpha)}.$$

But then by (iv) we must have

$$\mathscr{S}_\nu = s(P) \cap s(B_\nu),$$

contradicting $P \wedge B_\nu = 0$.

Case 2. $E(\theta) \leq \alpha$. Then by (8.12), $s(P) \cap \aleph_{E(\alpha)}$ has fewer than $\aleph_\theta$ members. Again, by (8.21) and (8.22) we must come to a $\nu < \aleph_\alpha$ for which

$$\mathscr{S}_\nu = s(P) \cap \aleph_{E(\alpha)},$$

and again we get a contradiction.

Theorem 8.4. For $\tau < \aleph_\alpha$ and for $k \in K_\tau$ let $Q_{\tau,k} \in A$. Take α and Q as in Theorem 8.3. Then there are basis sets R_τ and sets Π_τ of basis sets such that for $\tau < \aleph_\alpha$ (i) through (vi) of Theorem 8.3 hold with R_τ, Π_τ, K_τ, and $Q_{\tau,k}$ in place of R, Π, K, and Q_k. Also, for $\mu \leq \tau < \aleph_\alpha$ we have

(vii) $R_\tau \leq R_\mu$.

PROOF. We define R_τ and Π_τ by induction on τ. If $\tau = 0$, we take the K of Theorem 8.3 to be K_0. Then Theorem 8.3 gives us an R and Π which we take to be R_0 and Π_0. Now suppose we have defined R_μ and Π_μ for $\mu < \tau$. In Theorem 8.3 we take K to be K_τ and Q to be $\prod_{\mu<\tau} R_\mu$. Then Theorem 8.3 gives us an R and Π which we take to be R_τ and Π_τ.

Theorem 8.5. Suppose that either $E(\theta) \leq \beta$ or $\beta < E(\theta)$ and $\aleph_\beta$ is regular. For $\tau < \aleph_\beta$ and for $k \in K_\tau$ let $Q_{\tau,k} \in A$. Let Q be a basis set. Then there is a basis set R and sets Π_τ of basis sets such that for $\tau < \aleph_\beta$:

(i) $R \leq Q$;

(ii) $\aleph(\Pi_\tau) \leq \aleph_\beta$;

(iii) if $B \in \Pi_\tau$, then $s(B) \subseteq \aleph_{E(\beta)}$;

(iv) if $B \in \Pi_\tau$, then either there is a $k \in K_\tau$ such that $B \wedge R \leq Q_{\tau,k}$ or else $B \wedge R \wedge Q_{\tau,k} = 0$ for each $k \in K_\tau$;

(v) if P is a basis set then there is a $B \in \Pi_\tau$ such that $P \wedge B \neq 0$;

(vi) if we form the β-decompositions of Q and R, then $Q^L = R^L$.

PROOF. We take the β-decomposition of Q into Q^L and Q^U. In Theorem 8.4 take β for α and Q^U for Q. Then we get R_τ and Π_τ with

$$s(R_\tau) \cap \aleph_{E(\beta)} = \Lambda.$$

We then take

$$R = Q^L \wedge \prod_{\tau < \aleph_\beta} R_\tau .$$

Now let $B \in \Pi_\tau$. Then either there is a $k \in K_\tau$ such that $B \wedge R_\tau \leq Q_{\tau,k}$ or else $B \wedge R_\tau \wedge Q_{\tau,k} = 0$ for each $k \in K_\tau$. As $R \leq R_\tau$, we get $B \wedge R \leq Q_{\tau,k}$ in the first case and $B \wedge R \wedge Q_{\tau,k} = 0$ in the second case.

Theorem 8.6. Let f be a function from ordinals to nonlimiting ordinals such that if $\eta < \tau$ then $f(\eta) < f(\tau)$. Let

$$\aleph_\alpha = \sum_{\eta < \gamma} \aleph_{f(n)} .$$

For $\tau < \aleph_\alpha$ and for $k \in K_\tau$ let $Q_{\tau,k} \in A$. Let Q be a basis set. Then there are basis sets R_η and set $\Pi s_{\tau,\eta}$ of basis sets such that for $n < \gamma$ and $\tau < \aleph_{f(\eta)}$:

(i) $R_\eta \leq Q$;

(ii) $R_\eta \leq R_\sigma$ for $\sigma \leq \eta$;

(iii) $\aleph(\Pi_{\tau,\eta}) \leq \aleph_{f(\eta)}$;

(iv) if $B \in \Pi_{\tau,\eta}$, then $s(B) \subseteq \aleph_{E(f(\eta))}$;

(v) if $B \in \Pi_{\tau,n}$, then either there is a $k \in K_\tau$ such that $B \wedge R_\eta \leq Q_{\tau,k}$ or else $B \wedge R_\eta \wedge Q_{\tau,k} = 0$ for each $k \in K_\tau$;

(vi) if P is a basis set then there is a $B \in \Pi_{\tau,\eta}$ such that $P \wedge B \neq 0$;

(vii) if we form the $f(\eta+1)$-decompositions of R_η and $R_{\eta+1}$, then $(R_\eta)^L = (R_{\eta+1})^L$;

(viii) If $\sigma < \gamma$ and σ is a limiting ordinal, and we form $f(\sigma)$-decompositions, then

$$(R_\sigma)^L = \Big(\prod_{\eta<\sigma} R_\eta\Big)^L.$$

PROOF. We carry out a series of definitions by induction on η. Let $\eta = 0$. Take β to be $f(0)$ in Theorem 8.5. Then for our Q there is a basis set R and sets Π_τ. We take R_0 to be R and

$$\Pi_{\tau,0} = \Pi_\tau .$$

To go from η to $\eta + 1$, we take $\beta = f(\eta + 1)$ in Theorem 8.5 and take Q to be R_η. Take the R that we get to be $R_{\eta+1}$ and take the Π_τ that we get to be $\Pi_{\tau,n+1}$. Let $\sigma < \gamma$ and σ a limiting ordinal. Then take $\beta = f(\sigma)$ in Theorem 8.5 and take Q to be $\prod_{n<\sigma} R_n$. Take the R that we get to be R_σ and take the Π_τ that we get to be $\Pi_{\tau,\sigma}$.

Theorem 8.7. Let α be an ordinal. For $\tau < \aleph_\alpha$ and for $k \in K_\tau$ let $Q_{\tau,k} \in A$. Let Q be a basis set. Then there is a basis set R and sets Π_τ of basis sets such that for $\tau < \aleph_\alpha$:

(i) $R \leq Q$;

(ii) $\aleph(\Pi_\tau) \leq \aleph_\alpha$;

(iii) if $B \in \Pi_\tau$, then $s(B) \subseteq \aleph_{E(\alpha)}$;

(iv) if $B \in \Pi_\tau$, then either there is a $k \in K_\tau$ such that $B \wedge R \leq Q_{\tau,k}$ or else $B \wedge R \wedge Q_{\tau,k} = 0$ for each $k \in K_\tau$;

(v) if P is a basis set then there is a $B \in \Pi_\tau$ such that $P \wedge B \neq 0$;

(vi) if $B \in \Pi_\tau$, then $\aleph(s(B)) < \aleph_\alpha$.

PROOF. If $\aleph_\alpha$ is regular and $\alpha < E(\theta)$, or if $E(\theta) \leq \alpha$, then we use Theorem 8.5. So let $\alpha < E(\theta)$, and let $\aleph_\alpha$ be singular. Then there is a $\gamma < \aleph_\alpha$ and a function g such that

$$g(\eta) < \aleph_\alpha \quad \text{if} \quad \eta < \gamma$$

$$\aleph_\alpha = \sum_{\eta<\gamma} g(\eta).$$

Clearly we can take g increasing. For each η, there is a β such that $g(\eta) = \aleph_\beta$. Define $f(\eta) = \beta + 1$ for this β. Then f satisfies the conditions of Theorem 8.6. We take

$$R = \prod_{\eta<\gamma} R_\eta$$

and

$$\Pi_\tau = \sum_{\eta<\gamma} \Pi_{\tau,\eta},$$

where in the summation we use only those η's for which $\tau < \aleph_{f(\eta)}$ so that $\Pi_{\tau,n}$ will be defined.

D. Cardinality Relations

As Requirement 2 involves cofinality, we need to show something about cofinality in the model. Our next theorem is an important step in that direction.

Theorem 8.8. If η and μ are cardinals and $\eta < \mathrm{Cf}(\mu)$, then

$$\models \sim(Ef) : G(\check{\eta}, \check{\mu}, f) \,.\, H(\check{\eta}, \check{\mu}, f) \tag{8.23}$$

where $G(u, v, f)$ denotes

$$(x) : x \in u \,.\supset.\, (E_1 y) \,.\, y \in v \,.\, \langle x, y\rangle \in f \tag{8.24}$$

and $H(u, v, f)$ denotes

$$(z) : z \in v \,.\supset.\, (Ex, y) \,.\, x \in u \,.\, y \in v \,.\, z \leq y \,.\, \langle x, y\rangle \in f. \tag{8.25}$$

PROOF. Suppose not. Therefore if we write

$$S = \|(Ef) : G(\check{\eta}, \check{\mu}, f) \,.\, H(\check{\eta}, \check{\mu}, f)\| \tag{8.26}$$

then $S \neq 0$. Then by Theorem 3.54 there is an $f \in V$ such that

$$S = \|G(\check{\eta}, \check{\mu}, f) \,.\, H(\check{\eta}, \check{\mu}, f)\|.$$

From this we have

$$S \leq \|G(\check{\eta}, \check{\mu}, f)\| \tag{8.27}$$

$$S \leq \|H(\check{\eta}, \check{\mu}, f)\|. \tag{8.28}$$

So for each $\tau < \eta$, we obtain by (8.27)

$$S \leq \|(E_1 y) \,.\, y \in \check{\mu} \,.\, \langle \check{\tau}, y \rangle \in f\|. \tag{8.29}$$

Then by Theorem 3.13, there is a $y \in V$ such that

$$S \leq \|y \in \check{\mu} \,.\, \langle \check{\tau}, y \rangle \in f\|. \tag{8.30}$$

We write $f(\check{\tau})$ for this y, so that

$$S \leq \|f(\check{\tau}) < \check{\mu}\|.$$

Then by Theorem 3.19

$$S \leq \sum_{\sigma < \mu} \|f(\check{\tau}) = \check{\sigma}\|. \tag{8.31}$$

Lemma 1. There is a basis set R with

$$R \leq S \tag{8.32}$$

and sets Π_τ of basis sets such that for $\tau < \eta$

$$\aleph(\Pi_\tau) \leq \eta; \tag{8.33}$$

and, if P is a basis set with $P \leq R$, then there is a $B \in \Pi_\tau$ and a $\sigma < \mu$ such that

$$P \wedge B \neq 0 \tag{8.34}$$

$$B \wedge R \leq \|f(\check{\tau}) = \check{\sigma}\|. \tag{8.35}$$

PROOF. As $S \neq 0$, there is a basis set Q with $Q \leq S$. Take this Q in Theorem 8.7. Take also $\aleph_\alpha = \eta$, $K_\tau = \mu$, and

$$Q_{\tau,\sigma} = \|f(\check{\tau}) = \check{\sigma}\|.$$

Consider the R and set of Π_τ whose existence is asserted by Theorem 8.7. As $Q \leq S$, we have (8.32) by (i), while (8.33) follows by (ii). Now let P be a basis set with $P \leq R$. Then by (v) there is a $B \in \Pi_\tau$ such that (8.34) holds. Moreover, (iv) tells us that either there is a $\sigma < \mu$ such that (8.35) holds, or else

$$B \wedge R \wedge \|f(\check{\tau}) = \check{\sigma}\| = 0 \tag{8.36}$$

for each $\sigma < \mu$. So we must show that this cannot be the case. As $P \wedge B \leq P \leq R \leq Q \leq S$, we have by (8.31) and (8.34)

$$P \wedge B \wedge \sum_{\sigma < \mu} \|f(\check{\tau}) = \check{\sigma}\| \neq 0.$$

So by Theorem 2.27 there is a basis set B_1 and an index $\sigma < \mu$ such that

$$B_1 \leq P \wedge B \wedge \|f(\check{\tau}) = \check{\sigma}\|.$$

As $P \leq R$, this gives

$$B_1 \leq B \wedge R \wedge \|f(\check{\tau}) = \check{\sigma}\|,$$

contradicting (8.36).

As $P \leq R$, we have

$$B \wedge R \neq 0 \tag{8.37}$$

by (8.34).

For each basis set B with $B \wedge R \neq 0$ and for each $\tau < \eta$ there is at most one σ for which (8.35) holds. For if (8.35) holds for σ_1 and σ_2, then

$$\begin{aligned} 0 \neq B \wedge R &\leq \|f(\check{\tau}) = \check{\sigma}_1\| \wedge \|f(\check{\tau}) = \check{\sigma}_2\| \\ &\leq \|\check{\sigma}_1 = \check{\sigma}_2\|, \end{aligned}$$

which can happen only if $\sigma_1 = \sigma_2$.

We may order the members of Π_τ as $B_{\tau,\nu}$ with $\nu < \eta$. Then for $\tau < \eta$ and $\nu < \eta$, we write $\sigma_{\tau,\nu}$ for the unique $\sigma < \mu$ such that

$$0 \neq B_{\tau,\nu} \wedge R \leq \|f(\check{\tau}) = \check{\sigma}\| \tag{8.38}$$

if there is one; otherwise take $\sigma_{\tau,\nu} = 0$. Take

$$\sigma = \left(\sum_{\substack{\tau<\eta \\ \nu<\eta}} \sigma_{\tau,\nu}\right) + 1. \tag{8.39}$$

As in fact $\eta < \mathrm{Cf}(\mu)$, we must have $\sigma < \mu$.

***Lemma* 2.** For $\tau < \eta$ and $\sigma \leq \gamma < \mu$

$$R \wedge \|f(\check{\tau}) = \check{\gamma}\| = 0. \tag{8.40}$$

PROOF. Suppose otherwise. Then there is a basis set P with

$$P \leq R \wedge \|f(\check{\tau}) = \check{\gamma}\|. \tag{8.41}$$

So by Lemma 1 there must be a $B_{\tau,\nu} \in \Pi_\tau$ and a $\delta < \mu$ such that

$$P \wedge B_{\tau,\nu} \neq 0 \tag{8.42}$$

$$B_{\tau,\nu} \wedge R \leq \|f(\check{\tau}) = \check{\delta}\|. \tag{8.43}$$

By (8.41) and (8.42)

$$0 \neq B_{\tau,\nu} \wedge R \wedge \|f(\check{\tau}) = \check{\gamma}\|. \tag{8.44}$$

So by (8.43)

$$0 \neq \|f(\check{\tau}) = \check{\delta}\| \wedge \|f(\check{\tau}) = \check{\gamma}\|.$$

Therefore $0 \neq \|\check{\delta} = \check{\gamma}\|$, so that $\delta = \gamma$ by Theorem 3.24. But by (8.38), (8.43), and (8.44), we see that $\delta = \sigma_{\tau,\nu}$. So by (8.39), we have $\delta < \sigma$, whereas $\gamma \geq \sigma$.

Then by Lemma 2 we have

$$\|f(\check{\tau}) = \check{\gamma}\| \leq R'$$

for $\sigma \leq \gamma < \mu$. However, if $\gamma < \sigma$, then $\|\check{\gamma} \geq \check{\sigma}\| = 0$. So for $\gamma < \mu$

$$\|f(\check{\tau}) = \check{\gamma} \,.\, \check{\gamma} \geq \check{\sigma}\| \leq R'.$$

Then by Theorem 3.20

$$\|(E\gamma) \,.\, \gamma < \check{\mu} \,.\, f(\check{\tau}) = \gamma \,.\, \gamma \geq \check{\sigma}\| \leq R'.$$

By a standard transformation of the predicate calculus with equality

$$\|\check{\sigma} \leq f(\check{\tau}) < \check{\mu}\| \leq R'.$$

As this holds for $\tau < \eta$, we obtain by Theorem 3.20

$$\|(Ex) \,.\, x \in \check{\eta} \,.\, \check{\sigma} \leq f(x) < \check{\mu}\| \leq R'.$$

Recalling the meaning of $f(x)$, we may write this as

$$\|(Ex, y) \,.\, x \in \check{\eta} \,.\, y < \check{\mu} \,.\, \check{\sigma} \leq y \,.\, \langle x, y\rangle \in f\| \leq R'.$$

But by (8.28) and (8.25)

$$S \leq \|(Ex, y) \,.\, x \in \check{\eta} \,.\, y < \check{\mu} \,.\, \check{\sigma} \leq y \,.\, \langle x, y\rangle \in f\|.$$

So $S \leq R'$. But this contradicts (8.32).

If we know that $\check{\eta}$ and $\check{\mu}$ are formal cardinals whenever η and μ are intuitive cardinals, this theorem will tell us that if η and μ are cardinals and $\eta < \mathrm{Cf}(\mu)$, then $\vDash \check{\eta} < \mathrm{Cf}(\check{\mu})$. So we proceed through a succession of theorems which will lead to the conclusion that $\check{\mu}$ is a formal cardinal whenever μ is an intuitive cardinal.

Theorem 8.9. If η and μ are ordinals and $\aleph(\eta) \leq \aleph(\mu)$, then $\models \aleph(\check{\eta}) \leq \aleph(\check{\mu})$.

PROOF. If $\aleph(\eta) \leq \aleph(\mu)$, then there is a one-to-one correspondence from η to a subset of μ. Transferring this correspondence into the formal system gives our theorem.

Corollary. If η and μ are ordinals and $\aleph(\eta) = \aleph(\mu)$, then $\models \aleph(\check{\eta}) = \aleph(\check{\mu})$.

Theorem 8.10. If σ and α are ordinals and $\sigma < \aleph_{\alpha+1}$, then

$$\models \aleph(\check{\sigma}) < \aleph(\mathrm{Img}(\aleph_{\alpha+1})).$$

PROOF. Let $\beta \leq \alpha$. If we take $\eta = \aleph_\beta$ and $\mu = \aleph_{\alpha+1}$, then $\eta < \mathrm{Cf}(\mu)$. So by Theorem 8.8, the formula (8.23) holds. If $\aleph(\check{\eta}) \geq \aleph(\check{\mu})$, this would say that there is a g which establishes a one-to-one correspondence between all of $\check{\mu}$ and part of $\check{\eta}$. By letting the other members of $\check{\eta}$ correspond to 0, we could infer the existence of an f of the sort whose existence is denied by (8.23). So a consequence of (8.23) is

$$\models \aleph(\mathrm{Img}(\aleph_\beta)) < \aleph(\mathrm{Img}(\aleph_{\alpha+1})).$$

Let $\sigma < \aleph_{\alpha+1}$. Then there is a $\beta \leq \alpha$ such that $\aleph(\sigma) = \aleph(\aleph_\beta)$. So by the corollary to Theorem 8.9

$$\models \aleph(\check{\sigma}) = \aleph(\mathrm{Img}(\aleph_\beta)).$$

Combining the last two formulas gives our theorem.

Theorem 8.11. If η and μ are ordinals and $\aleph(\eta) < \aleph(\mu)$, then

$$\models \aleph(\check{\eta}) < \aleph(\check{\mu}).$$

PROOF. There must be an α such that $\aleph(\mu) = \aleph_\alpha$. So by the corollary to Theorem 8.9

$$\models \aleph(\check{\mu}) = \aleph(\mathrm{Img}(\aleph_\alpha)). \tag{8.45}$$

Case 1. α is not a limiting ordinal. Then our theorem follows by (8.45) and Theorem 8.10.

Case 2. α is a limiting ordinal. Then there is a $\beta < \alpha$ such that $\eta < \aleph_{\beta+1}$. So by Theorem 8.10

$$\models \aleph(\check{\eta}) < \aleph(\mathrm{Img}(\aleph_{\beta+1})).$$

However, by Theorem 8.9

$$\models \aleph(\mathrm{Img}(\aleph_{\beta+1})) \leq \aleph(\mathrm{Img}(\aleph_\alpha)).$$

Then our theorem follows by (8.45).

This theorem is the equivalent of Theorem 3.44. From it we prove the equivalents of Theorems 3.45–3.47 by analogous proofs. Then, as noted earlier, Theorem 8.8 becomes a formal theorem about cofinality.

E. Proof of Easton's Theorem

We are finally ready for our key result, which we do in three steps.

Theorem 8.12. If α is an ordinal, then

$$\models \mathrm{Img}(\aleph_{E(\alpha)}) \leq \aleph(SC(\aleph_{\check{\alpha}})).$$

PROOF. First take the case where $\alpha < E(\theta)$ and $\aleph_\alpha$ is regular. Then as $\aleph_\alpha \times \aleph_{E(\alpha)} = \aleph_{E(\alpha)}$, we may identify coordinates less than $\aleph_{E(\alpha)}$ by two subscripts, the first $<\aleph_\alpha$ and the second $<\aleph_{E(\alpha)}$. Hence we may define q_μ with $D(q_\mu) = V_{\aleph_\alpha}$ by the condition that if $x \in V_{\aleph_\alpha}$ then

$$q_\mu(x) = \sum_{\eta < \aleph_\alpha} B^1_{\eta,\mu} \wedge \|x = \check{\eta}\|. \tag{8.46}$$

This is analogous to Definition 6.3. Then a proof like that of Theorem 6.3 gives

$$\models q_\mu \subseteq \aleph_{\check{\alpha}} \tag{8.47}$$

for $\mu < \aleph_{E(\alpha)}$. A proof like that of Theorem 6.4 gives

$$\models q_\sigma \neq q_\mu \tag{8.48}$$

for $\sigma < \mu < \aleph_{E(\alpha)}$. Thus we have at least $\aleph_{E(\alpha)}$ distinct subsets of $\aleph_{\check{\alpha}}$. To prove our theorem, we define a formal one-to-one correspondence between $\check{\mu}$ and q_μ.

Write momentarily $\beta = \aleph_{E(\alpha)} + 3$. We define f with $D(f) = V_\beta$ by the condition that if $x \in V_\beta$ then

$$f(x) = \sum_{\mu < \aleph_{E(\alpha)}} \|x = \langle \check{\mu}, q_\mu \rangle\|.$$

We verify without difficulty that f is extensional, so that by Theorem 3.9 $f \in V$ and

$$\|x \in f\| \leq \sum_{\mu < \aleph_{E(\alpha)}} \|x = \langle \check{\mu}, q_\mu \rangle\|. \tag{8.49}$$

Lemma 1.

$$\models (y, z) : \langle y, z \rangle \in f . \supset . y \in \operatorname{Img}(\aleph_{E(\alpha)}) . z \subseteq \aleph_{\check{\alpha}}.$$

PROOF. By (8.47) we have for $\mu < \aleph_{E(\alpha)}$

$$\|\langle y, z \rangle = \langle \check{\mu}, q_\mu \rangle\| \leq \|y \in \operatorname{Img}(\aleph_{E(\alpha)}) . z \subseteq \aleph_{\check{\alpha}}\|.$$

Summing on μ and using (8.49) gives

$$\|\langle y, z \rangle \in f\| \leq \|y \in \operatorname{Img}(\aleph_{E(\alpha)}) . z \subseteq \aleph_{\check{\alpha}}\|.$$

Lemma 2.

$$\models (y) : y \in \operatorname{Img}(\aleph_{E(\alpha)}) . \supset . (Ez) . \langle y, z \rangle \in f.$$

PROOF. Take $\sigma < \aleph_{E(\alpha)}$. Then

$$\sum_{\mu < \aleph_{E(\alpha)}} \|\langle \check{\sigma}, q_\sigma \rangle = \langle \check{\mu}, q_\mu \rangle\| = 1.$$

But $\langle \check{\sigma}, q_\sigma \rangle$ is in $D(f)$. So by the definition of f,

$$\models \langle \check{\sigma}, q_\sigma \rangle \in f.$$

Therefore

$$\models (Ez) . \langle \check{\sigma}, z \rangle \in f.$$

As this holds for each $\sigma < \aleph_{E(\alpha)}$, our lemma follows by Theorem 3.20.

Lemma 3.

$$\vDash(x, y, z) : \langle x, z\rangle \in f . \langle y, z\rangle \in f . \supset . x = y.$$

PROOF. We wish to show first that

$$\|\langle x, z\rangle = \langle \check{\mu}, q_\mu\rangle . \langle y, z\rangle = \langle \check{\sigma}, q_\sigma\rangle\| \leq \|x = y\|.$$

Case 1. $\mu \neq \sigma$. Since

$$\|\langle x, z\rangle = \langle \check{\mu}, q_\mu\rangle . \langle y, z\rangle = \langle \check{\sigma}, q_\sigma\rangle\| \leq \|q_\mu = q_\sigma\|$$

we conclude by (8.48) that the left side must be 0. Hence the left side is $\leq \|x = y\|$.

Case 2. $\mu = \sigma$. Then the result to be proved reduces to

$$\|\langle x, z\rangle = \langle \check{\mu}, q_\mu\rangle . \langle y, z\rangle = \langle \check{\mu}, q_\mu\rangle\| \leq \|x = y\|$$

which is certainly valid.

If we now sum on μ and σ on the left, we can use (8.49) to conclude our lemma.

Lemma 4.

$$\vDash(x, y, z) : \langle x, y\rangle \in f . \langle x, z\rangle \in f . \supset . y = z.$$

PROOF. Proceed as in the proof of Lemma 3.

From these four lemmas, our theorem follows.

Next consider the case where $\alpha < E(\theta)$ and $\aleph_\alpha$ is singular. By (i) and (ii) of Easton's theorem, $E(\alpha)$ has the minimum value allowed by Requirements 1 and 2. As these reflect classical theorems of set theory, we can use these classical theorems of set theory to prove our theorem.

Finally, let $E(\theta) \leq \alpha$. Then a reference to (iv) of Definition 8.3 discloses that we have

$$E(\alpha) = \alpha + 1.$$

So our theorem takes the form

$$\vDash \operatorname{Img}(\aleph_{\alpha+1}) \leq \aleph(SC(\aleph_{\check{\alpha}})).$$

Since $\alpha + 1$ is the minimum value allowed by Requirements 1 and 2, we could parallel the proof of the previous case. However, Cantor's theorem gives the desired result more simply.

Definition 8.7. We define Σ to be the set of all pairs $\langle \Pi, s \rangle$ such that:

(i) Π is a nonempty set of basis sets;

(ii) $\aleph(\Pi) \leq \aleph_\alpha$;

(iii) if $B \in \Pi$, then $s(B) \subseteq \aleph_{E(\alpha)}$;

(iv) $s \subseteq \Pi \times \aleph_\alpha$;

(v) if $B \in \Pi$, then $\aleph(s(B)) < \aleph_\alpha$.

Theorem 8.13. $\aleph(\Sigma) = \aleph_{E(\alpha)}$.

PROOF. Clearly there are at least $\aleph_{E(\alpha)}$ subsets of $\aleph_{E(\alpha)}$ with fewer than $\aleph_\alpha$ members because there are that many with one member. On the other hand, there are certainly no more than $(\aleph_{E(\alpha)})^{\aleph_\alpha}$ such subsets.

Lemma.

$$(\aleph_{E(\alpha)})^{\aleph_\alpha} = \aleph_{E(\alpha)}.$$

Case 1. $E(\alpha)$ is not limiting. Say $E(\alpha) = \beta + 1$. Recalling that $E(\alpha) > \alpha$ by Requirement 2, we have

$$(\aleph_{E(\alpha)})^{\aleph_\alpha} = (2^{\aleph_\beta})^{\aleph_\alpha} = 2^{\aleph_\beta \times \aleph_\alpha} = 2^{\aleph_\beta} = \aleph_{E(\alpha)}.$$

Case 2. $E(\alpha)$ is limiting. Note that since $\aleph_\alpha < \aleph_{E(\alpha)}$, we can see that $(\aleph_{E(\alpha)})^{\aleph_\alpha}$ is just the number of ways of choosing $\aleph_\alpha$ elements out of $\aleph_{E(\alpha)}$. Recall that by Requirement 2, $\aleph_\alpha < \mathrm{Cf}(\aleph_{E(\alpha)})$. Hence any subset of $\aleph_{E(\alpha)}$ with $\aleph_\alpha$ elements must be bounded. Take a sequence of nonlimiting ordinals whose sum is $E(\alpha)$. Clearly we can take each of them greater than α. As in Case 1, if β is one of these, then the number of subsets of $\aleph_\beta$ with $\aleph_\alpha$ members is just $\aleph_\beta$. Adding these for each $\beta < E(\alpha)$, we conclude that there are $\aleph_{E(\alpha)}$ subsets of $\aleph_{E(\alpha)}$ with $\aleph_\alpha$ members.

By our lemma, the number of supports for basis sets satisfying (iii) and (v) is $\aleph_{E(\alpha)}$. For each such support, there are at most $\aleph_\alpha$ basis sets with that support. Hence there are $\aleph_{E(\alpha)}$ basis sets B satisfying (iii) and (v). As each Π contains at most $\aleph_\alpha$ of these B's, the number of Π's is at most $(\aleph_{E(\alpha)})^{\aleph_\alpha}$, which is $\aleph_{E(\alpha)}$ by our lemma. On the other hand, there are $\aleph_{E(\alpha)}$ Π's which contain one member each. So there are exactly $\aleph_{E(\alpha)}$ Π's. For each such Π, there are $\aleph_\alpha$ members of $\Pi \times \aleph_\alpha$, and hence $\aleph_{\alpha+1}$ possible s's. But $\alpha + 1 \leq E(\alpha)$, so that the number of pairs $\langle \Pi, s \rangle$ is

$$\aleph_{E(\alpha)} \times \aleph_{\alpha+1} = \aleph_{E(\alpha)}.$$

Corollary. $\models \aleph(\check{\Sigma}) = \mathrm{Img}(\aleph_{E(\alpha)})$.

The reader should note the parallelism between the present Σ and that of Definition 7.1. Also the theorem just proved parallels Theorem 7.5. The lemmas of the next theorem parallel Theorems 7-6–7.8, and their proofs have many similarities. The reader will find it helpful to review the proofs of Theorems 7.6–7.8 before commencing to read the next theorem and its proof.

Definition 8.8. Let $\langle \Pi, s \rangle \in \Sigma$ and $y \in V$. We define $\|\Phi(\langle \Pi, s \rangle, y)\|$ to be the sum of all basis sets R such that:

(i) If P is a basis set with $P \leq R$, and if $\gamma < \aleph_\alpha$, then there is a $B \in \Pi$ such that

$$P \wedge B \neq 0 \tag{8.50}$$

and either

$$B \wedge R \leq \|\check{\gamma} \in y\| \tag{8.51}$$

or

$$B \wedge R \leq \|{\sim}\check{\gamma} \in y\|. \tag{8.52}$$

(ii) $s = \{\langle B, \gamma \rangle \mid B \in \Pi \,.\, \gamma < \aleph_\alpha \,.\, B \wedge R \leq \|\check{\gamma} \in y\|\}$.

Definition 8.9. Choose β large enough so that if $y \in D(SC(\aleph_{\check{\alpha}}))$ and $\langle \Pi, s \rangle \in \Sigma$, then

$$\langle y, \mathrm{Img}(\langle \Pi, s \rangle) \rangle \in V_\beta.$$

Define f with $D(f) = V_\beta$ by the condition that if $x \in V_\beta$, then

$$f(x) = \sum_{w \in \Sigma} \|(Ev) \,.\, x = \langle v, \check{w} \rangle \,.\, \Phi(w, v) \,.\, v \subseteq \aleph_{\check{\alpha}}\|.$$

Theorem 8.14. If α is an ordinal, then

$$\models \mathrm{Img}(\aleph_{E(\alpha)}) = \aleph(SC(\aleph_{\check{\alpha}})).$$

PROOF. By Theorem 8.12, it suffices to prove

$$\models \aleph(SC(\aleph_{\check{\alpha}})) \leq \mathrm{Img}(\aleph_{E(\alpha)}). \tag{8.53}$$

This we do in a series of lemmas.

First we note that clearly f is extensional, so that by Theorem 3.9 $f \in V$ and

$$\|x \in f\| \leq \sum_{w \in \Sigma} \|(Ev) \,.\, x = \langle v, \check{w} \rangle \,.\, \Phi(w, v) \,.\, v \subseteq \aleph_{\check{\alpha}}\|. \tag{8.54}$$

Lemma 1.

$$\models (y, z) : \langle y, z \rangle \in f \,.\, \supset .\, y \subseteq \aleph_{\check{\alpha}} \,.\, z \in \check{\Sigma}$$

PROOF. For $w \in \Sigma$ and $v \in V$

$$\|\langle y, z \rangle = \langle v, \check{w} \rangle \,.\, \Phi(w, v) \,.\, v \subseteq \aleph_{\check{\alpha}}\| \leq \|y \subseteq \aleph_{\check{\alpha}} \,.\, z \in \check{\Sigma}\|.$$

Summing on v gives

$$\|(Ev) \,.\, \langle y, z \rangle = \langle v, z \rangle \,.\, \Phi(w, v) \,.\, v \subseteq \aleph_{\check{\alpha}}\| \leq \|y \subseteq \aleph_{\check{\alpha}} \,.\, z \in \check{\Sigma}\|.$$

Summing on $w \in \Sigma$ and using (8.54) gives

$$\|\langle y, z \rangle \in f\| \leq \|y \subseteq \aleph_{\check{\alpha}} \,.\, z \in \check{\Sigma}\|.$$

Lemma 2. Let $y \in V$. Then

$$\sum_{w \in \Sigma} \|\Phi(w, y)\| = 1.$$

PROOF. Suppose not. Then

$$\Big(\sum_{w \in \Sigma} \|\Phi(w, y)\|\Big)' \neq 0.$$

Choose a basis set Q included in the term on the left. Then

$$Q \wedge \sum_{w \in \Sigma} \|\Phi(w, y)\| = 0. \tag{8.55}$$

In Theorem 8.7 take this Q. Take also $K_\tau = \{0\}$ and $Q_{\tau,0} = \|\check{\tau} \in y\|$. Take

$$\Pi = \sum_{\tau < \aleph_\alpha} \Pi_\tau \tag{8.56}$$

and

$$s = \{\langle B, \gamma\rangle \mid B \in \Pi \,.\, \gamma < \aleph_\alpha \,.\, B \wedge R \leq \|\check{\gamma} \in y\|\}. \tag{8.57}$$

By Definition 8.7, $\langle \Pi, s\rangle \in \Sigma$. Also, (ii) of Definition 8.8 is satisfied. So we wish to verify (i) of Definition 8.8. Let P be a basis set with $P \leq R$ and let $\gamma < \aleph_\alpha$. Then by (v) of Theorem 8.7, there is a $B \in \Pi_\gamma$ such that (8.50) is satisfied. Also by (iv) of Theorem 8.7, either (8.51) holds or else

$$B \wedge R \wedge \|\check{\gamma} \in y\| = 0. \tag{8.58}$$

As $P \leq R$, we have $B \wedge R \neq 0$ by (8.50). So $B \wedge R$ is a basis set. Then by (8.58) and Definition 2.3

$$B \wedge R \wedge \mathrm{Cl}(\|\check{\gamma} \in y\|) = 0.$$

So by Definitions 2.4 and 2.6

$$B \wedge R \leq \mathrm{Cc}(\|\check{\gamma} \in y\|).$$

But then (8.52) holds by (2.8) and (3.1).

Hence by Definition 8.8

$$R \leq \|\Phi(\langle \Pi, s\rangle, y)\|.$$

Therefore

$$R < \sum_{w \in \Sigma} \|\Phi(w, y)\|.$$

As $R \leq Q$ by (i) of Theorem 8.7, we get a contradiction by (8.55).

Lemma 3.

$$\vdash (x) : x \subseteq \aleph_{\check{\alpha}} \,.\supset.\, (Ez) \,.\, \langle x, z\rangle \in f.$$

PROOF. By Lemma 2 and Theorem 2.22

$$\|y \subseteq \aleph_{\check{\alpha}}\| = \sum_{w \in \Sigma} \|\Phi(w, y) \,.\, y \subseteq \aleph_{\check{\alpha}}\|. \tag{8.59}$$

However

$$\|\Phi(w, y) \,.\, y \subseteq \aleph_{\check{\alpha}}\| = \|\langle y, \check{w}\rangle = \langle y, \check{w}\rangle \,.\, \Phi(w, y) \,.\, y \subseteq \aleph_{\check{\alpha}}\|$$

so that for $w \in \Sigma$

$$\|\Phi(w, y) \,.\, y \subseteq \aleph_{\check{\alpha}}\| \leq \sum_{a \in \Sigma} \|(Ev) \,.\, \langle y, \check{a} \rangle = \langle v, \check{w} \rangle \,.\, \Phi(w, v) \,.\, v \subseteq \aleph_{\check{\alpha}}\|.$$

Summing over $w \in \Sigma$ and using (8.59) gives

$$\|y \subseteq \aleph_{\check{\alpha}}\| \leq \sum_{w \in \Sigma} \sum_{a \in \Sigma} \|(Ev) \,.\, \langle y, \check{a} \rangle = \langle v, \check{w} \rangle \,.\, \Phi(w, v) \,.\, v \subseteq \aleph_{\check{\alpha}}\|.$$

By Theorem 2.21, we can interchange the order of summation in a double sum. Therefore

$$\|y \subseteq \aleph_{\check{\alpha}}\| \leq \sum_{a \in \Sigma} \sum_{w \in \Sigma} \|(Ev) \,.\, \langle y, \check{a} \rangle = \langle v, \check{w} \rangle \,.\, \Phi(w, v) \,.\, v \subseteq \aleph_{\check{\alpha}}\|.$$

Take $y \in D(SC(\aleph_{\check{\alpha}}))$. Then $\langle y, \check{a} \rangle$ is in $D(f)$. So by the definition of f

$$\|\langle y, \check{a} \rangle \in f\| = \sum_{w \in \Sigma} \|(Ev) \,.\, \langle y, \check{a} \rangle = \langle v, \check{w} \rangle \,.\, \Phi(w, v) \,.\, v \subseteq \aleph_{\check{\alpha}}\|.$$

Hence

$$\|y \subseteq \aleph_{\check{\alpha}}\| \leq \sum_{a \in \Sigma} \|\langle y, \check{a} \rangle \in f\|$$

so that by (3.7)

$$\|y \subseteq \aleph_{\check{\alpha}}\| \leq \|(Ez) \,.\, \langle y, z \rangle \in f\|.$$

This gives

$$\|x = y \,.\, y \in SC(\aleph_{\check{\alpha}})\| \leq \|(Ez) \,.\, \langle x, z \rangle \in f\|.$$

Summing over $y \in D(SC(\aleph_{\check{\alpha}}))$ and using (3.28) gives

$$\|x \in SC(\aleph_{\check{\alpha}})\| \leq \|(Ez) \,.\, \langle x, z \rangle \in f\|.$$

Lemma 4. If $w \in \Sigma$ and $x, y \in V$, then

$$\|\Phi(w, x) \,.\, x \subseteq \aleph_{\check{\alpha}} \,.\, \Phi(w, y) \,.\, y \subseteq \aleph_{\check{\alpha}}\| \leq \|x = y\|.$$

PROOF. If $w \in \Sigma$, then $w = \langle \Pi, s \rangle$ for some Π and s satisfying the conditions of Definition 8.7. Take $\gamma < \aleph_\alpha$, and suppose, if possible, that

$$\|\Phi(w, x) \,.\, \Phi(w, y) \,.\, \check{\gamma} \in x \,.\, \sim \check{\gamma} \in y\| \neq 0.$$

Then by Definition 8.8 and Theorems 2.22 and 2.25 there must be an R_1 and an R_2 such that

$$R_1 \wedge R_2 \wedge \|\check{\gamma} \in x \,.\, \sim\check{\gamma} \in y\| \neq 0,$$

where (i) and (ii) of Definition 8.8 hold for R_1 together with x and for R_2 together with y. Choose a basis set P such that

$$P \leq R_1 \wedge R_2 \wedge \|\check{\gamma} \in x \,.\, \sim\check{\gamma} \in y\|. \tag{8.60}$$

Take this P in (i) of Definition 8.8 and conclude that there is a $B \in \Pi$ such that (8.50) holds and either

$$B \wedge R_1 \leq \|\check{\gamma} \in x\| \tag{8.61}$$

or

$$B \wedge R_1 \leq \|\sim\check{\gamma} \in x\|. \tag{8.62}$$

By (8.60), we have

$$B \wedge P \leq B \wedge R_1 \tag{8.63}$$

and

$$B \wedge P \leq \|\check{\gamma} \in x\|. \tag{8.64}$$

If (8.62) could hold, then by (8.62) and (8.63) we would have

$$B \wedge P \leq \|\sim\check{\gamma} \in x\|,$$

contradicting (8.64). So (8.61) must hold. Then by (ii) of Definition 8.8, we have $\langle B, \gamma\rangle \in s$. But then by (ii) of Definition 8.8 we have

$$B \wedge R_2 \leq \|\check{\gamma} \in y\|. \tag{8.65}$$

But by (8.60)

$$B \wedge P \leq \|\sim\check{\gamma} \in y\|. \tag{8.66}$$

As $P \leq R_2$, we get

$$B \wedge P \leq \|\check{\gamma} \in y\|$$

by (8.65). With (8.50) and (8.66), this gives a contradiction.

Thus our supposition is false. So for each $\gamma < \aleph_\alpha$, we have

$$\|\Phi(w, x) \,.\, \Phi(w, y)\| \leq \|\check{\gamma} \in x \supset \check{\gamma} \in y\|.$$

By a similar argument, we conclude

$$\|\Phi(w, x) \,.\, \Phi(w, y)\| \le \|\check{\gamma} \in y \supset \check{\gamma} \in x\|$$

for each $\gamma < \aleph_\alpha$. So for each $\gamma < \aleph_\alpha$, we have

$$\|\Phi(w, y) \,.\, \Phi(w, y)\| \le \|\check{\gamma} \in x \equiv \check{\gamma} \in y\|.$$

Multiplying over $\gamma < \aleph_\alpha$ gives

$$\|\Phi(w, x) \,.\, \Phi(w, y)\| \le \|(t) : t \in \aleph_{\check{\alpha}} \,.\supset.\, t \in x \equiv t \in y\|.$$

Then by Theorem 3.6, we conclude the proof of the lemma.

Lemma 5.

$$\vDash (x, y, z) : \langle x, z\rangle \in f \,.\, \langle y, z\rangle \in f \,.\supset.\, x = y.$$

PROOF. We first show

$$\|\langle x, z\rangle = \langle v_1, \check{w}_1\rangle \,.\, \Phi(w_1, v_1) \,.\, v_1 \subseteq \aleph_{\check{\alpha}} \,.\, \langle y, z\rangle = \langle v_2, \check{w}_2\rangle \,.\, \Phi(w_2, v_2) \,.\, v_2 \subseteq \aleph_{\check{\alpha}}\| \le \|x = y\| \tag{8.67}$$

if $w_1 \in \Sigma$ and $w_2 \in \Sigma$.

Case 1. $w_1 \ne w_2$. But

$$\|\langle x, z\rangle = \langle v_1, \check{w}_1\rangle \,.\, \langle y, z\rangle = \langle v_2, \check{w}_2\rangle\| \le \|\check{w}_1 = \check{w}_2\|.$$

So by Theorem 3.24 the left side of (8.67) is zero, and so (8.67) holds.

Case 2. $w_1 = w_2$. Then by Lemma 4

$$\|\Phi(w_1, v_1) \,.\, v_1 \subseteq \aleph_{\check{\alpha}} \,.\, \Phi(w_2, v_2) \,.\, v_2 \subseteq \aleph_{\check{\alpha}}\| \le \|v_1 = v_2\|.$$

Therefore

$$A \le \|\langle x, z\rangle = \langle v_1, \check{w}_1\rangle \,.\, \langle y, z\rangle = \langle v_2, \check{w}_2\rangle \,.\, v_1 = v_2\|$$

where A is the left side of (8.67). So in this case also, (8.67) holds.

We now sum the left side of (8.67) on v_1 and v_2 and on w_1 for $w_1 \in \Sigma$ and on w_2 for $w_2 \in \Sigma$. Then by (8.54) we get

$$\|\langle x, z\rangle \in f \,.\, \langle y, z\rangle \in f\| \le \|x = y\|.$$

Finally, by Lemmas 1, 3, and 5, we conclude

$$\models \aleph(SC(\aleph_{\check{\alpha}})) \leq \aleph(\check{\Sigma}).$$

Then our theorem follows by means of the corollary to Theorem 8.13.

F. A Note on the Proof

We have left one question unresolved, namely whether for a fixed Π and s the formula $\Phi(\langle \Pi, s \rangle, y)$ is extensional as far as y is concerned. Perhaps it is, but no proof presented itself readily. As it turned out that we could evade the question, we simply did so, although this required that we proceed with some care, particularly in the proof of Lemma 5 in the proof of Theorem 8.14.

CHAPTER NINE

The Generalized GCH— The Unbounded Case

A. Preliminary Considerations

We now withdraw the boundedness restriction, and undertake to prove Easton's theorem in the form enunciated in Chapter 8. So we assume throughout this chapter that E satisfies Requirements 1 and 2, and also the further requirement that if $\aleph_\alpha$ is singular, then $E(\alpha)$ is the least γ such that: (i) $\gamma \geq E(\beta)$ for each $\beta < \alpha$, and (ii) $\mathrm{Cf}(\aleph_\gamma) > \aleph_\alpha$. We devote the chapter to defining a model in which

$$\vDash \mathrm{Img}(2^{\aleph_\alpha}) = \mathrm{Img}(\aleph_{E(\alpha)})$$

for each ordinal α. We shall actually show

$$\vDash \aleph(SC(\aleph_{\check{\alpha}})) = \mathrm{Img}(\aleph_{E(\alpha)}) \tag{9.1}$$

for each α, which amounts to the same thing in the presence of Theorems 3.45–3.47. We shall further verify Theorem 3.36.

We should like to stress the importance of Theorem 3.36. Let us look at a specific case, which would be of general interest.

Suppose we define

$$E(\alpha) = \begin{cases} \alpha + 1 & \text{if} \quad \alpha \text{ is limiting} \\ \alpha + 2 & \text{if} \quad \alpha \text{ is nonlimiting.} \end{cases}$$

Then $E(\alpha)$ satisfies the conditions we have set, so that (9.1) holds. That is, in our model we will have

$$\models \aleph(SC(\aleph_{\check{\alpha}})) = \aleph_{\check{\alpha}+1} \tag{9.2}$$

for limiting ordinals and

$$\models \aleph(SC(\aleph_{\check{\alpha}})) = \aleph_{\check{\alpha}+2} \tag{9.3}$$

for nonlimiting ordinals. We should like to infer the validity in the model of the formalization of the following statement:

If α is a limiting ordinal, then

$$2^{\aleph_\alpha} = \aleph_{\alpha+1}$$

while if α is a nonlimiting ordinal, then

$$2^{\aleph_\alpha} = \aleph_{\alpha+2}.$$

If theorem 3.36 holds (and also Theorems 3.45–3.47), then one can make such an inference from (9.2) and (9.3). That is, one can conclude that the formalization in question is consistent with the axioms of set theory and AxC.

If it were not for the indispensability of Theorem 3.36, one might be tempted to try a shortcut along the following lines. First assert that (9.2) and (9.3) can be added consistently to the axioms of set theory; if not, a contradiction would be forthcoming from their addition, but its proof would involve only a finite number of instances of (9.2) and (9.3), whereas the consistency of any finite number of instances of (9.2) and (9.3) could be established by taking θ sufficiently great in Chapter 8 and appealing to Theorem 8.1. There are subtle difficulties in the above argument, one such being the question of what meaning is to be attached to $\check{\alpha}$ in the absence of a specific model. However, there is no point in trying to resolve these difficulties, since one needs also the have Theorem 3.36 as well as (9.2) and (9.3) to infer the validity of the formalization referred to above.

Thus it appears that there is no way to dispense with devising a model in which we would have (9.1) holding for all ordinals. It will not suffice to have it holding for a bounded set of ordinals, as we could easily arrange by taking θ sufficiently large and appealing to Theorem 8.1.

B. Specification of the Boolean Algebra

In essence we get the unbounded version of Easton's theorem by taking the limit of the bounded case as θ increases without limit. The first result of this is that we get a Boolean algebra in which the totality of elements is a class rather than a set. This produces a variety of complications. The first of these is the difficulty of giving a precise definition of the Boolean algebra.

The effect we wish to achieve is as if we had defined X by (2.24) with I taken to be the class of all ordinals, and then had taken basis sets P of the form (8.11) subject to the requirement that $s(P)$ be a set and (8.12) hold for each ordinal α for which $\aleph_\alpha$ is regular. However it is not practicable to do exactly this, since each member of X would be a class, so that the basis sets would have to be sets whose members were proper classes; this is not possible. However, since $s(P)$ is a set, it must be bounded by some β. It turns out that we can get the effect we wish by proceeding rather as though (8.11) were a subset of X with X taken to be

$$\{0, 1\}^\beta. \tag{9.4}$$

Let us temporarily write $X^{(\beta)}$ for (9.4). To consider P, as given by (8.11), as a subset of $X^{(\beta)}$ it suffices for β to be an upper bound of $s(P)$. Thus there are many possible interpretations of P as a subset of $X^{(\beta)}$. We cannot really dispense with any of them, since we might wish to form $P \vee Q$; if the least upper bound of $s(Q)$ is a very large β, we will need to consider P as a subset of $X^{(\beta)}$ for at least that large a β in order to form $P \vee Q$. On the other hand, we wish to think of P as a unique element of the Boolean algebra. We cannot very well consider P as the totality of its interpretations, since this totality is a class. One may handle this problem in various ways. We have chosen basically to identify P with the subset of $X^{(\beta)}$ for the minimum possible β. However, some subtlety is required to have adequate freedom with the Boolean operations, as well as to assure that the specification of P is not ambiguous.

Thus, let $2 < \gamma$. Consider the basis sets

$$B_2{}^0 \wedge B_\gamma{}^0 \tag{9.5}$$

and

$$B_2{}^0 \wedge B_\gamma{}^1. \tag{9.6}$$

They can be considered as subsets of $X^{(\beta)}$ for each $\beta > \gamma$. Basically we consider them as identified with the subsets of $X^{(\beta)}$ for $\beta = \gamma + 1$. In this way (or with any greater β) we can form their sum. And for each $\beta > \gamma$, we will get

$$(B_2{}^0 \wedge B_\gamma{}^0) \vee (B_2{}^0 \wedge B_\gamma{}^1) = B_2{}^0.$$

But then the $B_2{}^0$ which appears as their sum is a subset of the same $X^{(\beta)}$ in which we formed the sum of (9.5) and (9.6). We would prefer to identify $B_2{}^0$ as a subset of $X^{(3)}$. Indeed, we shall do so, but clearly we must exercise some care in framing the definition of the sum.

The same problem can arise about forming a product. Thus we may consider

$$B_2{}^0 \vee B_\gamma{}^0$$

and

$$B_2{}^0 \vee B_\gamma{}^1$$

as subsets of $X^{(\beta)}$ for $\beta > \gamma$. As such, we may form their product. But we have

$$(B_2{}^0 \vee B_\gamma{}^0) \wedge (B_2{}^0 \vee B_2{}^1) = B_2{}^0.$$

Note that in defining

$$B_i{}^n = \{x \mid x(i) = n\},$$

there is a hidden parameter β in that the x's are to be taken as points in $X^{(\beta)}$; clearly we must have $i < \beta$. To proceed without causing confusion, we must make this parameter explicit. To do this, we shall speak of "$B_i{}^n$ at the level β."

More generally, let B be given by (8.11) .That is

$$B = \bigcap \{B_j^{g(j)} \mid j \in J\}.$$

Then we can speak of "B at the level β" if we interpret each $B_j^{g(j)}$ in the product as being at the level β; we must have $J \subseteq \beta$, of course. Explicitly we are interpreting B as a subset of $X^{(\beta)}$. If $J = \Lambda$, then B is all of $X^{(\beta)}$, and can be thought of as the Boolean element 1 at the level β. The Boolean element 0 at any level will be Λ.

We now wish to define the notion of a subset of X at an arbitrary level. In preparation, we note that if B is given by (8.11) it is a basis set if we impose the restriction (8.12). However, if we relax the restriction (8.12), then (8.11) can represent other things. Thus consider

$$B = \bigcap \{B_i^{x(i)} \mid i < \beta\},$$

where we take each $B_i^{x(i)}$ at the level β. This is the unit class whose sole member is the point x of $X^{(\beta)}$.

Thus we see that if P is a subset of $X^{(\beta)}$ we can write

$$P = \bigcup \{B_k \mid k \in K\}, \tag{9.7}$$

where K is a set and each B_k is given by (8.11) and is taken at the level β; this entails that each corresponding J have the property $J \subseteq \beta$. If for each k we further assume

$$\aleph(J \cap \aleph_{E(\alpha)}) < \aleph_\alpha$$

for each α for which $\aleph_\alpha$ is regular, then each B_k is a basis set, and then P as given by (9.7) is open. By Definition 2.2, P is open only if it can be so given. However, an open set P can be given by (9.7) without it necessarily being the case that each B_k is a basis set; indeed, as we noted earlier, one could take each B_k to be a unit set.

Definition 9.1. Suppose that P is a subset of $X^{(\beta)}$. We say that P is at the level β. Write P in the form (9.7), with each B_k at the level β. Suppose it is possible to take each B_k at the level γ. That is, each B_k still has the form (8.11), with the same g and J as before; however now B_k is a subset of

$$\{0, 1\}^\gamma, \tag{9.8}$$

so that necessarily $J \subseteq \gamma$. If we still take P as given by (9.7) but with each B_k at the level γ, then P is a subset of (9.8); we speak of P being at the level γ. Alternatively, we may say that we take P at the level γ.

Theorem 9.1. Suppose

$$Q = \bigcup \{B'_{k'} \mid k' \in K'\} \tag{9.9}$$

where K' is a set and each $B'_{k'}$ is given by (8.11) and is taken at the level β; thus each $J \subseteq \beta$. Suppose that it is possible to take each $B'_{k'}$ at the level γ, so that by Definition 9.1 we can take Q at the level γ. As before let P be given by (9.7). If $P \subseteq Q$ at level β, then $P \subseteq Q$ at level γ.

PROOF. For each B_k and $B'_{k'}$ we must have the corresponding $J \subseteq \beta$. Indeed, since both the B_k and $B'_{k'}$ can be taken at the level γ, we must have $J \subseteq \gamma$ for each J. As $P \subseteq Q$ at level β, we must have $B_k \subseteq Q$ for each k. Hence

$$B_k = \bigcup \{B_k B'_{k'} \mid k' \in K'\},$$

both at level β and γ. (We leave out those products $B_k B'_{k'}$ which are 0. Thus each $B_k B'_{k'}$ has the form (8.11) with $J \subseteq \beta$ and $J \subseteq \gamma$.) If we substitute such a sum for each B_k in (9.7), we write

$$P = \bigcup \{B''_k \mid k \in K''\}$$

where each B''_k is included in some $B'_{k'}$. When we go to level γ, P will have the same form, and hence $P \subseteq Q$ at level γ.

Corollary. Start with P at level β. If it can be taken at level γ, it can be done so uniquely.

PROOF. The point is that while one can write P in the form (9.7), one can usually do so in many different ways at level β. We wish to show that each such leads to the same subset of X as given by (9.8) when one goes to level γ. To be specific, suppose the Q of (9.9) is the same set as P at level β. Will they be the same at level γ? At level β, we have $P \subseteq Q$ and $Q \subseteq P$. So by our theorem we have the same at level γ. So $P = Q$ at level γ.

We call attention to the fact that it may be the case that some of the B_k in (9.7) cannot be taken at a lower level than β, but that this does not necessarily mean that P cannot be taken at a lower level than β. Note that each of (9.5) and (9.6) cannot be taken at a lower level than $\gamma + 1$, but their sum can be taken at level 3. This is why we have to be able to talk of a set at various levels in order to treat sums adequately.

Definition 9.2. A set is at minimal level if it cannot be taken at any lower level.

Clearly each set has a minimal level at which it can be taken; one makes a special provision for 1 and 0, perhaps saying that the ordinals 1 and 0 are 1 and 0 at the level 0. Given a set, it is unique at its minimal level by the corollary to Theorem 9.1. A set can clearly be taken at any level above its minimal level, and uniquely so.

Theorem 9.2. If a set is open at one level, it will be open at all levels (that is, all levels at or higher than its minimal level). Given a set S of sets at level β, the join can be taken at any level γ at which all members of S can be taken; at that level it will be the join of the members of S. Similarly for the intersection. The complement of P can be taken at any level at which P can; at that level it will be the complement of P. Similarly for the closure of P.

PROOF. Suppose P is open at level β. Then it can be taken in the form (9.7) with each B_k a basis set. If we use the same B_k at level γ, with $\gamma > \beta$, we will see that P is open at level γ by Definition 2.2. However, suppose P is open at level β and can be taken at level γ with $\gamma < \beta$. Then P must have the form (9.7), where for each B_k the corresponding $J \subseteq \gamma$. Take a point x in P at level γ. Then x must be in one of the B_k at level γ. So an "extension" of x at level β must be in the same B_k at level β. As P is open at level β, there must be a basis set B which contains the "extension" of x and which is included in P. For this basis set B we have

$$B = \bigcap \{B_j^{g(j)} \mid j \in J\}.$$

Take

$$B^L = \bigcap \{B_j^{g(j)} \mid j \in J \cap \gamma\}.$$

Because each B_k had its $J \subseteq \gamma$, we see that B^L is included in P at level β. But we can take B^L at level γ, and it will be included in P at level γ by Theorem 9.1. Also B^L is a basis set, and will contain the point x. Repeating this for each x in P at level γ, we conclude that P at level γ is open.

Suppose each $P \in S$ can be taken at level γ. Then each P must be expressible in the form (9.7), where each B_k has $J \subseteq \gamma$. At level β, the join of the members of S will consist of the join of all the B_k for all the $P \in S$. The same is true at level γ. For intersections, we write the intersection as the complement of a join of complements, and apply the next part of the theorem, to which we now turn.

We first need a very special case of the intersection result, namely that if P and Q have a zero intersection at level β, they will do the same at any level γ with $\gamma > \beta$. So let P and Q be given by (9.7) and (9.9) at level β. Then they can be taken as given similarly at level γ for $\gamma > \beta$. Suppose that at level γ they have a point x in common. But as P still has the form (9.7) at level γ, the point x^L got by restricting the argument of x to β must be in one of the B_k of P. Similarly x^L must be in one of the $B'_{k'}$ of Q. So x^L is common to P and Q at level β.

Given P at level β, take it at its minimal level μ. At this level, take the complement, Co(P). Then P and Co(P) have zero intersection at level μ, and so must have zero intersection at each higher level. Also P and Co(P) have sum 1 at level μ, and hence this must be so at each higher level. So at each level Co(P) is the complement of P.

To handle the closure, we start out similarly. Given P at level β, take it at its minimal level μ. At this level, form its closure Cl(P). We desire to show that this is the closure at each level γ, with $\gamma > \mu$. Suppose $x \in$ Cl(P) at level γ, and let B be a basis set at level γ which contains x. That is

$$B = \bigcap \{B_j^{g(j)} \mid j \in J\}$$

where J is a set such that $J \subseteq \gamma$ and

$$\aleph(J \cap \aleph_{E(\alpha)}) < \aleph_\alpha$$

for each α for which $\aleph_\alpha$ is regular. Let x^L be the point obtained by restricting the argument of x to μ. Similarly, put

$$B^L = \bigcap \{B_j^{g(j)} \mid j \in J \cap \mu\}.$$

Then x^L is in $\mathrm{Cl}(P)$ at level μ. Also B^L is a basis set at both level μ and level γ. So, by Definition 2.3, B^L and P at level μ must have a nonzero intersection. Hence they must have a nonzero intersection at level γ. Hence B and P must have a nonzero intersection. So $\mathrm{Cl}(P)$ at level γ is a subset of the closure of P at level γ. Now take x in the closure of P at level γ. Choose a basis set B at level μ which contains x^L. Then B at level γ contains x. So by Definition 2.3, B and P at level γ have a nonzero intersection. So B and P at level μ have a nonzero intersection. As this is true of each B at level μ which contains x^L, we see by Definition 2.3 that x^L is in $\mathrm{Cl}(P)$ at level μ. Then x is in $\mathrm{Cl}(P)$ at level γ. So $\mathrm{Cl}(P)$ at level γ is the closure of P at level γ.

Corollary. If P is a regular open set at level β, it is a regular open set at all levels at which it can be taken . If a set S of regular open sets has a regular open set as a supremum at level β, then this supremum can be taken at any level γ at which all members of S can be taken; at that level it will be the supremum of the members of S. Similarly for the infimum.

PROOF. By Definitions 2.6–2.8, we see that if P is regular at one level, it will be so at all other levels. By the proof of Theorem 2.26 we see that the supremum is Cc^2 of the join. Thus the supremum is invariant under change of level.

Indeed, all the features of sets which are of interest to us for forming a Boolean algebra are invariant under change of level. That is, it does not matter at which level we are .

Definition 9.3. The "Boolean algebra" which we are to use shall have as elements each regular open set taken at its minimal level. 0 and 1 are to be Λ and X respectively, at minimal levels. P' is to be just P' at the same level as P. If S is a set of elements, then we define the sum of the members of S as follows. Take an upper bound β of the levels of the members of S. Take all the members of S at the level β. Form their sum, and then take it at its minimal level. We use a similar procedure for products.

This is not exactly a Boolean algebra, because it was stipulated that the totality of elements of a Boolean algebra should form a set. However, it has enough of the properties of a Boolean algebra to be adequate for our purposes.

We take $\mathcal{G}$ to consist of all finite products of automorphisms induced by interchanging B_i^0 with B_i^1. We take Γ to consist of all subgroups of $\mathcal{G}$.

Theorem 9.3. With $\mathcal{G}$, Γ, and the "Boolean algebra" as given, we verify that sums and products are uniquely determined. Also, each of (2.9) through (2.23) holds. Also B_i^0 and B_i^1 are elements of the "Boolean algebra" for i any ordinal. Also Theorems 2.19–2.25 hold for our "Boolean algebra." Furthermore, our "Boolean algebra" is complete in the sense that every set of elements has a supremum in the "Boolean algebra"; in fact, it is just the sum of the elements of the set as given in Definition 9.3. Similarly for the infimum. Similarly, Theorem 2.27 holds if I is a set. Also, Theorems 2.28 and 2.29 hold. Certainly the countable chain condition fails. However, Theorems 8.3–8.7 hold with the following modifications: in Theorem 8.3 replace "either $E(\theta) \leq \alpha$ or $\alpha < E(\theta)$" by "α is an ordinal"; in Theorem 8.5 replace "either $E(\theta) \leq \beta$ or $\beta < E(\theta)$" by "β is an ordinal."

Note that we do not require K or K_τ to be sets in any of Theorems 8.3–8.7. This is important.

C. Definition of the Universe

We first try to duplicate as much as possible of Section B of Chapter 3. We undertake to define subuniverses, V_α, for each ordinal α, so that (3.13)–(3.41) are valid. The only difficulty arises when we go from V_α to $V_{\alpha+1}$. We must refrain from generating *each* function a from V_α to A. As A is now a class, this procedure would result in a class of new functions. Then $V_{\alpha+1}$ would be a class, and we could not generate functions a with $D(a) = V_{\alpha+1}$ with which to form $V_{\alpha+2}$. What we do instead is to take each function a from V_α to A for which its values are all at a level not greater than $\aleph_{\alpha+1}$. Thus we shall have the condition that if $a \in V_\alpha$ and $x \in D(a)$, then $a(x)$ is at a level not greater than $\aleph_\alpha$. We were careful to choose $\mathscr{G}$ so that (3.30) would hold with this restricted version of V_α. As Γ consists of all subgroups of $\mathscr{G}$, (3.24) will be satisfied trivially.

Theorem 9.4. If a, $b \in V_\alpha$, then $\|a \in b\|$ and $\|a = b\|$ are both at level not greater than $\aleph_\alpha$. Furthermore the results (3.13) through (3.41) are all valid.

The proof presents no difficulty.

There is an important relationship between the universe we have just described and the universes used in the previous chapter. As in the proof of Theorem 8.1, define $E^*(\alpha) = E(\alpha)$ for $\alpha < \theta$, $E^*(\alpha) = E(\theta) + 1$ for $\theta \leq \alpha \leq E(\theta)$, and $E^*(\alpha) = \alpha + 1$ for $E(\theta) < \alpha$. Define X by (2.24) with $I = \aleph_{E^*(\theta)}$. Take basis sets of the form (8.11) for each J such that

$$\aleph(J \cap \aleph_{E^*(\alpha)}) < \aleph_\alpha$$

for each $\alpha < E^*(\theta)$ for which $\aleph_\alpha$ is regular. Let $V_\alpha^{\ \theta}$ denote the corresponding subuniverses.

Theorem 9.5. If $\alpha < \theta$ then there is a many-to-one correspondence from V_α to a subset V_α^* of $V_\alpha^{\ \theta}$ such that:

(i) for $\beta < \alpha$ the elements corresponding to elements of V_β form a subset V_β^* of $V_\beta^{\ \theta}$;

(ii) if $\beta + 1 \leq \alpha$ and $a \in V_{\beta+1}$ and $\sim a \in V_\beta$, then the element a^* corresponding to a is obtained by taking V_β^* as its Scott domain and $a^{(S)}$ as its Scott core, with $a^{(S)}$ defined as follows: if $b^* \in D(a^{(S)})$ then $b^* \in V_\beta^*$, so that it is the correspondent of a $b \in V_\beta$, and we take $a^{(S)}(b^*)$ to be $a(b)$ at the level $\aleph_{E^*(\theta)}$;

(iii) if a, $b \in V_\alpha$ and a^* and b^* are the corresponding elements of V_α^*, then $\|a^* \in b^*\|$, $\|a^* = b^*\|$, and $\|a^* \subseteq b^*\|$ are $\|a \in b\|$, $\|a = b\|$, and $\|a\ b\|, \subseteq$ respectively, at the level $\aleph_{E^*(\theta)}$;

(iv) if s is an intuitive set and $\check{s} \in V_\alpha$, then $\check{s}$ is the correspondent of $\check{s}$.

PROOF BY INDUCTION ON β FOR $\beta \leq \alpha$. Precisely what is meant in (ii) by saying that $V_\beta{}^*$ is a Scott domain of a^* and $a^{(S)}$ (as defined) is a Scott core of a^* is that the equivalent of (3.60) shall hold. That is,

$$a^*(x) = \sum_{y \in V_\beta^*} a^{(S)}(y) \wedge \|x = y\|$$

for each $x \in V_\beta{}^\theta$. That is

$$a^*(x) = \sum_{b \in V_\beta} a(b) \wedge \|x = b^*\|,$$

where $a(b)$ is taken at the level $\aleph_{E^*(\theta)}$.

As there may not be a unique b of which b^* is the correspondent, it is not immediately obvious that this is a well posed definition of a^*. However, suppose that b^* is a correspondent of both b and b'. As $\|b^* = b^*\| = 1$, it would follow by (iii) that $\|b = b'\| = 1$. Hence $a(b) = a(b')$, so that the value of $a^*(x)$ is indeed uniquely defined.

We proceed to define a^* by (ii), and so set up a many-to-one correspondence from V_α to a subset $V_\alpha{}^*$ of $V_\alpha{}^\theta$. It is clear that under this procedure (i) will hold.

We proceed with (iii) as follows. Let $b \in V_{\beta+1}$ and $\sim b \in V_\beta$, with $\beta + 1 \leq \alpha$. Then $D(b) = V_\beta$. Hence $V_\beta{}^*$ is a Scott domain of b^*. So by Theorem 3.16

$$\|a^* \in b^*\| = \sum_{y^* \in V_\beta^*} b^{(S)}(y^*) \wedge \|a^* = y^*\|.$$

However, for $y^* \in V_\beta{}^*$, y^* is the correspondent of a $y \in D(b)$, and by definition

$$b^{(S)}(y^*) =_\theta b(y)$$

($P =_\theta Q$ means that Q at level $\aleph_{E^*(\theta)}$ is P). If also $a \in V_\beta$, then

$$\|a^* = y^*\| =_\theta \|a = y\|$$

by the hypothesis of the induction. Therefore

$$\|a^* \in b^*\| =_\theta \sum_{y \in D(b)} b(y) \wedge \|a = y\|.$$

By (3.32) and (3.28), this gives

$$\|a^* \in b^*\| =_\theta \|a \in b\|.$$

For the moment, this has been established for $b \in V_{\beta+1}$ and $a \in V_\beta$.

Analogously, we have by (3.61) in Theorem 3.15

$$\|b^* \subseteq a^*\| = \prod_{y^* \in V_\beta{}^*} b^{(S)}(y^*) \Rightarrow \|y^* \in a^*\|.$$

This reduces to

$$\|b^* \subseteq a^*\| =_\theta \prod_{y \in D(b)} b(y) \Rightarrow \|y \in a\|.$$

So by (3.64)

$$\|b^* \subseteq a^*\| =_\theta \|b \subseteq a\|.$$

A similar proof gives

$$\|a^* \subseteq b^*\| =_\theta \|a \subseteq b\|.$$

By Theorem 3.4 (which will be available shortly)

$$\|a = b\| = \|a \subseteq b\| \wedge \|b \subseteq a\|.$$

As a similar result is available in $V_\alpha{}^\theta$, we get

$$\|a^* = b^*\| =_\theta \|a = b\|.$$

With this, we can now complete the proof that

$$\|a^* \in b^*\| =_\theta \|a \in b\|.$$

We turn to (iv). By (ii) of our theorem and Theorem 3.16

$$\check{s}^*(x) = \sum_{y \in V_\beta} \check{s}(y) \wedge \|x = y^*\|$$

for $x \in V_\beta{}^\theta$. However, by (3.69) we obtain

$$\check{s}^*(x) = \sum_{y \in V_\beta} \left(\sum_{t \in s} \|y = \check{t}\|\right) \wedge \|x = y^*\|.$$

So by the hypothesis of the induction

$$\check{s}^*(x) = \sum_{t \in s} \sum_{y \in V_\beta} \|y^* = \check{t}\| \wedge \|x = y^*\|.$$

Now

$$\|y^* = \check{t}\| \wedge \|x = y^*\| \leq \|x = \check{t}\|$$

so that

$$\sum_{y \in V_\beta} \|y^* = \check{t}\| \wedge \|x = y^*\| \leq \|x = \check{t}\|.$$

However, one of the y's in the summation is $\check{t}$. Therefore

$$\sum_{y \in V_\beta} \|y^* = \check{t}\| \wedge \|x = y^*\| \geq \|x = \check{t}\|.$$

Thus

$$\sum_{y \in V_\beta} \|y^* = \check{t}\| \wedge \|x = y^*\| = \|x = \check{t}\|.$$

So

$$\check{s}^*(x) = \sum_{t \in s} \|x = \check{t}\|.$$

So by (3.69)

$$\check{s}^*(x) = \check{s}(x).$$

D. Definition of the Boolean Value of a Statement

Having defined the universe and the Boolean values $\|a \in b\|$ and $\|a = b\|$ for a, $b \in V$, we turn to the definition of Boolean values generally. We proceed to make the definitions (3.1)–(3.3), as before, but immediately face a problem with (3.3). The right side of (3.3) is an infimum over a class, and we have no assurance that there will be such an infimum.

Recall that we have proved the existence of an infimum for a set of elements, but not for a class of elements.

The way out of this difficulty is provided by a bit of black magic.

Theorem 9.6. Let $F(x_1, \ldots, x_n, y)$ be a formula such that for each $a_1, \ldots, a_n, b \in V$ there is assigned a value

$$\|F(a_1, \ldots, a_n, b\|.$$

Suppose further that for $G \in \mathscr{G}$

$$G(\|F(a_1, \ldots, a_n, b)\|) = \|F(G(a_1), \ldots, G(a_n), G(b))\|. \quad (9.10)$$

Then for each $a_1, \ldots, a_n \in V$ there is a γ such that

$$\sum_{b \in V_\gamma} \|F(a_1, \ldots, a_n, b)\| \tag{9.11}$$

is a supremum for the class of values

$$\|F(a_1, \ldots, a_n, b)\|$$

for this choice of $a_1, \ldots, a_n$ and any $b \in V$.

PROOF. Take a specific choice $a_1, \ldots, a_n \in V_\beta$. Take α so that $\aleph_\alpha$ is regular and there is a function h so that $h(\tau)$ enumerates (perhaps with repetitions) all ordered n-tuples $\langle x_1, \ldots, x_n\rangle$ with $x_1, \ldots, x_n \in V_\beta$ as τ runs over all ordinals less than $\aleph_\alpha$. In Theorem 8.4 take $Q = 1$. For $\tau < \aleph_\alpha$ take $\langle x_1, \ldots, x_n\rangle = h(\tau)$, take K_τ as the class of all ordinals, and put

$$Q_{\tau,\sigma} = \sum_{b \in V_\sigma} \|F(x_1, \ldots, x_n, b)\|. \tag{9.12}$$

Take the R_τ of Theorem 8.4 and put

$$R = \prod_{\tau < \aleph_\alpha} R_\tau. \tag{9.13}$$

For each τ, let $B_{\eta,\tau}$ be an enumeration of Π_τ for $\eta < \aleph_\alpha$. For each $\eta < \aleph_\alpha$ and $\tau < \aleph_\alpha$ define $\sigma_{\eta,\tau}$ as the least σ such that

$$B_{\eta,\tau} \wedge R \leq Q_{\tau,\sigma} \tag{9.14}$$

if there is one; zero otherwise. Take γ the least upper bound of the $\sigma_{\eta,\tau}$.

Lemma. For each $\delta \geq \gamma$ and each $\tau < \aleph_\alpha$

$$R \leq Q_{\tau,\delta} \Rightarrow Q_{\tau,\gamma}. \tag{9.15}$$

PROOF. Suppose not. Then there is a $\delta \geq \gamma$ and a $\tau < \aleph_\alpha$ such that

$$R \wedge Q_{\tau,\delta} \wedge (Q_{\tau\gamma})' \neq 0.$$

Then there is a basis set P such that

$$P \leq R \tag{9.16}$$

$$P \leq Q_{\tau,\delta} \tag{9.17}$$

$$Q_{\tau,\gamma} \leq P'. \tag{9.18}$$

By (vi) of Theorem 8.4 there is a $B \in \Pi_\tau$ such that

$$P \wedge B \neq 0. \tag{9.19}$$

Also, by (v) of Theorem 8.4, either there is a σ such that

$$B \wedge R_\tau \leq Q_{\tau,\sigma} \tag{9.20}$$

or else

$$B \wedge R_\tau \wedge Q_{\tau,\sigma} = 0 \tag{9.21}$$

for all σ. However, (9.21) must fail for $\sigma = \delta$, since by (9.16) and (9.17)

$$P \wedge B \leq B \wedge R \wedge Q_{\tau,\delta}$$

so that by (9.13),

$$P \wedge B \leq B \wedge R_\tau \wedge Q_{\tau,\delta},$$

which would contradict (9.19) and (9.21) for $\sigma = \delta$.

Hence (9.20) holds for some σ. Then by (9.13),

$$B \wedge R \leq Q_{\tau,\sigma}. \tag{9.22}$$

Then by (9.14), we can take the σ to be $\sigma_{\eta,\tau}$, because B is a $B_{\eta,\tau} \in \Pi_\tau$. But $\sigma_{\eta,\tau} \leq \gamma$, so that (9.22) gives

$$B \wedge R \leq Q_{\tau,\gamma}$$

by (9.12). From this by (9.16), we obtain

$$P \wedge B \leq P \wedge Q_{\tau,\gamma}.$$

Then by (9.18)

$$P \wedge B \leq P \wedge P' = 0.$$

This contradicts (9.19).

The lemma tells us by (9.12) that for $x_1, \ldots, x_n \in V_\beta$ and $\delta \geq \gamma$

$$R \leq \sum_{b \in V_\delta} \|F(x_1, \ldots, x_n, b)\| \Rightarrow \sum_{b \in V_\gamma} \|F(x_1, \ldots, x_n, b)\|.$$

Multiplying over all $x_1, \ldots, x_n \in V_\beta$ gives

$$R \leq \prod_{x_1, \ldots, x_n \in V_\beta} \left\{ \sum_{b \in V_\delta} \|F(x_1, \ldots, x_n, b)\| \Rightarrow \sum_{b \in V_\gamma} \|F(x_1, \ldots, x_n, b)\| \right\}.$$

By (3.30), an automorphism G from $\mathcal{G}$ merely permutes the elements of V_β, and similarly for V_γ and V_δ. Hence by (9.10) the right side above is unchanged under transformation by G. So by Theorem 2.29, it must be 0 or 1. But it is greater than or equal to R. So it must be 1. So by Theorem 2.25 each factor is 1. Recall that we chose β so that $a_1, \ldots, a_n \in V_\beta$. Thus

$$\sum_{b \in V_\delta} \|F(a_1, \ldots, a_n, b)\| \Rightarrow \sum_{b \in V_\gamma} \|F(a_1, \ldots, a_n, b)\|$$

is one of the factors, and so must have the value 1. That is, for each $\delta \geq \gamma$

$$\sum_{b \in V_\delta} \|F(a_1, \ldots, a_n, b)\| \leq \sum_{b \in V_\gamma} \|F(a_1, \ldots, a_n, b)\|.$$

Consider any $b \in V$. There must be a $\delta \geq \gamma$ such that $b \in V_\delta$. So

$$\|F(a_1, \ldots, a_n, b)\| \leq \sum_{b \in V_\gamma} \|F(a_1, \ldots, a_n, b)\|. \tag{9.23}$$

So (9.11) is an upper bound of

$$\|F(a_1, \ldots, a_n, b)\|$$

for any $b \in V$. To show that it is a supremum, suppose that

$$\|F(a_1, \ldots, a_n, b)\| \leq Q$$

for each $b \in V$. Summing over all $b \in V_\gamma$ gives

$$\sum_{b \in V_\gamma} \|F(a_1, \ldots, a_n, b)\| \leq Q.$$

So indeed (9.11) is the supremum.

Theorem 9.7. If S is a statement, then S has a Boolean value $\|S\|$ in the "Boolean algebra." Furthermore $\|S\|$ can be determined by (3.1)–(3.3). Indeed, for each application of (3.3), there will be a γ such that

$$\|(x)F(x)\| = \prod_{a \in V_\gamma} \|F(a)\|. \tag{9.24}$$

Proof by Induction on the Number of Symbols in S. The only step which presents any difficulty is when S is $F(x)$. Then, as $F(x)$ may contain constants $a_1, \ldots, a_n$, we can write $G(a_1, \ldots, a_n, x)$ for $\sim F(x)$. Then by Theorem 9.6, there is a γ such that

$$Q = \sum_{b \in V_\gamma} \|G(a_1, \ldots, a_n, b)\|$$

is a supremum for $\|\sim F(a)\|$ for $a \in V$. Then Q' is an infimum for $\|F(a)\|$, and can be used as the right side of (3.3). This verifies (9.24). The hypothesis (9.10) of Theorem 9.6 is handled just as in the proof of Theorem 3.7.

Thus we are able to handle quantification for statements. We can also handle "bounded" quantification for more general formulas provided the formulas are extensional (see the next theorem).

Theorem 9.8. Suppose that Φ is extensional. Let $a \in V$. Then

$$\prod_{x \in D(a)} a(x) \Rightarrow \Phi(x) \tag{9.25}$$

is an infimum for

$$\|b \in a\| \Rightarrow \Phi(b) \tag{9.26}$$

for $b \in V$. Also

$$\sum_{x \in D(a)} a(x) \wedge \Phi(x) \tag{9.27}$$

is a supremum for

$$\|b \in a\| \wedge \Phi(b) \tag{9.28}$$

for $b \in V$.

PROOF. Let $x \in D(a)$. Then by (3.32)

$$\|x \in a\| = a(x).$$

As Φ is extensional, we get

$$\|x \in a \,.\, b = x\| \wedge \Phi(b) \leq a(x) \wedge \Phi(x).$$

Summing both sides over $x \in D(a)$ and using (3.28) gives

$$\|b \in a\| \wedge \Phi(b) \leq \sum_{x \in D(a)} a(x) \wedge \Phi(x).$$

So (9.27) is an upper bound for (9.28). That it is indeed a supremum follows easily. To treat (9.25) and (9.26), we replace $\Phi(x)$ and $\Phi(b)$ by $(\Phi(x))'$ and $(\Phi(b))'$, respectively, and take the primes of (9.27) and (9.28).

These results are comparable to (3.64) and (3.65). Indeed, they reduce to (3.64) and (3.65) when $\Phi(x)$ is $\|F(x)\|$.

E. Proof of the Axioms of Set Theory, Except the Power Set Axiom

We are now able to proceed much as in Chapter 3. Theorems 3.1–3.8 present no difficulty. Theorems 3.9 and 3.10 fail as stated if the values of $\Phi(x)$ or $\|F(x, a_1, \ldots, a_n)\|$ are at too high a level, since then (3.44) and (3.47) are not permitted as definitions of $a(x)$. If the values of $\Phi(x)$ or $\|F(x, a_1, \ldots, a_n)\|$ are not at too high a level, the proofs of Theorems 3.9 and 3.10 go through as stated. However, even when $\Phi(x)$ or $\|F(x, a_1, \ldots, a_n)\|$ are at too high a level, the following stratagem may give an acceptable substitute.

We shall take V_α as a Scott domain of a. With x restricted to V_α, there will be an upper bound for the levels taken by $\Phi(x)$. Suppose $\aleph_\mu$ is an upper bound. Then $\mu > \alpha$, else the levels of $\Phi(x)$ would not have been too high for us to proceed with the proof of Theorem 3.9 as written. We now take $D(a) = V_\mu$. We take

$$a^{(S)}(x) = \Phi(x)$$

for $x \in V_\alpha$ as a Scott core of a. That is, by (3.60) we set

$$a(x) = \sum_{y \in V_\alpha} \Phi(y) \wedge \|x = y\|$$

for $x \in V_\mu$. With this definition, the values of $a(x)$ are all at a level not greater than $\aleph_\mu$. Also, a is extensional; this is true whether Φ is extensional or not. So (as we are assuming that Γ is the filter of all subgroups of $\mathcal{G}$) $a \in V_{\mu+1}$.

By Theorem 3.16, we conclude that

$$\|x \in a\| = \sum_{y \in V_\alpha} \Phi(y) \wedge \|x = y\|$$

for each $x \in V$. This is a useful result.

Although we do not need the hypothesis that Φ is extensional to conclude that a is extensional or to conclude that $a \in V_{\mu+1}$, we do need the hypothesis to conclude (3.45). With the hypothesis that Φ is extensional, we have

$$\Phi(y) \wedge \|b = y\| \leq \Phi(b).$$

Summing over $y \in V_\alpha$, we get

$$\sum_{y \in V_\alpha} \Phi(y) \wedge \|b = y\| \leq \Phi(b).$$

But this gives

$$\|b \in a\| \leq \Phi(b),$$

which is (3.45).

A similar stratagem yields a substitute for Theorem 3.10.

The nearest substitutes we have for Theorem 3.11 are Theorems 9.6–9.8. We have to do the best we can with these. Thus, we cannot prove Theorem 3.12 except in special cases, but we can use Theorem 9.7 in place of Theorem 3.11 in order to carry out a proof of Theorem 3.13. The details are as follows.

Let us write briefly $F(x)$ for $F(x, a_1, \ldots, a_n)$. In Theorem 9.7, we take $\sim F(x)$ rather than $F(x)$ in (9.24). This gives

$$\|(Ex)F(x)\| = \sum_{a \in V_\gamma} \|F(a)\|,$$

which will play the role of (3.52). By Theorem 9.6 there is a δ for each $z \in V_\gamma$ such that

$$\|(Ex) . F(x) . z \in x\| = \sum_{a \in V_\delta} \|F(a) . z \in a\|.$$

If we take the least upper bound of these δ's for each $z \in V_\gamma$, we get a δ for which the relation above holds for each $z \in V_\gamma$. Then there is a μ such that $\mu > \gamma$ and $\mu > \delta$ and the values on the right are at a level $\leq \aleph_\mu$ for each $z \in V_\gamma$. So we define $c \in V_{\mu+1}$ by taking

$$SD(c) = V_\gamma$$

$$c^{(S)}(z) = \|(Ex) . F(x) . z \in x\|$$

for $z \in V_\gamma$. We obtain

$$\models F(c) \supset (Ex)F(x),$$

the equivalent of (3.55).

Analogous to (3.56), take $a \in V_\gamma$. Therefore

$$\|F(a) \,.\, z \in a\| \leq c^{(S)}(z)$$

for $z \in D(a)$, since if $z \in D(a)$, then $z \in SD(c)$. So by Theorem 3.16,

$$\|F(a) \,.\, z \in a\| \leq \|z \in c\|.$$

Then we obtain

$$\|F(a)\| \leq \prod_{z \in D(a)} \|z \in a \supset z \in c\|,$$

analogous to (3.57).

We write

$$R = (x, y) \,.\, F(x)F(y) \supset x = y.$$

So for $z \in V_\gamma$,

$$\|F(a) \,.\, R\| \wedge \|F(x) \,.\, z \in x\| \leq \|z \in a\|.$$

Summing the left over x gives

$$\|F(a) \,.\, R\| \wedge c^{(S)}(z) \leq \|z \in a\|.$$

Hence

$$\|F(a) \,.\, R\| \leq c^{(S)}(z) \Rightarrow \|z \in a\|.$$

Then

$$\|F(a) \,.\, R\| \leq \prod_{x \in SD(c)} c^{(S)}(x) \Rightarrow \|x \in a\|.$$

So by Theorem 3.15

$$\|F(a) \,.\, R\| \leq \|(x) \,.\, x \in c \supset x \in a\|.$$

Then

$$\|F(a) \,.\, R\| \leq \prod_{z \in D(c)} \|z \in c \supset z \in a\|.$$

Hence

$$\|F(a) \,.\, R\| \leq \|a = c\|,$$

so that

$$\|F(a) \,.\, R\| \leq \|F(c)\|.$$

But this holds for each $a \in V_\gamma$. So we can sum on the left over V_γ and obtain

$$\|(Ex)F(x)\| \wedge \|R\| \leq \|F(c)\|.$$

So

$$\|R\| \leq \|(Ex)F(x) \, . \supset . \, F(c)\|.$$

So finally

$$\vDash R \, . \supset . \, F(c) \equiv (Ex)F(x).$$

As this leans heavily on Theorems 3.15 and 3.16, we cannot conclude Theorem 3.13 until after we have verified Theorems 3.15 and 3.16. However, there is no difficulty with the proofs of Theorems 3.14–3.16. Indeed, Theorem 3.15 holds under the weaker assumption that $F(x)$ is an extensional formula, since we can assign values for the various quantifiers by Theorem 9.8. In Theorem 3.17, we must not only choose α large enough so that $D(b) \subseteq V_\alpha$, but we must have the level of $b(y)$ less than or equal to $\aleph_{\alpha+1}$ for each $y \in D(b)$. Then the proof goes through as written.

We have little trouble with the proofs of Theorems 3.18–3.32. In the proof of Theorem 3.28, we have to use Theorem 9.8 to assure that the value for $a(x)$ is not at too high a level. In the proof of Theorem 3.31 we take $SD(a) = V_\alpha$ and put

$$a^{(S)}(y) = \|(Ex) \, . \, x \in b \, . \, F(x, y)\|$$

for each $y \in V_\alpha$. Then

$$\vDash (y) : y \in a \, . \supset . \, (Ex) \, . \, x \in b \, . \, F(x, y)$$

follows by Theorem 3.15.

As $y_x \in SD(a)$, we obtain

$$R \wedge \|x \in b\| \leq \|x \in b \, . \, F(x, y_x)\| \leq a^{(S)}(y_x).$$

Then we obtain

$$R \wedge \|x \in b\| \leq \|x \in b \, . \, F(x, y_x)\| \leq \|y_x \in a\|$$

by Theorem 3.16. The rest of the proof proceeds as written.

We shall have to postpone the proof of Theorem 3.33 for some time. Fortunately, as we noted earlier, much can be done without the axiom of the power set.

We have no trouble with the proofs of Theorems 3.34–3.36. In the corollary to Theorem 3.36, a momentary difficulty appears because we ask for the supremum of a class. However, we note that $\|a = \check{\eta}\| = 0$ for all sufficiently large η, so that we have no real problem. We have no trouble with the proofs of Theorems 3.37–3.43.

We postpone further cardinality results for the moment, and turn to the axiom of choice. We assume that $V = L$ holds in our "intuitive" logic.

The definition given for Ord(x, y) presents no problem because $\|x = \check{\eta}\| = 0$ for all sufficiently large η by Theorem 3.23. Then we have no trouble with the proofs of Theorems 3.48–3.51.

One may raise the question as to how one is to interpret the quantifiers appearing in Theorems 3.48–3.51, since we cannot appeal to Theorem 9.7 or 9.8. However, the theorems themselves provide a trivial interpretation. That is, Theorem 3.50 says that the Boolean value 1 is the infimum for the set of values

$$\|(Ex) . \mathrm{Od}(x) . \mathrm{Ord}(x, y)\|$$

for $y \in V$. That is, each of these values is 1, which says that for each $y \in V$ the Boolean value 1 is the supremum for the set of values

$$\|\mathrm{Od}(x) . \mathrm{Ord}(x, y)\|$$

for $x \in V$. Similarly for the other theorems.

We have to work with a modified definition of Mord(x, y), namely

$$\mathrm{Ord}(x, y) : (w) . w < x \supset {\sim}\mathrm{Ord}(w, y).$$

As $w < x$ is the same as $w \in x$, we can use Theorem 9.8 to give a value to this formula. Then by Theorem 3.51

$$\models \mathrm{Mord}(x, y) . \mathrm{Ord}(z, y) . \supset . \mathrm{Od}(x) . \mathrm{Od}(z).$$

So by 1.11 on p. 84 of Bernays and Fraenkel [1]

$$\models \mathrm{Mord}(x, y) . \mathrm{Ord}(z, y) : \supset : z < x . \vee . x \leq z.$$

But

$$\models \mathrm{Mord}(x, y) . z < x . \supset . {\sim}\mathrm{Ord}(z, y)$$

by our definition of Mord (x, y). So

$$\vDash \text{Mord}(x, y) \,.\, \text{Ord}(z, y) \,.\supset .\, x \leq z.$$

Thus we can carry through the proof of Theorem 3.52.

When we come to Theorem 3.53, we must make the additional hypothesis that there is an α for which (3.84) holds. The sense of (3.84) is that

$$\sum_{x \in V_\alpha} \|F(x)\|$$

is the supremum of $\|F(a)\|$ for $a \in V$.

Besides taking an additional hypothesis for Theorem 3.53, we have to give it the following conclusion:

If Hyp(Γ), then there are $a, b \in V$ such that if $z \in V$ then

$$\vDash (Ex)F(x) :: \supset :: \text{Ord}(a, b) :. F(b) :. \\ (w) : F(z) \,.\, w < a \,.\supset .\, \sim \text{Ord}(w, z). \qquad (9.29)$$

Our hypothesis that (3.84) holds insures that a value is assigned to $(Ex)F(x)$. Because $w < a$ means $w \in a$, we can appeal to Theorem 9.8 to assign a value to

$$(w) : F(z) \,.\, w < a \,.\supset .\, \sim \text{Ord}(w, z).$$

In (3.85) a value is given to the formula on the left side of the implication by (3.84) and a value is given to the formula on the right side by Theorem 9.8.

We take $SD(c) = V_\sigma$ and put

$$c^{(S)}(x) = \|x < \check{\sigma} : (Ez) \,.\, z \in U_\beta \,.\, \text{Ord}(x, z) \,.\, F(z)\|$$

for $x \in V_\sigma$. Then (3.86) follows by Theorem 3.15, while the subsequent displayed formula follows by Theorem 3.16.

Our use of Theorem 3.13 to derive (3.88) is justified because

$$\text{Od}(x) \,.\, x \in c : (w) : \text{Od}(w) \,.\, w \in c \,.\supset .\, x \leq w$$

is a statement. To derive (3.90), we cannot appeal to Theorem 3.13 as we did in Chapter 3, because there we were assuming that the elements of the Boolean algebra form a set. However, we can carry through a modification of the proof of Theorem 3.12, as follows. We take $\Phi(x)$ to be

$$\|x \in U_\beta \,.\, \mathrm{Ord}(a, x) \,.\, F(x)\|.$$

Then by Theorem 9.8

$$\sum_{b \in V} \Phi(b) = \sum_{x \in D(U_\beta)} \Phi(x).$$

But $D(U_\beta) = V_\beta$, so that we conclude that for $\gamma \geq \beta$

$$\sum_{b \in V} \Phi(b) = \sum_{b \in V_\gamma} \Phi(b).$$

That is

$$\|(Ez) \,.\, z \in U_\beta \,.\, \mathrm{Ord}(a, z) \,.\, F(z)\| = \sum_{b \in V_\gamma} \Phi(b).$$

This can be used in place of (3.52). Appealing again to Theorem 9.8 gives

$$\sum_{x \in V} \Phi(x) \wedge \|z \in x\| = \sum_{x \in D(U_\beta)} \Phi(x) \wedge \|z \in x\|.$$

With this we can assign a value to the right side of (3.54). We can choose $\mu \geq \beta$ and large enough so that for each $x \in D(U_\beta)$ the value of $\Phi(x)$ is at a level $\leq \aleph_\mu$. Then we define c with $D(c) = V_\mu$ by the condition that (3.54) shall hold for each $z \in V_\mu$. Then we can proceed with the proof of Theorem 3.12 as written, except that we use V_μ instead of V_β. Then we justify (3.90).

Now take $z \in V$. We wish to show

$$\vdash a < \check{\sigma} \,.\, w < a \,.\, \mathrm{Ord}(w, z) \,.\, \supset \,.\, z \in U_\beta. \tag{9.30}$$

To this end, we show

$$\|a < \check{\sigma} \,.\, w < a \,.\, w = \check{\eta} \,.\, z = \xi_\eta\| \leq \|z \in U_\beta\|. \tag{9.31}$$

Case 1. $\eta \geq \sigma$. Then

$$\|a < \check{\sigma} \,.\, w < a \,.\, w = \check{\eta}\| = 0$$

by Theorems 3.19 and 3.23.

Case 2. $\eta < \sigma$. Then $\xi_\eta \in V_\beta$. So $\|\xi_\eta \in U_\beta\| = 1$. Therefore

$$\|z = \xi_\eta\| \leq \|z \in U_\beta\|.$$

So we establish (9.31). Summing over all η gives (9.30).

Next, our lemma should be revised to read

$$\vDash a < \check{\sigma} \,.\, S : \supset : (w) : F(z) \,.\, w < a \,.\, \supset \,.\, \sim\mathrm{Ord}(w, z), \quad (9.32)$$

where S is

$$(z, w) : w < \check{\sigma} \,.\, z \in U_\beta \,.\, \mathrm{Ord}(w, z) \,.\, F(z) \,.\, \supset \,.\, a \leq w. \quad (9.33)$$

By Theorem 3.29 and Definition 1.1 on p. 80 of Bernays and Fraenkel [1]

$$\vDash a < \check{\sigma} \,.\, w < a \,.\, \supset \,.\, w < \check{\sigma}.$$

So by (9.30) and (9.33)

$$\vDash a < \check{\sigma} \,.\, S \,.\, F(z) \,.\, w < a \,.\, \mathrm{Ord}(w, z) \,.\, \supset \,.\, a \leq w. \quad (9.34)$$

However, by Theorem 3.35 and 1.5 on p. 82 of Bernays and Fraenkel [1],

$$\vDash a < \check{\sigma} \,.\, w < a \,.\, \supset \,.\, \mathrm{Od}(a) \,.\, \mathrm{Od}(w).$$

Then by 1.11 on p. 84 of Bernays and Fraenkel [1]

$$\vDash a < \check{\sigma} \,.\, w < a \,.\, \supset \,.\, \sim(a \leq w).$$

So by (9.34)

$$\| a < \check{\sigma} \,.\, S \,.\, F(z) \,.\, w < a \,.\, \mathrm{Ord}(w, z) \| = 0.$$

From this our revised lemma follows. Then Theorem 3.53 follows by (3.89), (3.90) and the lemma.

For Theorem 3.54, we must hypothecate (3.84) as well as (3.83). However, if $F(x)$ is a statement, then (3.83) follows by Theorem 3.5 and (3.84) follows by Theorem 9.7. Similarly there will be cases in which we can infer (3.84) by use of Theorem 9.8. In the derivation of Theorem 3.55, $F(x)$ is taken to be a statement, and so we can use Theorem 3.53 as indicated. Then Theorem 3.56 follows; the theorem itself supplies the interpretation for the quantifiers, as with Theorems 3.48–3.51.

From Theorem 3.56 we conclude $\vDash$AxC.

F. Cardinality Relations

We note that the proof of Theorem 8.8 goes through without modification. So do the proofs of Theorems 8.9–8.11. Then we infer the equivalents of Theorems 3.44–3.47. So in effect the formal images $\check{\eta}$ of intuitive cardinals η constitute the totality of formal cardinals. For example, one can prove that "there is no cardinal between $\mathrm{Img}(\aleph_\alpha)$ and $\mathrm{Img}(\aleph_{\alpha+1})$." This is implicit in Theorem 3.47, but let us make it more explicit. Suppose $\aleph(\eta) < \aleph_{\alpha+1}$. Then $\aleph(\eta) \le \aleph_\alpha$. So by Theorems 8.9 and 3.45

$$\models \aleph(\check{\eta}) \le \mathrm{Img}(\aleph_\alpha).$$

As this holds for each $\eta < \aleph_{\alpha+1}$, we can appeal to Theorem 3.20 to conclude

$$\models (x) : x < \mathrm{Img}(\aleph_{\alpha+1}) \,.\supset.\, \aleph(x) \le \mathrm{Img}(\aleph_\alpha). \tag{9.35}$$

This is the formal analog of the statement in quotations just given.

Another way to put this is to say that the formal cardinality of a set is the same as its intuitive cardinality.

G. The Axiom of the Power Set

First we need some preparatory theorems.

Theorem 9.9. Let α be an ordinal. Then

$$\models (f, x) : \mathrm{Od}(x) \,.\, G(\aleph_{\check{\alpha}}, x, f) \,.\supset.\, \aleph(x) \le \mathrm{Img}(\aleph_{E(\alpha)})$$

where $G(y, x, f)$ denotes

$$\begin{aligned}(u, v, w) : \langle v, u\rangle \in f \,.\, \langle w, u\rangle \in f \,.\subset.\, v = w :. \\ (v) : v < x \,.\supset.\, (E_1 u) \,.\, u \subseteq y \,.\, \langle v, u\rangle \in f.\end{aligned} \tag{9.36}$$

PROOF. By Theorems 2.29, 3.7, and 3.18, the statement in question must take either the value 0 or the value 1. Let it take the value 0. By Theorem 3.54, applied twice, there are $f, x \in V$ such that

$$\|\mathrm{Od}(x)\| = 1 \tag{9.37}$$

$$\|G(\aleph_{\check{\alpha}}, x, f)\| = 1 \tag{9.38}$$

$$\|\aleph(x) \le \mathrm{Img}(\aleph_{E(\alpha)})\| = 0. \tag{9.39}$$

From (9.39), (9.35), and (9.37), we get

$$\|\text{Img}(\aleph_{E(\alpha)+1}) \leq x\| = 1.$$

So for $\mu < \aleph_{E(\alpha)+1}$

$$\|\check{\mu} \in x\| = 1$$

follows by (9.37) and Theorem 3.21. Then by (9.36) and (9.38)

$$\|(E_1 u) \,.\, u \subseteq \aleph_{\check{\alpha}} \,.\, \langle \check{\mu}, u \rangle \in f\| = 1.$$

By Theorem 3.13 there is a u_μ such that

$$\|u_\mu \subseteq \aleph_{\check{\alpha}} \,.\, \langle \check{\mu}, u_\mu \rangle \in f\| = 1. \tag{9.40}$$

Then by (9.36) and (9.38)

$$\|\langle \check{\sigma}, u_\mu \rangle \in f \,.\supset.\, \check{\mu} = \check{\sigma}\| = 1. \tag{9.41}$$

But since $\|\langle \check{\sigma}, u_\sigma \rangle \in f\| = 1$ by the same argument as we had for (9.40), we have

$$\|u_\mu = u_\sigma\| \leq \|\langle \check{\sigma}, u_\mu \rangle \in f\|.$$

So by (9.41)

$$\|u_\mu = u_\sigma\| \leq \|\check{\mu} = \check{\sigma}\|.$$

So if $\mu \neq \sigma$, then

$$\|u_\mu = u_\sigma\| = 0. \tag{9.42}$$

There is some β such that $\text{Img}(\aleph_\alpha) \in V_\beta$, and also $u_\mu \in V_\beta$ for each $\mu < \aleph_{E(\alpha)+1}$. Take $\theta > \beta$ and apply Theorem 9.5. So in $V_\beta{}^\theta$ we have elements corresponding to $\text{Img}(\aleph_\alpha)$ and u_μ for $\mu < \aleph_{E(\alpha)+1}$. By (iv) of Theorem 9.5, we see that $\text{Img}(\aleph_\alpha)$ is the element corresponding to $\text{Img}(\aleph_\alpha)$.

By (9.42) and (iii) of Theorem 9.5, we have

$$\vDash u_\mu{}^* \neq u_\sigma{}^* \tag{9.43}$$

in $V_\beta{}^\theta$ if $\mu \neq \sigma$ and $\mu < \aleph_{E(\alpha)+1}$ and $\sigma < \aleph_{E(\alpha)+1}$. By (9.40) and (iii) of Theroem 9.5

$$\vDash u_\mu{}^* \subseteq \text{Img}(\aleph_\alpha) \tag{9.44}$$

in $V_\beta{}^\theta$ for $\mu < \aleph_{E(\alpha)+1}$.

By (9.43) and (9.44) we have $\aleph_{E(\alpha)+1}$ distinct subsets of $\mathrm{Img}(\aleph_\alpha)$ in $V_\beta{}^\theta$ .Thus we can proceed as in the proof of Theorem 8.12 to prove

$$\models \mathrm{Img}(\aleph_{E(\alpha)+1}) \leq \aleph(SC(\aleph_{\check{\alpha}}))$$

in $V_\beta{}^\theta$. But this contradicts Theorem 8.14.

In effect, this theorem says that there are not more than $\aleph_{E(\alpha)}$ formal subsets of $\aleph_{\check{\alpha}}$. The motivation for our next steps is the following classical argument. We define by induction on η a function f from ordinals to subsets of $\aleph_{\check{\alpha}}$: if at η the elements $f(\check{\tau})$ for $\tau < \eta$ do not exhaust all subsets of $\aleph_{\check{\alpha}}$, then we take $f(\check{\eta})$ to be the "next" remaining subset of $\aleph_{\check{\alpha}}$; if we have exhausted all subsets of $\aleph_\alpha$, we take

$$f(\check{\eta}) = \check{\Lambda}.$$

As long as we have not exhausted all subsets of $\aleph_{\check{\alpha}}$, the newly defined subset $f(\check{\eta})$ must be "different" from $f(\check{\tau})$ for each $\tau < \eta$. But if we have not exhausted all subsets of $\aleph_{\check{\alpha}}$ at η, we will not have exhausted them at any earlier point, so that for $\tau < \eta$, $\sigma < \eta$, and $\tau \neq \sigma$ we must have $f(\check{\tau})$ "different" from $f(\check{\sigma})$. However, by Theorem 9.9 we must be getting repetitions among the $f(\check{\tau})$ before we get to $\aleph_{E(\alpha)+1}$. So we must before this time have exhausted all subsets of $\aleph_{\check{\alpha}}$. So if we take the set of all $f(\check{\tau})$ for $\tau < \aleph_{E(\alpha)+1}$, this set must be $SC(\aleph_{\check{\alpha}})$; the set in question will exist by the axiom of replacement. Once we are able to form $SC(\aleph_{\check{\alpha}})$ for each α, we can proceed to power sets of general sets by an argument which we will present later. For the moment, we have to circumvent certain hazards in the argument just outlined.

Classically, at η we have either exhausted all the subsets of $\aleph_{\check{\alpha}}$, or we have not. Thus it is definite whether to take $f(\check{\eta})$ to be the "next" remaining subset or to be $\check{\Lambda}$. However, in our model, the statement that we have exhausted all subsets may have a value different from 0 or 1, and then the proper choice for $f(\check{\eta})$ presents difficulties. Also, we would like to use Theorem 3.53 to define the "next" remaining subset. However, Theorem 3.53 involves formulas which are not statements, and this may involve us in difficulties about quantifiers. We shall avoid these troubles by carrying out the definition by induction in the intuitive logic. Specifically, we define by intuitive induction on η sets $b_\eta \in V$ which are to be the values of $f(\check{\eta})$. To define b_η we need to have in the formal system a function f_η consisting of f with its arguments restricted to η. Specifically, we require of f_η that for each $x \in V$

$$\|x \in f_\eta\| = \sum_{\sigma < \eta} \|x = \langle \check{\sigma}, b_\sigma \rangle\|. \tag{9.45}$$

According to the plan outlined above, we expect to show that for $\eta = \aleph_{E(\alpha)+1}$ the range of f_η will consist exactly of all subsets of $\aleph_{\check{\alpha}}$. We introduce $F_1(y, f)$ to signify that every subset of $\aleph_{\check{\alpha}}$ is a value $f(u)$ for some $u < y$. Specifically, we take $F_1(y, f)$ to be

$$(v) : . v \subseteq \aleph_{\check{\alpha}} : \supset : (Eu) . u < y . \langle u, v \rangle \in f. \tag{9.46}$$

We would like also to express the property that as long as the $f(t)$ for $t < z$ do not exhaust all subsets of $\aleph_{\check{\alpha}}$, then for $t < z$, $s < z$, and $t \neq s$ we must have $f(t)$ "different" from $f(s)$. We indicate a slightly sharpened version of this by $F_2(z, f)$, which shall denote

$$(y) : : y < z . \sim F_1(y, f) . : \supset : . (u, v, w) : u \leq y . v \leq y .$$
$$\langle u, w \rangle \in f . \langle v, w \rangle \in f . \supset . u = v. \tag{9.47}$$

We wish also to express the property that as soon as the elements $f(t)$ for $t < y$ do exhaust all subsets of $\aleph_{\check{\alpha}}$, then $f(y) = \check{\Lambda}$, for all $y < z$. This we indicate by $F_3(z, f)$, which will denote

$$(y) : . y < z . F_1(y, f) . \supset . \langle y, \check{\Lambda} \rangle \in f. \tag{9.48}$$

Note that if we take y, z, and f to be variables or specific elements of V in $F_1(y, f)$, $F_2(z, f)$, and $F_3(z, f)$, then these formulas and their various parts will be statements, so that by Theorem 9.7 the quantifiers appearing therein are perfectly determinate. The same applies to (9.50), (9.51), and other auxiliary formulas which we shall use.

Theorem 9.10.

$$\vDash (f, y)(Ev) : : v \subseteq \aleph_{\check{\alpha}} : . v = \check{\Lambda} . F_1(y, f) : \vee :$$
$$(u) : u < y . \supset . \sim \langle u, v \rangle \in f.$$

PROOF. This follows from the axioms of set theory (excluding the power set axiom). One makes a "proof by cases" (see paragraph 6 on p. 35 of Rosser [7]), first assuming $F_1(y, f)$ and second assuming $\sim F_1(y, f)$.

Theorem 9.11. Suppose that for each $\tau < \eta$ there is an element $b_\tau \in V$ such that

$$\vDash b_\tau \subseteq \aleph_{\check{\alpha}}. \tag{9.49}$$

Suppose also that f_η is an element of V such that (9.45) holds for each $x \in V$. Then

$$\vDash (u, v) : \langle u, v \rangle \in f_\eta . \supset . u < \check{\eta} . v \subseteq \aleph_{\check{\alpha}} \tag{9.50}$$

$$\vDash (u) : u < \check{\eta} . \supset . (E_1 v) . \langle u, v \rangle \in f_\eta . \tag{9.51}$$

PROOF. The proof of (9.50) parallels the proof of Lemma 1 in the proof of Theorem 8.12.

Lemma. If $\tau < \eta$ then $\vDash (v) : \langle \check{\tau}, v \rangle \in f_\eta . \equiv . v = b_\tau$.

PROOF. By (9.45)

$$\vDash v = b_\tau . \supset . \langle \check{\tau}, v \rangle \in f_\eta$$

is immediate. Now

$$\| \langle \check{\tau}, v \rangle = \langle \check{\sigma}, b_\sigma \rangle \| \leq \| v = b_\tau \|$$

by a familiar argument (see the proof of Theorem 3.49, for example). Summing over $\sigma < \eta$ gives

$$\vDash \langle \check{\tau}, v \rangle \in f_\eta . \supset . v = b_\tau .$$

Thus we infer the lemma.

By the lemma, we conclude

$$\vDash (E_1 v) . \langle \check{\tau}, v \rangle \in f_\eta$$

for each $\tau < \eta$. Then (9.51) follows by Theorem 3.20.

Theorem 9.12. We can for each ordinal η define f_η and b_η, elements of V, in such a way that for each η the results (9.45) and (9.49) hold, and also

$$\vDash F_2(\check{\eta}, f_\eta) \tag{9.52}$$

$$\vDash F_3(\check{\eta}, f_\eta). \tag{9.53}$$

PROOF. We proceed by induction on η. We take f_0 to be $\check{\Lambda}$, which trivially satisfies (9.45). Also (9.52) and (9.53) hold with $\eta = 0$. We will wait to define b_τ when we define $f_{\tau+1}$.

First let η be a limiting ordinal μ. We assume that b_τ and f_τ have been defined for $\tau < \mu$, and that (9.45), (9.52), and (9.53) hold for $\eta < \mu$, and that (9.49) holds for $\tau < \mu$. Take β the least ordinal such that $\langle \check{\sigma}, b_\sigma \rangle \in V_\beta$ for $\sigma < \mu$. Define f_μ with $D(f_\mu) = V_\beta$ by taking

$$\{\langle \check{\sigma}, b_\sigma \rangle \mid \sigma < \mu\}$$

as a Scott domain, and defining the corresponding Scott core by

$$f_\mu^{(S)}(x) = 1.$$

Then by (3.60)

$$f_\mu(x) = \sum_{\sigma<\mu} \| x = \langle \check{\sigma}, b_\sigma \rangle \|$$

for $x \in D(f_\mu)$. Then (9.45) holds for $\eta = \mu$ by Theorem 3.16.

Lemma 1. If $\tau < \mu$, then

$$\vDash (u) \therefore u < \check{\tau} : \supset : (v) \,.\, \langle u, v \rangle \in f_\tau \equiv \langle u, v \rangle \in f_\mu \,.$$

PROOF. Let $\sigma < \tau < \mu$. By the lemma in the proof of Theorem 9.11

$$\vDash (v) \,.\, \langle \check{\sigma}, v \rangle \in f_\tau \equiv \langle \check{\sigma}, v \rangle \in f_\mu \,.$$

Since this holds for each $\sigma < \tau$, our lemma follows by Theorem 3.20.

Lemma 2. If $\tau < \mu$, then

$$\vDash (y) : y \leq \check{\tau} \,.\, \supset \,.\, F_1(y, f_\tau) \equiv F_1(y, f_\mu).$$

PROOF. Use Lemma 1 with (9.46).

We write $F_4(y,f)$ for

$$(u, v, w) : u \leq y \,.\, v \leq y \,.\, \langle u, w\rangle \in f \,.\, \langle v, w\rangle \in f \,.\supset.\, u = v. \quad (9.54)$$

Then by (9.47), we can write $F_2(z,f)$ as

$$(y) : y < z \,.\, {\sim}F_1(y,f) \,.\supset.\, F_4(y,f).$$

Lemma 3. If $\tau < \mu$, then

$$\models (y) : y < \check{\tau} \,.\supset.\, F_4(y,f_\tau) \equiv F_4(y,f_\mu).$$

PROOF. Use Lemma 1 with (9.54).

We now show that (9.52) holds for $\eta = \mu$. Take $\tau < \mu$. By the hypothesis of the induction, (9.52) holds for $\eta = \tau + 1$. In this we take y to be $\check{\tau}$, and conclude

$$\models {\sim}F_1(\check{\tau},f_{\tau+1}) \supset F_4(\check{\tau},f_{\tau+1}).$$

Then by Lemmas 2 and 3

$$\models {\sim}F_1(\check{\tau},f_\mu) \supset F_4(\check{\tau},f_\mu). \quad (9.55)$$

As this holds for each $\tau < \mu$, we conclude by Theorem 3.20

$$\models (y) : y < \check{\mu} \,.\supset.\, {\sim}F_1(y,f_\mu) \supset F_4(y,f_\mu),$$

from which we conclude that (9.52) holds for $\eta = \mu$.

Similarly, take $\tau < \mu$. As (9.53) holds for $\eta = \tau + 1$, we may take y to be $\check{\tau}$ therein and get

$$\models F_1(\check{\tau},f_{\tau+1}) \,.\supset.\, \langle \check{\tau}, \check{\Lambda}\rangle \in f_{\tau+1}.$$

Then by Lemmas 1 and 2.

$$\models F_1(\check{\tau},f_\mu) \,.\supset.\, \langle \check{\tau}, \check{\Lambda}\rangle \in f_\mu. \quad (9.56)$$

Then by Theorem 3.20

$$\models (y) :. y < \check{\mu} :\supset: F_1(y,f_\mu) \,.\supset.\, \langle y, \check{\Lambda}\rangle \in f_\mu,$$

from which we conclude that (9.53) holds for $\eta = \mu$.

Turn to the case where η is nonlimiting. Say $\eta = \mu = \rho + 1$. We assume that b_τ has been defined for $\tau < \rho$ and that (9.49) holds for each such τ. We assume that f_τ has been defined for $\tau \leq \rho$, and that (9.45), (9.52), and (9.53) hold for $\eta \le \rho$. By Theorem 9.10

$$\vDash (Ev) :: v \subseteq \aleph_{\breve{\alpha}} :. v = \breve{\Lambda} . F_1(\breve{\rho}, f_\rho) : \vee :$$
$$(u) : u < \breve{\rho} . \supset . \sim \langle u, v \rangle \in f_\rho.$$

Then by Theorem 3.54 there is a $b \in V$ such that

$$\vDash b \subseteq \aleph_{\breve{\alpha}} \tag{9.57}$$

$$\vDash b = \breve{\Lambda} \cdot F_1(\breve{\rho}, f_\rho) : \vee : (u) : u < \breve{\rho} . \supset . \sim \langle u, b \rangle \in f_\rho. \tag{9.58}$$

Take this b to be b_ρ, and take f_μ to be

$$f_\rho \cup \{\langle \breve{\rho}, b_\rho \rangle\}.$$

Clearly (9.45) holds with $\eta = \mu$. Also, by (9.57) we have (9.49) holding for $\tau < \mu$.

Note that by (9.58) we have

$$\vDash F_1(\breve{\rho}, f_\rho) \supset b_\rho = \breve{\Lambda} \tag{9.59}$$

$$\vDash \sim F_1(\breve{\rho}, f_\rho) : \supset : (u) : u < \breve{\rho} . \supset . \sim \langle u, b_\rho \rangle \in f_\rho. \tag{9.60}$$

What (9.59) tells us is that if the range of f_ρ exhausts all subsets of $\aleph_{\breve{\alpha}}$ then we chose $f(\breve{\rho})$ (that is, b_ρ) to be $\breve{\Lambda}$. Alternatively (9.60) tells us that if the range of f_ρ does not exhaust all subsets of $\aleph_{\breve{\alpha}}$, then $f(\breve{\rho})$ was chosen different from $f(u)$ for $u < \breve{\rho}$; by (9.57) $f(\breve{\rho})$ is a subset of $\aleph_{\breve{\alpha}}$. Indeed, it is the "next" subset, because we appealed to Theorem 3.54 to obtain b_ρ. However, Theorem 3.54 relies on Theorem 3.53, which picks the "first" element of the sort in question.

In point of fact, most likely $\|F_1(\breve{\rho}, f_\rho)\|$ is neither 0 or 1, so that neither $\|b_\rho = \breve{\Lambda}\|$ nor

$$\|(u) : u < \breve{\rho} . \supset . \sim \langle u, b_\rho \rangle \in f_\rho \|$$

is equal either to 0 or 1. Thus it is unclear just what sort of object b_ρ is. However, by (9.57), it is certainly a subset of $\aleph_{\breve{\alpha}}$. Also, as long as $\|F_1(\breve{\rho}, f_\rho)\| \neq 1$, the "new" subset b_ρ will not be exactly equal to any previously chosen b_τ. Thus, as long as we have not completely exhausted the subsets of $\aleph_{\breve{\alpha}}$, the b_ρ will scavenge part of the residue of subsets of $\aleph_{\breve{\alpha}}$. Before we get to $\rho = \aleph_{E(\alpha)+1}$ the residue will be wholly purged.

To show this, we must get on with the present proof; we must still show that (9.52) and (9.53) hold for $\eta = \mu$.

As before, Lemmas 1–3 hold. Then the same arguments as before will show that (9.55) and (9.56) will hold for $\tau < \rho$. If we prove them also for $\tau = \rho$, we can finish the proof as before.

Lemma 4.

$$\vdash (y, z, f) : \mathrm{Od}(z) \,.\, y < z \,.\, F_1(y, f) \,.\supset.\, F_1(z, f).$$

PROOF. Use (9.46) with Definitions 1.1 and 1.4 on p. 80 of Bernays and Fraenkel [1].

Lemma 5.

$$\vdash (y) : y < \check{\rho} \,.\, \sim F_1(\check{\rho}, f_\mu) \,.\supset.\, F_4(y, f_\mu).$$

PROOF. By Lemma 2

$$\vdash \sim F_1(\check{\rho}, f_\mu) \equiv \sim F_1(\check{\rho}, f_\rho).$$

But by Lemma 4

$$\vdash (y) < \check{\rho} \,.\, \sim F_1(\check{\rho}, f_\rho) \,.\supset.\, \sim F_1(y, f_\rho).$$

Therefore

$$\vdash y < \check{\rho} \,.\, \sim F_1(\check{\rho}, f_\mu) \,.\supset.\, y < \check{\rho} \,.\, \sim F_1(y, f_\rho).$$

Since (9.52) holds for $\eta = \rho$ by hypothesis, we obtain

$$\vdash y < \check{\rho} \,.\, \sim F_1(\check{\rho}, f_\mu) \,.\supset.\, F_4(y, f_\rho).$$

Our lemma follows by Lemma 3.

Lemma 6. $\vdash \sim F_1(\check{\rho}, f_\mu) \supset F_4(\check{\rho}, f_\mu)$.

PROOF. Let $\theta < \rho$ and $\phi < \rho$. Take $\nu = \max(\theta, \phi)$. Then in Lemma 5 we can take $\check{\nu}$, $\check{\theta}$, $\check{\phi}$ for y, u, and v, respectively. This gives

$$\vdash \sim F_1(\check{\rho}, f_\mu) \,.:\supset:.\, (w) : \langle \check{\theta}, w \rangle \in f_\mu \,.\, \langle \check{\phi}, w \rangle \in f_\mu \,.\supset.\, \check{\theta} = \check{\phi}.$$

Two uses of Theorem 3.20 give

$$\vdash \sim F_1(\check{\rho}, f_\mu) \,.:\supset:.\, (u, v, w) : u < \check{\rho} \,.\, v < \check{\rho} \,.\, \langle u, w \rangle \in f_\mu \,.\, \langle v, w \rangle \in f_\mu \,.\supset.\, u = v. \qquad (9.61)$$

By the lemma in the proof of Theorem 9.11

$$\models v = \check{\rho} \,.\, \langle v, w \rangle \in f_\mu \,.\supset.\, w = b_\rho \,.$$

So by Lemma 1

$$\models u < \check{\rho} \,.\, v = \check{\rho} \,.\, \langle u, w \rangle \in f_\mu \,.\, \langle v, w \rangle \in f_\mu \,.\supset.\, \langle u, b_\rho \rangle \in f_\rho \,.$$

Hence by (9.60) and Lemma 2

$$\models \sim F_1(\check{\rho}, f_\mu) \,.\, u < \check{\rho} \,.\, v = \check{\rho} \,.\, \langle u, w \rangle \in f_\mu \,.\, \langle v, w \rangle \in f_\mu \,.\supset.\, u = v.$$

Thus we infer

$$\models \sim F_1(\check{\rho}, f_\mu) \,.:\supset:.\, (u, v, w) : u < \check{\rho} \,.\, v = \check{\rho} \,.\, \langle u, w \rangle \in f_\mu \,.\, \langle v, w \rangle \in f_\mu \,.\supset.\, u = v. \tag{9.62}$$

A change of bound variables gives

$$\models \sim F_1(\check{\rho}, f_\mu) \,.:\supset:.\, (u, v, w) : u = \check{\rho} \,.\, v < \check{\rho} \,.\, \langle u, w \rangle \in f_\mu \,.\, \langle v, w \rangle \in f_\mu \,.\supset.\, u = v. \tag{9.63}$$

Our lemma follows easily from (9.61)–(9.63).

Lemma 6, together with the fact that (9.55) holds for $\tau < \rho$, gives us what we need to conclude that (9.52) holds for $\eta = \mu$.

Lemma 7. $\models F_1(\check{\rho}, f_\mu) \supset \langle \check{\rho}, \check{\Lambda} \rangle \in f_\mu \,.$

PROOF. Use Lemma 2 and (9.59) together with the result

$$\models \langle \check{\rho}, b_\rho \rangle \in f_\mu \,.$$

Lemma 7, together with the fact that (9.56) holds for $\tau < \rho$, gives us what we need to conclude that (9.53) holds for $\eta = \mu$.

Thus the proof of our theorem is complete.

Theorem 9.13. The power set of $\aleph_{\check{\alpha}}$ exists. That is, there is an $a \in V$ such that

$$\models (y) : y \in a \,.\equiv.\, y \subseteq \aleph_{\check{\alpha}} \,.$$

We shall refer to such an a as $SC(\aleph_{\check{\alpha}})$.

PROOF. Write temporarily σ for $\aleph_{E(\alpha)+1}$. By Theorems 9.11 and 9.12, we can take η to be σ in (9.50) and (9.51), giving

$$\vDash (v) : v < \check{\sigma} . \supset . (E_1 u) . u \subseteq \aleph_{\check{\alpha}} . \langle v, u \rangle \in f_\sigma . \tag{9.64}$$

Let $\theta < \sigma$ and $\phi < \sigma$, and put $v = \max(\theta, \phi)$. Take η to be σ in (9.52) and put $\check{v}$, $\check{\theta}$, and $\check{\phi}$ for y, u, and v. This gives

$$\vDash \sim F_1(\check{v}, f_\sigma) . : \supset : . (w) : \langle \check{\theta}, w \rangle \in f_\sigma . \langle \check{\phi}, w \rangle \in f_\sigma . \supset . \check{\theta} = \check{\phi}.$$

Then by Lemma 4 in the proof of Theorem 9.12 we infer

$$\vDash \sim F_1(\check{\sigma}, f_\sigma) . : \supset : . (w) : \langle \check{\theta}, w \rangle \in f_\sigma . \langle \check{\phi}, w \rangle \in f_\sigma . \supset . \check{\theta} = \check{\phi} .$$

As this holds for each $\theta < \sigma$ and each $\phi < \sigma$, we can apply Theorem 3.20 twice to get

$$\vDash \sim F_1(\check{\sigma}, f_\sigma) . : \supset : . (u, v, w) : u < \check{\sigma} . v < \check{\sigma} .$$
$$\langle u, w \rangle \in f_\sigma . \langle v, w \rangle \in f_\sigma . \supset . u = v.$$

So by (9.50)

$$\vDash \sim F_1(\check{\sigma}, f_\sigma) . : \supset : . (u, v, w) : \langle u, w \rangle \in f_\sigma . \langle v, w \rangle \in f_\sigma . \supset . u = v.$$

By (9.64) and (9.36), this gives

$$\vDash \sim F_1(\check{\sigma}, f_\sigma) \supset G(\aleph_{\check{\alpha}}, \check{\sigma}, f_\sigma).$$

So by Theorem 9.9

$$\vDash \sim F_1(\check{\sigma}, f_\sigma) . \supset . \aleph(\check{\sigma}) \leq \mathrm{Img}(\aleph_{E(\alpha)}).$$

Since $\sigma = \aleph_{E(\alpha)+1}$, we have

$$\vDash \sim \aleph(\check{\sigma}) \leq \mathrm{Img}(\aleph_{E(\alpha)})$$

by Theorems 8.10 and 3.45. Hence

$$\vDash F_1(\check{\sigma}, f_\sigma). \tag{9.65}$$

In the corollary to Theorem 3.31, take u to be $\check{\sigma}$ and $F(x, y)$ to be $\langle x, y \rangle \in f_\sigma$. Then by (9.51)

$$\vDash (Ew)(y) : y \in w . \equiv . (Ex) . x \in \check{\sigma} . \langle x, y \rangle \in f_\sigma .$$

So by Theorem 3.54 there is an $a \in V$ such that

$$\vdash (y) : y \in a \,.\equiv.\, (Ex) \,.\, x \in \check{\sigma} \,.\, \langle x, y \rangle \in f_\sigma \,. \tag{9.66}$$

By (9.50)

$$\vdash (Ex) \,.\, x \in \check{\sigma} \,.\, \langle x, y \rangle \in f_\sigma : \supset : y \subseteq \aleph_{\check{\alpha}} \,.$$

By (9.65) and (9.46)

$$\vdash y \subseteq \aleph_{\check{\alpha}} : \supset : (Ex) \,.\, x \in \check{\sigma} \,.\, \langle x, y \rangle \in f_\sigma \,.$$

Hence

$$\vdash (y) :.\, (Ex) \,.\, x \in \check{\sigma} \,.\, \langle x, y \rangle \in f_\sigma : \equiv : y \subseteq \aleph_{\check{\alpha}} \,.$$

Combining this with (9.66) gives our theorem.

It is perhaps worth remarking that the proof of the corollary to Theorem 3.31 actually furnished an a which could have been used in (9.66). Thus it was not necessary to appeal to Theorem 3.54 for this purpose, but it was handier than trying to identify a from the proof of the corollary.

The result (9.65) is the goal which was set after Theorem 9.9, namely to find a function f whose range exhausts all the subsets of $\aleph_{\check{\alpha}}$. It sufficed to deal with functions f_η of bounded domain. This had the advantage that all f_η are elements of V.

Theorem 9.14.

$$\vdash (z) :.\, z \subseteq \aleph_{\check{\alpha}} : \supset : (Ew)(y) \,.\, y \in w \equiv y \subseteq z.$$

Proof. In Theorem 3.31 take z a constant element of V, $F(x, y)$ to be $y = x \cap z$, and b to be $SC(\aleph_{\check{\alpha}})$. Then there is an $a \in V$ such that

$$\vdash (y) : y \in a \,.=.\, (Ex) \,.\, x \subseteq \aleph_{\check{\alpha}} \,.\, y = x \cap z.$$

However, we have

$$\vdash z \subseteq \aleph_{\check{\alpha}} : \supset : y \subseteq z \,.\equiv.\, (Ex) \,.\, x \subseteq \aleph_{\check{\alpha}} \,.\, y = x \cap z$$

by standard theorems of set theory. Combining these two results gives our theorem.

We now have the needed preparatory theorems, and can proceed to a proof of the axiom of the power set. The idea of the proof is as follows. Let $b \in V$. We can set up a one-to-one correspondence f from b to some set z of ordinals by well-ordering b. As z is a set, there must be an α such that $z \subseteq \aleph_{\check{\alpha}}$. Then by Theorem 9.14, $SC(z)$ exists. However, by means of f, we can set up a one-to-one correspondence g between subsets of b and subsets of z. As $SC(z)$ exists, we can apply the axiom of replacement to find the set of all elements related by g to members of $SC(z)$. Clearly this must be $SC(b)$.

We have the axiom of choice, and so could carry through the program outlined above. However, it would be risky to use the developments of Bernays and Fraenkel [1] as a model, since Bernays and Fraenkel introduce the power set axiom before they introduce the axiom of choice. Thus one would have to scrutinize any of their developments from the axiom of choice with the greatest care to make sure that they had not used the power set axiom. So we feel it desirable to develop the proof in detail. It turns out that some simplifications are possible. For instance, we do not need a one-to-one correspondence from b to a set of the ordinals; a one-many correspondence will suffice. Thus, we do not need to start by well-ordering b. However, the overall pattern of the proof remains much the same as indicated above.

Theorem 9.15. The axiom of the power set holds in the model.

PROOF. Let $b \in V$. Choose β so that $b \in V_\beta$. Let ξ_η be an ordering of V_β. It may as well be a portion of the ordering used to define $\mathrm{Ord}(x, y)$. Choose σ large enough so that each $x \in V_\beta$ is a ξ_η for some $\eta < \sigma$. Take γ large enough so that $\langle \check{\eta}, \xi_\eta \rangle \in V_\gamma$ for each $\eta < \sigma$. Define c with $D(c) = V_\gamma$ by taking

$$\{\langle \check{\eta}, \xi_\eta \rangle \mid \eta < \sigma\}$$

as a Scott domain, and defining the corresponding Scott core by

$$c^{(S)}(x) = 1.$$

Then by (3.60)

$$c(x) = \sum_{\eta < \sigma} \|x = \langle \check{\eta}, \xi_\eta \rangle\|$$

for $x \in D(c)$. Then Theorem 3.16 gives

$$\|x \in c\| = \sum_{\eta<\sigma} \|x = \langle \check{\eta}, \xi_\eta \rangle\| \tag{9.67}$$

for each $x \in V$. As in Theorem 9.11, we can show

$$\models (u, v) : \langle u, v \rangle \in c \, . \supset . \, u < \check{\sigma} \tag{9.68}$$

and

$$\models (u) : u < \check{\sigma} \, . \supset . \, (E_1 v) \, . \, \langle u, v \rangle \in c. \tag{9.69}$$

Lemma 1.

$$\models (v) : v \in b \, . \supset . \, (Eu) \, . \, u < \check{\sigma} \, . \, \langle u, v \rangle \in c.$$

PROOF. Take $w \in D(b)$. As $b \in V_\beta$, we must have $D(b) \subseteq V_\beta$ by (3.31) and (3.14). Therefore $w \in V_\beta$. So there is an $\eta < \sigma$ such that w is ξ_η. Therefore

$$\models \langle \check{\eta}, w \rangle \in c.$$

Hence

$$\models (Eu) \, . \, u < \check{\sigma} \, . \, \langle u, w \rangle \in c.$$

Hence

$$\|w \in b \, . \, v = w\| \leq \|(Eu) \, . \, u < \check{\sigma} \, . \, \langle u, v \rangle \in c\|.$$

Summing over $w \in D(b)$ and using (3.28) establishes the lemma.

Write $F(x, y)$ for

$$x \subseteq b \, . \, y \subseteq \check{\sigma} : (u) : u \in y \, . \equiv . \, (Ev) \, . \, v \in x \, . \, \langle u, v \rangle \in c. \tag{9.70}$$

Lemma 2.

$$\models (x) : x \subseteq b \, . \supset . \, (E_1 y) \, . \, F(x, y).$$

PROOF. Take $x \in V$. Take $\delta > \sigma$ and large enough so that the level of

$$\|(Ev) \, . \, v \in x \, . \, \langle \check{\tau}, v \rangle \in c\|$$

is less than $\aleph_\delta$ for each $\tau < \sigma$. Define y with $D(y) = V_\delta$ by taking

$$\{\check{\tau} \mid \tau < \sigma\}$$

as a Scott domain, and defining the corresponding Scott core by

$$y^{(S)}(\check{\tau}) = \|(Ev) \,.\, v \in x \,.\, \langle \check{\tau}, v \rangle \in c\|$$

for $\tau < \sigma$. Then by (3.60)

$$y(u) = \sum_{\tau < \sigma} \|u = \check{\tau} : (Ev) \,.\, v \in x \,.\, \langle \check{\tau}, v \rangle \in c\|$$

for $u \in D(y)$. Then Theorem 3.16 gives

$$\|u \in y\| = \sum_{\tau < \sigma} \|u = \check{\tau} : (Ev) \,.\, v \in x \,.\, \langle \check{\tau}, v \rangle \in c\| \tag{9.71}$$

for $u \in V$. Now

$$\|u = \check{\tau} : (Ev) \,.\, v \in x \,.\, \langle \check{\tau}, v \rangle \in c\| \leq \|(Ev) \,.\, v \in x \,.\, \langle u, v \rangle \in c\|.$$

Summing the left over $\tau < \sigma$ gives

$$\models u \in y \,.\, \supset .\, (Ev) \,.\, v \in x \,.\, \langle u, v \rangle \in c \tag{9.72}$$

by (9.71). Also by (9.71),

$$\models (Ev) \,.\, v \in x \,.\, \langle \check{\tau}, v \rangle \in c : \supset : \check{\tau} \in y$$

for $\tau < \sigma$. So by Theorem 3.20

$$\models (u) :: u < \check{\sigma} \,.: \supset :.\, (Ev) \,.\, v \in x \,.\, \langle u, v \rangle \in c : \supset : u \in y.$$

So by (9.68)

$$\models (u) :.\, (Ev) \,.\, v \in x \,.\, \langle u, v \rangle \in c : \supset : u \in y.$$

Then by (9.72)

$$\models (u) : u \in y \,.\, \equiv .\, (Ev) \,.\, v \in x \,.\, \langle u, v \rangle \in c.$$

So by (9.68)

$$\models y \subseteq \check{\sigma}.$$

Then by (9.70)

$$\models x \subseteq b \,.\, \supset .\, F(x, y).$$

So the lemma follows by Theorem 3.4.

By taking x to be b in Lemma 2, and using Theorem 3.54, we determine that there is a $z \in V$ such that

$$\vDash F(b, z). \tag{9.73}$$

Then by (9.70) and (9.69)

$$\vDash (u) : u \in z \,.\supset .\, (E_1 v) \,.\, v \in b \,.\, \langle u, v \rangle \in c. \tag{9.74}$$

Thus $\langle u, v \rangle \in c$ defines a one-many correspondence from b to z, and by (9.73) and (9.70)

$$\vDash z \subseteq \check{\sigma}. \tag{9.75}$$

Write $G(x, y)$ for

$$x \subseteq b \,.\, y \subseteq z : (v) : v \in x \,.\equiv .\, (Eu) \,.\, u \in y \,.\, \langle u, v \rangle \in c. \tag{9.76}$$

Lemma 3.

$$\vDash (y) : y \subseteq z \,.\supset .\, (E_1 x) \,.\, G(x, y).$$

PROOF. Take $y \in V$. By (9.74)

$$\vDash y \subseteq z \,.:\supset :.\, (u) : u \in y \,.\supset .\, (E_1 v) \,.\, v \in b \,.\, \langle u, v \rangle \in c.$$

So by the corollary to Theorem 3.31

$$\vDash y \subseteq z \,.:\supset :.\, (Ew)(v) : v \in w \,.\equiv .\, (Eu) \,.\, u \in y \,.\, v \in b \,.\, \langle u, v \rangle \in c.$$

So by Theorem 3.54 there is an $x \in V$ such that

$$\vDash y \subseteq z \,.:\supset :.\, (v) : v \in x \,.\equiv .\, (Eu) \,.\, u \in y \,.\, v \in b \,.\, \langle u, v \rangle \in c. \tag{9.77}$$

This gives

$$\vDash y \subseteq z \,.\supset .\, x \subseteq b. \tag{9.78}$$

Assume

(i) $y \subseteq z$

(ii) $u \in y \,.\, \langle u, v \rangle \in c$.

Then by (9.74)

$$(E_1 v) \,.\, v \in b \,.\, \langle u, v \rangle \in c.$$

So by Rule C (see Rosser [7, p. 128]),

$$w \in b \,.\, \langle u, w\rangle \in c.$$

Then by (ii), (9.75), and (9.69)

$$w \in b \,.\, w = v.$$

Therefore

(iii) $v \in b$.

We can appeal to Theorem VI.7.2 on p. 130 of Rosser [7] to conclude that there is a derivation of (iii) from (i) and (ii) without the use of Rule C. Then by two uses of the deduction theorem (see Rosser [7, p. 75])

$$\vdash y \subseteq z \,.:\supset:.\, u \in y \,.\, \langle u, v\rangle \in c :\supset: v \in b.$$

Hence

$$\vdash y \subseteq z \,.:\supset:.\, (u) : u \in y \,.\, \langle u, v\rangle \in c \,.\supset.\, v \in b.$$

With this and (9.77) we get

$$\vdash y \subseteq z \,.:\supset:.\, (v) : v \in x \,.\equiv.\, (Eu) \,.\, u \in y \,.\, \langle u, v\rangle \in c.$$

This with (9.78) gives

$$\vdash y \subseteq z \,.\supset.\, G(x, y).$$

So the lemma follows by Theorem 3.4.

Lemma 4. $SC(z)$ is an element of V.

PROOF. By (9.75) there is an α such that

$$\vdash z \subseteq \aleph_{\check{\alpha}}.$$

Hence we may use Theorem 9.14.

Lemma 5. There is an $a \in V$ such that

$$\vdash (x) : x \in a \,.\equiv.\, (Ey) \,.\, y \in SC(z) \,.\, G(x, y).$$

PROOF. Use Lemmas 3 and 4 with the corollary to Theorem 3.31, and then use Theorem 3.54.

Lemma 6.

$$\vDash (x, y, w) \,.\, F(x, y) \,.\, G(w, y) \,.\supset .\, x = w.$$

PROOF. Assume

(i) $F(x, y)$

(ii) $G(w, y)$

(iii) $v \in x$.

By (9.70), (i), and (iii)

$$v \in b.$$

So by Lemma 1 and Rule C of Rosser [7]

(iv) $\langle u, v\rangle \in c$.

Then by (9.70), (i), and (iii)

$$u \in y.$$

So by (9.76), (ii), and (iv)

$$v \in w.$$

Applying the deduction theorem gives

$$\vDash F(x, y) \,.\, G(w, y) \,.\supset .\, x \subseteq w.$$

Assume (i), (ii), and

(v) $v \in w$.

By (9.76), (ii), and Rule C

(vi) $u \in y$

(vii) $\langle u, v\rangle \in c$.

By (9.70), (i), (vi), and Rule C

(viii) $t \in x$

(ix) $\langle u, t\rangle \in c$.

By (9.70), (i), and (vi)

$$u < \check{\sigma}.$$

Then by (9.69), (vii), and (ix)

$$t = v.$$

So by (viii)

$$v \in x.$$

Applying the deduction theorem gives

$$\vdash F(x, y) \,.\, G(w, y) \,.\supset .\, w \subseteq x.$$

So our lemma is proved.

Lemma 7. $\vdash (x, y) \,.\, F(x, y) \supset y \subseteq z.$

PROOF. Assume

(i) $F(x, y)$
(ii) $u \in y.$

By (9.70), (i), and Rule C

$$v \in x \,.\, \langle u, v \rangle \in c.$$

By (9.70) and (i), $x \subseteq b$, so that

$$v \in b \,.\, \langle u, v \rangle \in c.$$

By (9.70) and (9.73)

$$u \in z.$$

Applying the deduction theorem proves the lemma.

Lemma 8.

$$\vdash (x) : x \subseteq b \,.\supset .\, (Ey) \,.\, y \in SC(z) \,.\, G(x, y).$$

PROOF. Assume

(i) $x \subseteq b.$

By Lemma 2 and Rule C

$$F(x, y).$$

By Lemma 7

(ii) $y \subseteq z$.

By Lemma 3 and Rule C

$$G(w, y).$$

By Lemma 6

$$x = w,$$

so that

$$G(x, y).$$

Since (ii) gives $y \in SC(z)$, our lemma follows.

By (9.76)

$$\vDash (x) :. (Ey) . y \in SC(z) . G(x, y) : \supset : x \subseteq b.$$

So by Lemma 8

$$\vDash (x) : x \subseteq b . \equiv . (Ey) . y \in SC(z) . G(x, y).$$

Then by Lemma 5

$$\vDash (x) : x \in a . \equiv . x \subseteq b.$$

This gives our theorem.

H. Proof of Easton's Theorem

We can give the same proof as before for Theorem 8.12, except that we may have to increase the value of β when we put $D(f) = V_\beta$. By Theorem 9.9 we easily infer

$$\vDash \aleph(SC(\aleph_{\breve{\alpha}})) \leq \text{Img}(\aleph_{E(\alpha)}).$$

So we conclude (9.1), namely

$$\vDash \aleph(SC(\aleph_{\breve{\alpha}})) = \text{Img}(\aleph_{E(\alpha)}),$$

which is Easton's theorem.

CHAPTER TEN

Resolution of Conceptual Difficulties

A. What Is Truth ?

In Chapter 3, we showed that if X is derivable from the axioms of set theory, then $\| X \| = 1$. As $\| Y \ \& \sim Y \| = 0$, we conclude that $Y \ \& \sim Y$ is not derivable from the axioms of set theory. Thus we have proved that set theory is consistent. We stated explicitly in Chapter 1 that the arguments of the subsequent chapters are considered to be carried out within set theory. If, indeed, we did this in Chapter 3, then we have proved within set theory that set theory is consistent. But then by a famous theorem of Gödel, it must be the case that set theory is inconsistent (see Cohen [3, pp. 42, 45]).

The reader who is well versed in logical matters will have encountered the same difficulty in connection with the proofs of independence by forcing, and will be familiar with its resolution there. We shall resolve the difficulty in the standard fashion, so that there will be no points of novelty in the present section. Certain points of novelty will appear in the next section.

In order that our presentation shall be self-contained for the reader who is less well versed in logical matters, we shall proceed with an explanation of how the difficulty is to be resolved. There is, in fact, a second difficulty. Tarski showed that the notion of truth in a formal logic (for example, set theory) cannot be formalized within that logic (see Cohen [3, pp. 43–44]). However, when we set up the definition of the value $\|X\|$ of a statement X (see (3.1)–(3.3), for instance) we did formalize a generalized notion of truth; had our Boolean algebra been the very simple one with 0 and 1 as the only elements, we would have formalized the usual notion of truth.

The resolution which disposes of this new difficulty also disposes of the earlier difficulty. The resolution is that in fact the definition of $\|X\|$ is not carried out wholly within set theory. Most of it is carried out within set theory, but a small residue is carried out in an external intuitive logic. Specifically, the definitions of $\|a \in b\|$ and $\|a = b\|$ can be carried out within set theory; we shall shortly elaborate this point. Then by (3.1)–(3.3), we can, *for each specific* X, derive a value for $\|X\|$; for each specific X this involves only a finite number of applications of (3.1)–(3.3), and so it can be performed within set theory.

What cannot be performed within set theory is the recognition that we have here a mechanism for assigning values $\|X\|$ for all X.

We reiterate. For each specific X, the mechanism for defining $\|X\|$ can be implemented within set theory. The fact that the mechanism is universally applicable can be recognized only outside set theory.

This same distinction recurs at other crucial points. Consider the axiom of replacement (see Theorem 3.32). It is really an infinite collection of axioms, one for each choice of $F(x, y, z_1, \ldots, z_n)$. *For each specific* F, we can carry out the proof of Theorem 3.32 within set theory. The fact that consequently Theorem 3.32 holds for all F can be recognized only outside set theory. Similar considerations apply to other results, such as Theorem 3.13.

In view of this, do our so-called proofs of independence really establish independence, as claimed? Let us look at a specific case, namely the proof in Chapter 4 of the independence of $V = L$. We chose a certain Boolean algebra. Then by taking one specific F, properly chosen, in Theorem 4.5, we concluded

$$\|V = L\| = 0 \tag{10.1}$$

(see Theorem 4.6). The proof given for Theorem 4.5 appeals to various earlier theorems. Amongst them is Theorem 3.13. However, we appealed to only a finite number of such earlier theorems, and if we are considering a specific F in Theorem 4.5 then each appeal to an earlier theorem will involve a specific statement. Thus, *for each specific* F, we can carry out the proof of Theorem 4.5 within set theory. If we needed to recognize that Theorem 4.5 holds for all F, this could be done only outside set theory. However, we do not need this. To conclude Theorem 4.6, and hence (10.1), we need to prove Theorem 4.5 only for a quite specific F. Thus (10.1) can be proved in set theory.

To complete the proof of independence, we reason as follows. Note that the arguments below are to be carried on outside set theory. Indeed, they are mostly concerned with what can be done within set theory, and so are most properly to be carried on outside set theory. Suppose, if possible, that there is a proof of $V = L$ from the axioms of set theory. Then this proof will be of finite length. It will involve only a finite number of statements, and these will be quite specific. Insofar as the proof may use the axiom of replacement (or any other axiom of set theory) at a number of points, it will do so only a finite number of times, and each time with a quite specific F. Hence, for each axiom $\mathscr{A}$ of set theory utilized in the proof, we can prove

$$\|\mathscr{A}\| = 1$$

in set theory. Then, by appealing to Theorem 3.1 a finite number of times, and each time with a specific X and Y, we can prove in set theory

$$\|\mathscr{S}\| = 1$$

for each statement $\mathscr{S}$ appearing as a step of the proof. But $V = L$ is supposedly the final step of the proof. Hence we can prove

$$\|V = L\| = 1 \tag{10.2}$$

in set theory.

Thus we can prove both (10.1) and (10.2) in set theory. However, this is possible if and only if set theory is inconsistent.

So, by an argument which takes place mainly outside set theory, but which repeatedly cites the possibility of carrying out key proofs within set theory, we conclude that $V = L$ is provable from the axioms of set theory if and only if these axioms are inconsistent.

The key to the arguments above is the capability to recognize within set theory that a finite number of specific instances of the axioms of set theory have the value 1. That this can be done without being able to recognize within set theory that *all* axioms of set theory have the value 1 is what rescues us from being able to prove the consistency of set theory within set theory (and hence being forced to conclude the inconsistency of set theory). Similarly, we require the capability to define the Boolean values for a limited class of statements within set theory (in fact, only a suitably chosen finite class would actually have Boolean values assigned in the argument above). This capability does exist, although the more general (and disastrous) capability to formulate the notion of truth value for *all* statements apparently does not exist within set theory.

This all comes about because the model V is a class, rather than a set. If it were a set, then one could prove within set theory that all instances of the axiom of replacement hold, one could formulate within set theory a general definition of $\|X\|$ for all X, etc. Indeed, the treatment would be so easy that Cohen [3, p. 78] dismissed the analogous case for two valued models with two sentences:

"In the discussion of models in Chapter I we used intuitive set theory. It is now clear that all that discussion can be easily formalized within *ZF*."

When a model is a class, specifically V, some capabilities are lost. The treatment is still fairly straightforward. However, some of our readers may be inexperienced in such matters. Also, it seems worthwhile to make it clear why we can handle specific cases of the replacement theorem, but not the general case, and similar points. So we shall give a rough outline of the treatment.

Each V_α is a set. So, by induction on σ within set theory, we can define functions f_σ, g_σ, and h_σ so that for $\alpha \leq \sigma$

$$f_\sigma(\alpha) = V_\alpha \tag{10.3}$$

and for $a, b \in V_\sigma$

$$g_\sigma(a, b) = \|a \in b\| \tag{10.4}$$

$$h_\sigma(a, b) = \|a = b\|. \tag{10.5}$$

This is done by paralleling formally the treatment of Section B of Chapter 3. Thus, let us have given f_σ, g_σ, and h_σ, and let us undertake to define $f_{\sigma+1}$, $g_{\sigma+1}$, and $h_{\sigma+1}$. Clearly we put

$$f_{\sigma+1}(\alpha) = f_\sigma(\alpha)$$

for $\alpha \leq \sigma$. Assuming we can define $V_{\sigma+1}$ in terms of f_σ, g_σ, and h_σ, we would complete the definition of $f_{\sigma+1}$ by setting

$$f_{\sigma+1}(\sigma + 1) = V_{\sigma+1}.$$

By taking α to be σ in (10.3), we have V_σ. Then of course we define

$$g_{\sigma+1}(a, b) = g_\sigma(a, b)$$
$$h_{\sigma+1}(a, b) = h_\sigma(a, b)$$

for $a, b \in V_\sigma$. To define $V_{\sigma+1}$, we first take all members of V_σ. We next generate each function from V_σ to A. We must then exclude those which are not extensional. Now by (3.33) and (10.5), a is extensional if and only if for each x and y in V_σ we have

$$a(x) \wedge h_\sigma(x, y) \leq a(y).$$

Since we have h_σ and V_σ, we can select the extensional a's.

Analogously to (3.32), we define

$$g_{\sigma+1}(x, a) = a(x) \tag{10.6}$$

for $x \in V_\sigma$ and a extensional over V_σ. Then, analogously to (3.29), we define

$$h_{\sigma+1}(a, b) = \left\{\prod_{x \in D(a)} g_{\sigma+1}(x, a) \Rightarrow g_{\sigma+1}(x, b)\right\} \wedge \left\{\prod_{x \in D(b)} g_{\sigma+1}(x, b) \Rightarrow g_{\sigma+1}(x, a)\right\}. \tag{10.7}$$

Next, analogously to (3.28), we define

$$g_{\sigma+1}(a, b) = \sum_{x \in D(b)} g_{\sigma+1}(x, b) \wedge h_{\sigma+1}(a, x). \tag{10.8}$$

Now we satisfy (3.24) by excluding all a's for which we do not have

$$\{G \mid G \in \mathcal{G} \,.\, h_{\sigma+1}(G(a), a) = 1\} \in \Gamma.$$

Thus finally we have defined $V_{\sigma+1}$, after which the definition of $f_{\sigma+1}$ can be completed.

The above sequence of steps to get from f_σ, g_σ, and h_σ to $f_{\sigma+1}$, $g_{\sigma+1}$, and $h_{\sigma+1}$ can be incorporated into a formal inductive relationship that the triple

$$\langle f_\sigma, g_\sigma, h_\sigma \rangle$$

must satisfy. We can prove by induction on σ that for each σ there is one and only one triple satisfying the inductive relationship up to σ.

Strictly speaking, we cannot define V, since it is a class, and we have no symbols for classes. However, we can define a predicate $V(x)$ which will be satisfied by just those x's which are in V. The predicate $V(x)$ will be a formalization of the statement that there is an α and a triple $\langle f, g, h \rangle$ such that the triple satisfies the inductive relationship up to α and $x \in f(\alpha)$.

Similarly, we cannot define functions $\|a \in b\|$ and $\|a = b\|$ of a and b, but we can define predicates G and H such that $G(y, a, b)$ if and only if $y = \|a \in b\|$ and $H(y, a, b)$ if and only if $y = \|a = b\|$. Specifically, the predicate $G(y, a, b)$ will be a formalization of the statement that there is an α and a triple $\langle f, g, h \rangle$ such that the triple satisfies the inductive relationship up to α, $a \in f(\alpha)$, $b \in f(\alpha)$, and $y = g(a, b)$. A similar definition can be made for $H(y, a, b)$.

In effect, G and H do define $\|a \in b\|$ and $\|a = b\|$ within set theory.

Now consider a specific statement $F(x_1, \ldots, x_n)$. It is built up from $\in$ and $=$ by $\sim$, &, and quantification. We have the predicates G and H to deal with $\in$ and $=$. So, corresponding to larger and larger pieces of $F(x_1, \ldots, x_n)$, we can parallel (3.1)–(3.3) to produce respective predicates, until finally we have a predicate J such that $J(y, a_1, \ldots, a_n)$ holds if and only if

$$y = \|F(a_1, \ldots, a_n)\|.$$

In effect, the predicate J defines $\|F(a_1, \ldots, a_n)\|$. Thus, for each specific X we can define $\|X\|$, but only by generating a predicate particular to that X. Thus there is no mechanism within set theory for formulating a universal definition for $\|X\|$.

We can now proceed to formalize all the developments of Chapter 3. We will succeed at each point where we are required to handle $\|X\|$ for at most a finite number of specific X's. Thus within set theory we can prove Theorems 3.13, 3.32, etc. for specific F's, but not in complete universality. However, as we saw above, this suffices for the independence proofs, without involving us in anything disastrous, such as a proof within set theory of the consistency of set theory.

In the form presented above, our independence proofs are really proofs of relative consistency. Thus the developments of Chapter 4 justify the following statement:

If set theory is consistent, then so is the system obtained by adding the additional axiom $V \neq L$.

Although Chapter 4 purports to produce a Boolean valued model, a careful analysis shows that only a partial model is actually given, as we have just been at some pains to explain. However, there is no real trouble if anyone wishes a model for the entire system. If set theory is consistent, then so is the system consisting of set theory plus $V \neq L$. Then by the Gödel completeness theorem (see Cohen [3, pp. 13–16]), it has a model, and indeed a denumerable one. Of course, this model does not have some of the attractive features of the models produced in connection with forcing arguments (amongst other things, these are standard, as defined by Cohen [3, p. 79]). However, even with forcing, one gets these standard models only by appealing to additional axioms (see the discussion in Section 11 of Chapter IV of Cohen [3, pp. 147–148]). If we appeal to additional axioms, we can likewise get improved results using Boolean algebra, a matter to which we now turn.

B. Appeal to Strong Axioms

Some people apparently hold a firm conviction that some inaccessible cardinals exist (see Cohen [3, p. 79]). They feel that one can add to the axioms of set theory an axiom affirming the existence of an inaccessible cardinal without introducing an inconsistency. More than that, they would have complete confidence in the truth of any theorem proved in such a system. If one wishes to convince such a person of the independence of $V = L$, it would be entirely adequate to carry out the proof in set theory augmented by the existence of an inaccessible cardinal.

This is an attractive approach, since the additional strong axiom allows one to simplify the development. Let Ω denote an inaccessible cardinal. Then we replace (3.13) by

$$V = \bigcup \{V_\alpha \mid \alpha < \Omega\}. \tag{10.9}$$

With this alternative definition, V is a set. If we take the triple $\langle f, g, h \rangle$ which satisfies the inductive relationship of the previous section up to Ω, then $f(\Omega)$ denotes V within set theory, and $g(a, b)$ and $h(a, b)$ denote $\|a \in b\|$ and $\|a = b\|$ within set theory. One can then formulate a universal definition for $\|X\|$ by induction (within set theory) on the number of symbols of X. Then one can prove as a theorem in the augmented set theory that Theorems 3.13, 3.32, and the rest hold for all F, provided the cardinality of A is less than Ω. This hypothesis is needed to carry through the proof of Theorem 3.11, for which the conditions $\alpha < \Omega$ and $\beta < \Omega$ should be adjoined. In this form, Theorem 3.11 suffices for the proofs of Theorems 3.12 and 3.13 in full universality. The proof of Theorem 3.31 proceeds without difficulty, since the definition of an inaccessible ordinal assures that $\alpha < \Omega$ for the α introduced in the proof. Hence we prove the axiom of replacement, and indeed universally for all F. All other proofs proceed within the augmented set theory without incident.

The material of subsequent chapters proceeds without change, except for Chapter 9. The difference is that we now prove a formal theorem within the augmented set theory which states the independence result in question. As we said, there are many persons who feel that the proof of such a formal theorem fully convinces them of the truth of the statement. Because we now have an additional strong axiom (the existence of an inaccessible cardinal Ω), the cost of making the formal proof is very slight; as V is now a set, the arguments of the first eight chapters are easily formalizable. The roundabout approach of the preceding section is avoided.

With regard to Chapter 9, an interesting prior question arises. One of the attributes of an inaccessible cardinal Ω is that if α is a cardinal and $\alpha < \Omega$, then

$$2^\alpha < \Omega.$$

Already, in Chapter 8, we have the possibility of choosing $E(\alpha) \geq \Omega$ for some $\alpha < \Omega$. If this were done, then Ω would cease to be an inaccessible cardinal in the model, although it would be regular. Further investigation of such an interesting situation is not suitable here.

If $E(\alpha) \geq \Omega$ for some $\alpha < \Omega$, we cannot avail ourselves of the definition (10.9). Then, even in Chapter 8 and equally so in Chapter 9, we are in the same position as if we had not assumed the existence of an inaccessible cardinal.

If $E(\alpha) < \Omega$ for each $\alpha < \Omega$, and either we are in the bounded case (Chapter 8) but with $\theta \geq \Omega$ or are in the unbounded case (Chapter 9), we can proceed as follows. We take X to be

$$\{0, 1\}^\Omega.$$

This is a set, which appreciably simplifies matters in the unbounded case. We restrict the elements of the Boolean algebra to be sets of the form (9.7), where K is bounded by an ordinal $\gamma < \Omega$. Then such a P is said to be at the level γ. If $\mathscr{S}$ is a set of Boolean elements, then $\mathscr{S}$ will have a supremum and an infimum if the cardinality of $\mathscr{S}$ is less than Ω.

As before, we hold the values of a to a level not greater than $\aleph_{\alpha+1}$ in forming $V_{\alpha+1}$. We define V by (10.9). We still have a problem with (3.3); our infimum will be over a set, but this set may have cardinality Ω, in which case we are not assured that an infimum exists in the Boolean algebra. However, we can use the same black magic as before. The rest of Chapter 9 proceeds without appreciable change.

A weaker axiom, which is commonly assumed for forcing arguments, is Axiom SM (see Cohen [3, p. 78]). From it, one concludes the existence of a minimal model. This is countable, standard, and transitive, and $V = L$ holds in it (see Cohen [3, pp. 104, 110]). We shall refer to this model as M. By an argument based on the presence of M in set theory, we can prove formal theorems in set theory plus M stating the desired independence results. However, the presence of M is an appreciably weaker assumption than the presence of Ω, and our proofs become quite appreciably more complicated. Indeed, they take on a startling resemblance to the forcing proofs.

We start by assuring that the Boolean algebra lies within M. As M is a part of the entire set theory, we need not distinguish between an element of the Boolean algebra inside M or as an object in its own right. (Analogously, forcing conditions are absolute; they all appear within M and have the same meaning there as anywhere else.) Next, we need to be able to define V_α, $\|a \in b\|$, and $\|a = b\|$ within M, and indeed by statements of M. This is done as in the preceding section, with formulas analogous to G and H being used to define $\|a \in b\|$ and $\|a = b\|$. Furthermore, the values assigned by G and H to $\|a \in b\|$ and $\|a = b\|$ are the true ones. (This is strictly analogous to the first lemma on p. 121 of Cohen [3], which says in effect that one can formalize within M the statement that P forces $a \in b$ or $a = b$, and that the resulting formalization is valid in M if and only if P indeed does force $a \in b$ or $a = b$.) Proceeding further, as in the introduction of J in the preceding section, we can, for each specific statement X, write a formal statement within M which defines the value of $\| X \|$, and indeed correctly. (This is strictly analogous to the second lemma on p. 121 of Cohen [3], which makes an analogous statement about forcing for each specific X.)

Let us look particularly at the proof of the independence of the continuum hypothesis in this context. We define the Boolean algebra within M by taking I to be $\omega \times \omega_2$ in (2.24) (using the ω_2 of M, of course). We define V_α within M (so that α is an ordinal of M) by using the analog of the f_σ, g_σ, and h_σ of the preceding section. Thus the functions a from V_α to A that we introduce to form $V_{\alpha+1}$ are all objects of M.

In point of fact, we define f_σ, g_σ, and h_σ within the full set theory observing (within set theory) that for $\sigma \leq \alpha_0$ this does not take us outside M (we are using α_0 in the sense of Cohen [3, pp. 104, 110]). Thus, by taking $\sigma = \alpha_0$ we can define $\|a \in b\|$ and $\|a = b\|$ by functions of set theory, although we are restricted to the use of predicates if we wish to deal with them inside M.

Similarly we can define $\|X\|$ in full generality by a function of set theory, although within M we are restricted to devising specific predicates to deal with specific X's.

From here on, the treatment parallels our discussion in the preceding section; "within M" will now play the role formerly played by "within set theory," and "within set theory" will now play the role formerly played by "outside set theory."

We call attention to one or two fine points whose analogs were glossed over in the broad discussion of the preceding section. In Theorems 3.9, 3.11, and 3.12, one has to invoke the hypothesis that Φ is expressible in M. Then, to complete the proofs of Theorems 3.10 and 3.13, we must show that one can find a statement of M equivalent to $F(x, a_1, \ldots, a_n)$ in which no constants $a_1, \ldots, a_n$ appear. This is done essentially by appealing to the theorem on p. 105 of Cohen [3]. (Really we need a slightly stronger result, namely that $A(y)$ is a formula of M, but this is proved incidentally in the proof of the theorem.) Thus our use of Theorem 3.10 in the proof of the axiom of the power set (Theorem 3.33) is permissible. In the proof of Theorem 3.31 (which provides the key to the proof of the axiom of replacement) we must take some pains to verify that the relation between x and α_x is expressible in M. Then the α defined will be less than α_0. (This is strictly analogous to the introduction of the function $g(P, c)$ at the bottom of p. 123 of Cohen [3]. This function in M plays the role for forcing analogous to the functional relationship in M that we have to introduce between x and α_x.)

Despite the analogy noted between parts of our proof of the axiom of replacement and the proof by forcing, our proof seems overall a bit simpler, since we can avoid an analog of the theorem on p. 124 of Cohen [3]. Furthermore, our proof of the power set axiom seems appreciably simpler than the proof given on pp. 122–123 of Cohen [3]. Indeed one overall simplification relative to the forcing treatment is the avoidance of the notion of "labeling" and "label space." (See Cohen [3, pp. 113–114].)

Because $V = L$ holds in M, our treatment of the axiom of choice in Section F of Chapter 3 goes through as presented. Finally, the material of Chapter 7 presents no difficulty at all; the arguments go through in M quite satisfactorily.

The net result is that we prove in set theory plus M that there is a Boolean valued model, within M, in which the axioms of set theory hold but the continuum hypothesis fails.

As M is countable, we may apply the well-known Rasiowa–Sikorski lemma and imbed our Boolean algebra in a two-valued Boolean algebra while preserving supremums and infimums. Then we have a two-valued model, with elements from M, in which the axioms of set theory hold but the continuum hypothesis fails. Naturally the $\in$-relationship of the model is not the $\in$-relationship of M.

This is an amusing variant on the model produced by forcing arguments, in which the $\in$-relationship is preserved but additional objects are adjoined to M.

In order to carry over the treatment of the generalized GCH (see Chapters 8 and 9), it seems essential that the function E be expressible in M. Otherwise, we proceed much as indicated above. One might think one could simplify the treatment of Chapter 9 by taking X to be

$$\{0, 1\}^{\alpha_0},$$

but the necessity for having the Boolean algebra within M seems to require something like the development actually presented.

BIBLIOGRAPHY

1. Bernays, P., and Fraenkel, A. A., "Axiomatic Set Theory," North-Holland Publ., Amsterdam, 1958.
2. Cohen, P. J., The Independence of the Continuum Hypothesis, *Proc. Natl. Acad. Sci. U.S.A.* **50**, 1143–1148 (1963); **51**, 105–110 (1964).
3. Cohen, P. J., "Set Theory and the Continuum Hypothesis," Benjamin, New York, 1966.
4. Easton, W. B., Powers of Regular Cardinals, Ph.D. dissertation, Princeton University, Princeton, New Jersey, October 1964.
5. Gödel, K., "The Consistency of the Axiom of Choice and of the Generalized Continuum-Hypothesis with the Axioms of Set Theory." Princeton Univ. Press, Princeton, New Jersey, 1940.
6. Halmos, P. R., "Lectures on Boolean Algebras." Van Nostrand, Princeton, New Jersey, 1963.
7. Rosser, J. B., "Logic for Mathematicians." McGraw–Hill, New York, 1953.
8. Scott, D., and Solovay, R., Boolean-Valued Models for Set Theory, to appear in *Proc. Amer. Math. Soc. Summer Inst. Axiomatic Set Theory, 1967, Univ. of California, Los Angeles, Proc. Symp. Pure Math.* **13** (1969).
9. Sochor, A., ∇-Model Over Generalized Boolean Algebra. Paper delivered at *Intern. Congr. for Logic, Methodology, and Philosophy of Sci., Amsterdam*, 1967.
10. Solovay, R., Independence Results in the Theory of Cardinals (abstract), *Notices Amer. Math. Soc.* **10**, 595 (1963).
11. Vopěnka, P., The limits of Sheaves and Applications on Constructions of Models, *Bull. Acad. Polon. Sci. Sér. Sci. Math., Astron. Phys.* **13**, 189–192 (1965).
12. Vopěnka, P., General Theory of ∇-models, *Comment. Math. Univ. Carolinae* **8**, 145–170 (1967).
13. Young, J. W. A., "Monographs on Topics of Modern Mathematics Relevant to the Elementary Field." Longmans, Green, New York, 1911 (republished by Dover, New York, 1955).

Subject Index

A

Agreement set, *see* Set
Automorphism, 27–31, 34, 43, 44, 53–55, 57, 89, 98, 105–107, 118, 132, 165
AxC, *see* Axiom of choice
Axiom 2.1, 12
Axiom 2.2, 12
Axiom(s)
  of choice, 2, 3, 81–88, 105–115, 178–181
  of constructibility, 2, 89–98
  of equality and extensionality, 41–51, esp. 43
  of extensionality, 65
  of infinity, 69
  of null set, 66
  of power set, 72–74, 182–201
  of regularity, 74
  of replacement, 72, 203, 209
  of restricted predicate calculus, 34–41
  of sum set, 67
  of unordered pairs, 66

B

Basis set, *see* Set
Boolean algebra, 20–27, 34, 37, 38, 89, 102, 103, 106, 118, 132, 158–165, 210, 211, 213
  complete, 23–26, 31, 34, 35, 38, 165
Boolean value, 34–38, 42–46, 100, 102–104, 166–174
Boundedness restriction, 131, 132

C

Cantor's theorem, 90, 116, 130, 148
Class, 20, 35, 56, 103, 158, 165, 169, 205
Closed set, *see* Set
Closure, 13, 162–164
Cohen combinatorial lemma, 121, 132–140
Combinatorial lemma, *see* Cohen combinatorial lemma
Complement, 14, 162, 163
Complete Boolean algebra, *see* Boolean algebra
Complete sequence, 102, 104
Condition, 99, 100, 102, 104, 211
Continuum hypothesis, 3, 116–126, 211
  generalized, 2, 3, 90–92, 106, 127–201
Countable chain condition, 31–33, 78, 80, 118, 119, 121, 122, 132

D

Disjoint elements, 31
Disjoint set, *see* Set

E

Easton's theorem, 127–131, 145–155, 201
Extensional function, 44, 45, 52, 54, 55, 63, 81, 83, 108, 150, 155, 173–175, 177, 206

F

Filter, 31, 34, 43, 44, 54, 55, 57, 81, 82, 84, 87, 89, 105–107, 118, 132, 165, 174
strongly normal, 31, 34, 107

G

GCH, *see* Continuum hypothesis, generalized
Generalized continuum hypothesis, *see* Continuum hypothesis
Generic set, *see* Set

I

Image, 62, 94
Inaccessible cardinal, 208–210
Infimum, 24, 28, 34, 35, 38, 39, 47, 164, 165, 169, 173, 210, 213

K

König's theorem, 128, 129

L

Lower bound, 24
Lusin, 119

M

Minimal model, 211

O

Open set, *see* Set

R

Rank, 62–64
Regular, 130, 132, 133, 135, 137, 139
Regular open set, *see* Set

S

Scott core, 59, 61, 62, 94, 110, 167, 174, 187, 194, 196
Scott domain, 59, 61, 62, 94, 110, 167, 174, 187, 194, 196
Set, 20, 35, 56, 103, 158, 165, 205, 210
agreement, 133, 136
basis, 12–15, 20, 26, 28–30, 32, 33, 89, 91, 99–101, 106, 110–112, 121, 122, 132–139, 141, 148–151, 158, 160, 162–164, 170
closed, 14–16, 21
disjoint, 31, 32, 80, 122
generic, 99, 103
open, 13–19, 21, 28, 91, 160, 162
regular open, 17, 18, 21, 25, 26, 28, 34, 91, 164
subbasis, 20, 29
Singular, 130, 139
Statement, 34–36, 50, 52, 53, 89, 90, 97–100, 105, 169–174
Strongly normal filter, *see* Filter
Subbasis set, *see* Set
Support, 28–30, 99, 106, 111, 112, 121, 132, 134–136, 149

Supremum, 23, 24, 26, 28, 29, 34, 38, 104, 111, 112, 164, 165, 170, 172, 173, 174, 210, 213

T

Topological spaces, 12–19, 34

U

Upper bound, 23, 24, 26, 172, 174

W

Weakly forces, 100, 103, 104

Pure and Applied Mathematics

A Series of Monographs and Textbooks

Edited by

Paul A. Smith and Samuel Eilenberg

Columbia University, New York

1: Arnold Sommerfeld. Partial Differential Equations in Physics. 1949 (Lectures on Theoretical Physics, Volume VI)

2: Reinhold Baer. Linear Algebra and Projective Geometry. 1952

3: Herbert Busemann and Paul Kelly. Projective Geometry and Projective Metrics. 1953

4: Stefan Bergman and M. Schiffer. Kernel Functions and Elliptic Differential Equations in Mathematical Physics. 1953

5: Ralph Philip Boas, Jr. Entire Functions. 1954

6: Herbert Busemann. The Geometry of Geodesics. 1955

7: Claude Chevalley. Fundamental Concepts of Algebra. 1956

8: Sze-Tsen Hu. Homotopy Theory. 1959

9: A. M. Ostrowski. Solution of Equations and Systems of Equations. Second Edition. 1966

10: J. Dieudonné. Foundations of Modern Analysis. 1960

11: S. I. Goldberg. Curvature and Homology. 1962

12: Sigurdur Helgason. Differential Geometry and Symmetric Spaces. 1962

13: T. H. Hildebrandt. Introduction to the Theory of Integration. 1963

14: Shreeram Abhyankar. Local Analytic Geometry. 1964

15: Richard L. Bishop and Richard J. Crittenden. Geometry of Manifolds. 1964

16: Steven A. Gaal. Point Set Topology. 1964

17: Barry Mitchell. Theory of Categories. 1965

18: Anthony P. Morse. A Theory of Sets. 1965

Pure and Applied Mathematics

A Series of Monographs and Textbooks

19: Gustave Choquet. Topology. 1966

20: Z. I. Borevich and I. R. Shafarevich. Number Theory. 1966

21: José Luis Massera and Juan Jorge Schaffer. Linear Differential Equations and Function Spaces. 1966

22: Richard D. Schafer. An Introduction to Nonassociative Algebras. 1966

23: Martin Eichler. Introduction to the Theory of Algebraic Numbers and Functions. 1966

24: Shreeram Abhyankar. Resolution of Singularities of Embedded Algebraic Surfaces. 1966

25: François Treves. Topological Vector Spaces, Distributions, and Kernels. 1967

26: Peter D. Lax and Ralph S. Phillips. Scattering Theory. 1967

27: Oystein Ore. The Four Color Problem. 1967

28: Maurice Heins. Complex Function Theory. 1968

29: R.M. Blumenthal and R. K. Getoor. Markov Processes and Potential Theory. 1968

30: L. J. Mordell. Diophantine Equations. 1969

31: J. Barkley Rosser. Simplified Independence Proofs: Boolean Valued Models of Set Theory. 1969

32: William F. Donoghue, Jr. Distributions and Fourier Transforms. 1969

33: Marston Morse and Stewart S. Cairns. Critical Point Theory in Global and Differential Topology. 1969

In preparation:

Hans Freudenthal and H. De Vries. Linear Lie Groups.

J. Dieudonné. Foundations of Modern Analysis *(enlarged and corrected printing)*

Edwin Weiss. Cohomology of Groups.